THE CELL PERIPHERY, METASTASIS, AND OTHER CONTACT PHENOMENA

FRONTIERS OF BIOLOGY

VOLUME 7

Under the General Editorship of

A. NEUBERGER

London

and

E. L. TATUM

New York

NORTH-HOLLAND PUBLISHING COMPANY

AMSTERDAM

THE CELL PERIPHERY,
METASTASIS AND
OTHER CONTACT PHENOMENA

LEONARD WEISS

Director and Research Professor,
Department of Experimental Pathology,
Roswell Park Memorial Institute,
Buffalo, New York

1967

NORTH-HOLLAND PUBLISHING COMPANY – AMSTERDAM

JOHN WILEY & SONS, INC. – NEW YORK

This book is published and distributed
in the United States by
AMERICAN ELSEVIER PUBLISHING COMPANY, INC.
52 Vanderbilt Avenue, New York, N.Y. 10017

1967 © NORTH-HOLLAND PUBLISHING CO. – AMSTERDAM

Library of Congress Catalog Card Number: 67-26465

PUBLISHERS:
NORTH-HOLLAND PUBLISHING CO. – AMSTERDAM

SOLE DISTRIBUTORS FOR U.S.A. AND CANADA:
INTERSCIENCE PUBLISHERS, A DIVISION OF
JOHN WILEY & SONS, INC. – NEW YORK

PRINTED IN THE NETHERLANDS

Editors' preface

The aim of the publication of this series of monographs, known under the collective title of *'Frontiers of Biology'*, is to present coherent and up-to-date views of the fundamental concepts which dominate modern biology.

Biology in its widest sense has made very great advances during the past decade, and the rate of progress has been steadily accelerating. Undoubtedly important factors in this acceleration have been the effective use by biologists of new techniques, including electron microscopy, isotopic labels, and a great variety of physical and chemical techniques, especially those with varying degrees of automation. In addition, scientists with partly physical or chemical backgrounds have become interested in the great variety of problems presented by living organisms. Most significant, however, increasing interest in and understanding of the biology of the cell, especially in regard to the molecular events involved in genetic phenomena and in metabolism and its control, have led to the recognition of patterns common to all forms of life from bacteria to Man. These factors and unifying concepts have led to a situation in which the sharp boundaries between the various classical biological disciplines are rapidly disappearing.

Thus, while scientists are becoming increasingly specialized in their techniques, to an increasing extent they need an intellectual and conceptual approach on a wide and non-specialized basis. It is with these considerations and needs in mind that this series of monographs, *'Frontiers of Biology'* has been conceived.

The advances in various areas of biology, including microbiology, biochemistry, genetics, cytology, and cell structure and function in general will be presented by authors who have themselves contributed significantly to these developments. They will have, in this series, the opportunity of bringing together, from diverse sources, theories and experimental data, and of integrating these into a more general conceptual framework. It is unavoidable, and probably even desirable, that the special bias of the individual authors will become evident in their contributions. Scope will also be given for presentation of new and challenging ideas and hypotheses for which complete evidence is at present lacking. However, the main emphasis will be on fairly complete and objective presentation of the more important and more rapidly advancing aspects of biology. The level will be advanced, directed primarily to the needs of the graduate student and research worker.

Most monographs in this series will be in the range of 200-300 pages, but on occasion a collective work of major importance may be included somewhat exceeding this figure. The intent of the publishers is to bring out these books promptly and in fairly quick succession.

It is on the basis of all these various considerations that we welcome the opportunity of supporting the publication of the series *'Frontiers of Biology'* by North-Holland Publishing Company.

A. NEUBERGER
E. L. TATUM, *Editors*

Author's preface

The study of the cell periphery and its contact reactions is currently of interest not only to biologists and pathologists, but also to those whose main background is in the physical sciences. Although this interdisciplinary approach is extremely stimulating for those of us working in the field, it also creates very real communication barriers. In the case of metastatic phenomena for example, biologists and physical chemists are often prone to consider just one small aspect of a very complex problem, and to give this an emphasis which is incompatible with the data known to pathologists. By the same token, pathologists and physicists are often unaware of the vast amount of data which are available in the more general fields of cell biology and embryology, where 'simpler', relevant biological systems have been explored. As much emphasis is now being placed on the physical approach to biology and pathology, anyone interested in cell contact phenomena should also be aware of not only the relevant physico-chemical data, but also the difficulties inherent in applying them to cellular systems. In a sense this monograph is therefore an essay in communication between biologists, pathologists and physical scientists who are interested in phenomena involving the cell periphery.

One of the great difficulties faced by workers entering the field, is in getting a guide to the vast multidisciplinary literature within the covers of one book. With this in mind, I have attempted to give a fairly exhaustive bibliography, but I must apologize for the many relevant and often important papers which have doubtless been unavoidably missed. Some of the chapters will probably be regarded as superficial by those who are specialists in those particular areas. For example, the chapter on the biophysical bases of cell contacts will probably not be detailed enough to satisfy the physicist; however, it will, I hope, serve as a fair critical introduction to biologists and pathologists.

Whenever possible I have given definite opinions on the interpretations of the experimental evidence described in the text, although very often my only definite opinion is that it is unwise to give an opinion at all.

I cannot possibly thank by name all of the many people who have generously helped me, in one way or another, in my studies, which have resulted in this monograph. My own work has certainly benefited over the years from the advice and particularly encouragement so freely given by Professor M. Abercrombie, Dr. N. A. de Bruyne, Professor Dame Honor Fell, Professor R. J. V. Pulvertaft and Professor P. Weiss, to whom my sincere thanks are due. In addition, I would thank Dr. M. E. Neiders for her stimulating discussions and help with the second part of this book.

LEONARD WEISS

Contents

PART I

The normal cell periphery and contact phenomena

Chapter 1. The cell periphery

Chapter 2. The dynamic nature of the cell periphery

PART II

The malignant cell periphery, metastasis and infiltration

Chapter 6. *The periphery of malignant cells*

Chapter 7. *Separation of malignant cells from the primary tumour*

Chapter 8. *Movements and transport of malignant cells*

To Bulgie
for introducing me
to heretical pathology
and the study of
living cells

and Stetson (1965), Takeuchi and Terayama (1965) and Skipski et al. (1965). A more recent, different approach, is due to Warren et al. (1966), in which the cell periphery is first strengthened with fluorescein mercuric acetate, 5,5′-dithiobis (2-nitrobenzoic acid) or zinc chloride. These reagents are used in hypotonic solutions which have the effect of raising the cell periphery off the underlying cytoplasm. The cells are then ruptured in a Dounce homogenizer, and the membranes are fractionated by differential centrifugation on sucrose, glycerol, or passage through glass bead columns. All variants of the technique yield 'membranes' showing the typical trilaminar structure under the electron microscope, in sufficient quantities for detailed chemical analyses.

When the cell surface has been breached, the question of the suspending fluid becomes important, and as pointed out by Allfrey, such a medium should resemble the soluble phase of the cytoplasm so that the various cell components are deranged as little as possible from their natural state. Unfortunately such a medium has not yet been devised for intracellular components, and it would be unwise to assume that we have optimal media for the cell periphery. Among the artifacts which can be introduced by media are: (1) loss of soluble components; (2) redistribution of components by desorption and resorption; (3) structural rearrangements; and (4) autolysis. Thus, nuclei fractionated in various sucrose solutions had lost the water-soluble enzymes adenosine deaminase and nucleoside phosphorylase (Stern and Mirsky 1953); mitochondrial fractions prepared by the usual sucrose techniques are usually found to be contaminated with lysosomes rich in hydrolytic enzymes (De Duve et al. 1955); freezing to $-79°$ produces structural changes in the double membrane systems of mitochondria, in the nucleus and in the endoplasmic reticulum (Weiss and Armstrong 1960); enzymes may be released and activated depending on the pH of the medium, with possible autolytic alteration of the cell surface. Non-aqueous techniques may theoretically be used in fractionation procedures for the cell surface, but lyophilization and lipid solvents are suspect because they will remove essential surface structural components including water.

1.2 *The constitution of the cell periphery*

Before the possible structure of the cell periphery can be discussed at the molecular level, it is as well to have some idea of the molecules actually present. This section will be concerned largely with analytical chemical data, although it must be emphasized that while such data are indispensable, they are unlikely to lead very far in terms of function, any more than chemical analysis of a wrist-watch will tell us how it works.

1.3 Lipids of the cell periphery

Because of the inherent difficulties in obtaining 'pure' specimens of the peripheries of cells other than erythrocytes, most of the analytical data to date have been obtained from either erythrocyte ghosts, or alternatively from the membranes of various subcellular organelles which can often be obtained in a reasonable degree of purity by differential centrifugation. As long as it is constantly borne in mind that in many respects the erythrocyte is functionally a bad model for other cells, and that these functional differences may cause, and/or be caused by, differences in the erythrocyte periphery, then erythrocyte data may be profitably used to provide hypotheses concerning structures in other cells. However, these will be at most the bases for further experimentation.

Following the early studies of Gorter and Grendel (1925, 1926) which will be discussed later, much emphasis has been placed on the lipids present in erythrocyte ghosts. Owing to technical limitations and difficulties, much of the older literature on membrane lipids presents conflicting and often confusing data. Partly on this account, and partly because of the recent advances in techniques of lipid chemistry, emphasis will be placed on more recent work. The literature generally is well-covered in the reviews of Ponder (1948, 1955 and 1961), Parpart and Ballentine (1952), Prankerd (1961) and Van Deenen and De Gier (1964). It must be remembered however, that although many workers (vide Parpart and Ballentine) consider that erythrocyte ghosts obtained by haemolysis may accurately represent the plasma membrane, this view is not universally accepted; Ponder (1961) has subjected this assumption to critical scrutiny and reasonably concludes that where differences in preparative technique give quite different types of ghosts (Ponder and Barreto 1953, 1957; Dodge et al. 1963), then the purely arbitrary statement that any one method gives a true representation of real structure is untenable.

Following haemolysis, the separation by centrifugation of mammalian erythrocyte ghosts from the other liberated material is greatly facilitated by previous agglutination of the ghosts by acidification of the medium to about pH 5. Using this technique, Parpart (1942) obtained ghosts containing only about 0.01% haemoglobin, and Williams et al. (1938) showed that most of the lipids present in the intact cell are also present in the ghost. In contrast to this, following haemolysis of erythrocytes in water, Dawson et al. (1960) reported that they could only recover about 60% of lipid phosphorus in the sediment following centrifugation at 90,000 *g* for 90 min.

It is often not possible to make comparisons between the lipid content of various cells from a survey of the literature, because many results have been expressed in the past, in terms of weight of lipid per unit volume of packed cells. As packed cell volumes are comparable only when standardized solutions and centrifugation techniques are used, the present discussion will be confined to those results expressed in weight of lipid per cell. Even these results are very variable, as is seen for example in table 1.1 where, as pointed out by Van Deenen and De Gier, estimates for the total lipid content of human erythrocytes differ considerably owing to differences in packing techniques, solvents used for lipid extraction, contaminants, etc. Also, since as stated above, the nature of erythrocyte ghosts may vary very considerably with the technique used to prepare them, data obtained from ghosts will not be quoted in connection with the estimation of total lipids.

TABLE 1.1

Total and percentage of cholesterol in the lipids of human erythrocytes

	Cholesterol (mg $\times 10^{-10}$/cell)	Total lipid (mg $\times 10^{-10}$/cell)	Cholesterol as per cent total lipid
Erickson et al. (1938)	1.20	3.94	30.4
Reed et al. (1960)	1.13	4.95	22.8
Dodge et al. (1963)	1.42	5.24	27.1
Ways (1964; cited by Van Deenen and De Gier)	1.27	4.82	23.4
Van Deenen and De Gier (1964)	1.13	4.80	23.6

Lipids may be chemically classified into the so-called 'neutral' lipids and more complex lipids, such as the phospholipids and glycolipids.

1.3.1 Neutral lipids

Among the 'neutral' lipids are the unesterified fatty acids, the mono-, di-, and tri-esters of glycerol, the glycerides, cholesterol and its esters (fig. 1.1).

The data concerned with the neutral lipids of the erythrocyte membrane has been summarized by Van Deenen and De Gier and their review has been used extensively as source material in the present section. The neutral lipids can be extracted from erythrocytes or ghosts with chloroform, leaving behind the polar lipids (phospholipids, glycolipids) which require polar solvents such as the lower alcohols. An estimate of the total neutral lipid content of an extract may be obtained by chromatography of such extracts on silicic acid columns (Borgström 1952).

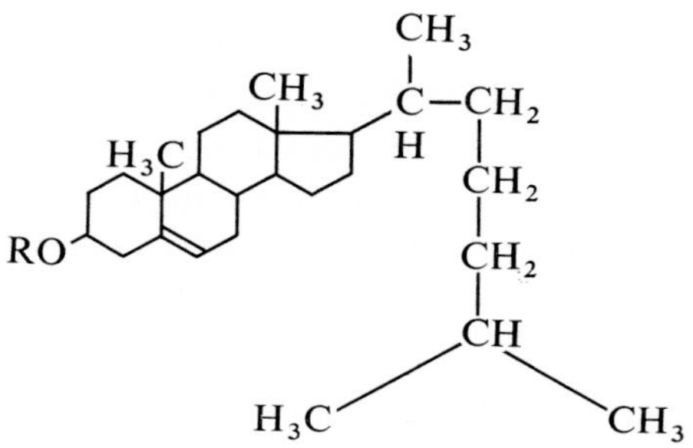

Cholesterol R=H

Cholesterol esters, $R = -\overset{\displaystyle \;}{\underset{\displaystyle \|}{C}}-R$
$$\overset{}{\underset{O}{\|}}$$

Fig. 1.1

In the human erythrocyte, neutral lipids comprise about 30% of the total lipids. From the data quoted in table 1.1 it can be seen that the cholesterol comprises the major part of the neutral lipids present; ranging from a high value of 100% (Erickson et al. 1938), to a low value of 76% (Reed et al. 1960) with a mean value of 85%.

Of the neutral lipids in human erythrocytes, the cholesterol esters compose about 4% of the total, and triglycerides, free fatty acids, hydrocarbon and possibly 'oxycholesterol' the remainder (Irie et al. 1961). Hanahan et al. (1960) observed that some 63% of the cholesterolester fatty acid was linoleic acid. Although the glycerides present form a small proportion of the neutral lipids, Vacca et al. (1960) have reported the presence of mono-, di-, and tri-glycerides in fixed amounts in the erythrocyte and the levels were different from the serum levels. Either they had been selectively adsorbed or alternatively were part of the cell from the synthetic viewpoint. Whatever their origin, the fact that they were present in fixed amounts would suggest that they must be considered functionally with the erythrocyte and probably its membrane. Van Deenen and De Gier feel that the free fatty acids and glycerides may possibly be intermediates in the metabolism of the lipids carrying most of the fatty acids.

1.3.2 Complex lipids

(a) *Glycolipids*. The glycolipids may be divided into several classes, starting with the cerebrosides (Colmer and Carter 1952) which consist of molar equivalents of sphingosine

$$(CH_3-(CH_2)_{12}-CH = CH-CHOH-\overset{\overset{\displaystyle NH_2}{\displaystyle |}}{CH}-CH_2OH),$$

fatty acid and hexose; progressing through the mucolipids which contain a second nitrogen atom which is part of a hexosamine, to gangliosides which include those mucolipids containing neuraminic acid or its derivatives. The classification is summarized in table 1.2 which is based on data collected by Van Deenen and De Gier.

The types of glycolipids present in erythrocytes as well as the actual amounts vary enormously between species (Yamakawa et al. 1956; Klenk and Lauenstein 1953; Rodin 1957; Yamakawa et al. 1962; Hakomori and Jeanloz 1961; Van Deenen and De Gier 1964), however it would appear that the total glycolipids compose up to 10% of the total lipids present in erythrocyte ghosts. As far as the human erythrocyte is concerned, a number of globosides have been separated chromatographically and the major component appears to be a lignocerylsphingosine, acetylgalactosamine trihexoside (Yamakawa et al. 1960).

(b) *Phospholipids*. The early literature on phospholipids is reviewed by Maclean and Smedley-Maclean (1927) and subsequent literature by Thierfelder and Klenk (1930) and Witcoff (1951). Among this class of compounds are the lecithins, cephalins and plasmalogens. The distinguishing feature in the lecithins and cephalins is an ester linkage between a hydroxyl group of glycerol with phosphoric acid, which itself is esterified by choline.

TABLE 1.2

Glycolipids

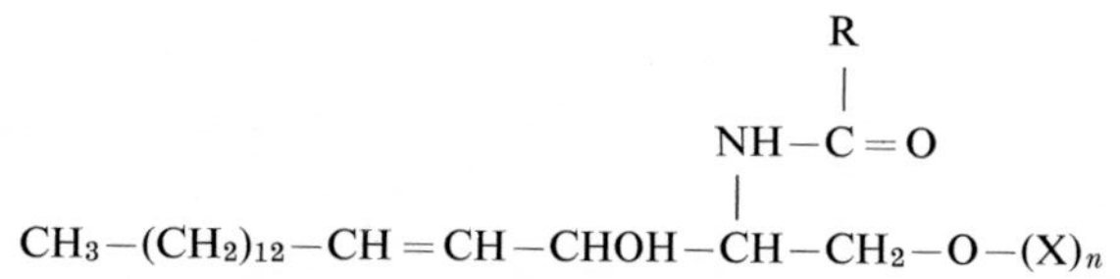

$$CH_3-(CH_2)_{12}-CH=CH-CHOH-CH-CH_2-O-(X)_n$$
$$NH-C=O$$
$$|$$
$$R$$

(a) ceramide monohexosides or cerebrosides	contain a second nitrogen
X = galactose or glucose	X = hexose(s) + hexosamine(s)
$N = 1$	e.g. galactosamine or glucosamine;
(b) ceramide oligohexosides	e.g. globosides from human erythrocytes
$N = 1$	$X = -(galactose)_3$
(a) and (b) contain molar equivalents of sphingosine, fatty acid R and hexose;	$|$ galactosamine
and contain only atom of N belonging to sphingosine;	$|$ acetyl
R includes tetracosanoic acid;	$R = C_{23}H_{47}$
$(CH_3-(CH_2)_{22}-COOH)$.	α-hydroxy-n-tetracosanoic acid;

mucolipids containing neuraminic acid (or derivative).
X = hexose(s) only and neuraminic acid.
e.g. in horse erythrocytes in molar proportions of sphingosine (1):
fatty acid (1): hexose (2):
neuraminic' acid (1),
or,
X = hexosamine(s) + neuraminic acid
Δ^{15}-α-N-tetracosanoic acid
Δ^{15}-α-hydroxy-n-tetracosanoic acid,

References to literature:
Van Deenen and De Gier (1964)

Klenk and Lauenstein (1953)
Yamakawa et al. (1956)
Yamakawa et al. (1960)
Yamakawa et al. (1962)

Yamakawa and Suzuki (1951, 1952)
Klenk and Wolter (1952)
Klenk and Lauenstein (1953)
Klenk and Padberg, (1962)
Klenk and Gielen (1962)
Ledeen (1966)

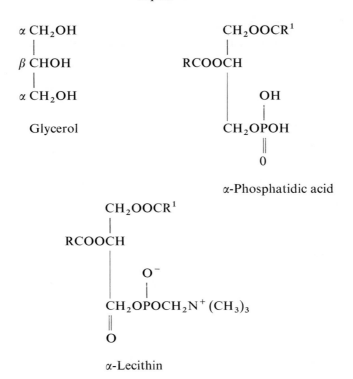

α CH$_2$OH
|
β CHOH
|
α CH$_2$OH

Glycerol

CH$_2$OOCR^1
|
RCOOCH
|
| OH
| |
CH$_2$OPOH
‖
0

α-Phosphatidic acid

CH$_2$OOCR^1
|
RCOOCH
|
| O$^-$
| |
CH$_2$OPOCH$_2$N$^+$(CH$_3$)$_3$
‖
O

α-Lecithin

Most lecithins contain both saturated and unsaturated fatty acids, and in those isolated from liver and egg yolk, the unsaturated fatty acids appear to be linked only in the α-position of glycerol (R^1), and the saturated fatty acids in the β-position (R) (Hanahan 1954). However, in studies on glycerolipids isolated from the rabbit liver, Moore and Williams (1965) showed that stearic and palmitic acids were mainly in the α or α$_1$ or α^1 positions, whereas the unsaturated acids occurred mainly in the β-positions. Nonetheless, it was also noted that a greater proportion of saturated fatty acids were found in the β-positions of the lecithin fraction than in the cephalin fraction. The main point here is that 'lecithin' is the name of a whole heterogeneous group of compounds, rather than one pure substance. The terminology of the lecithins may be based on phosphatidic acid (α-glycerylphosphoric acid), and α-lecithin may therefore be termed α-phosphatidylcholine. The 'α' may be omitted, since β-lecithins are not thought to occur naturally (Baer and Kates 1950).

Although it was at one time thought that all naturally occurring materials classified as cephalins were analogous to α-lecithins with ethanolamine

($HOCH_2 \cdot CH_2 \cdot NH_2$) substituted for choline, it is now realized that cephalins are also a heterogeneous group of substances which include phosphatidylethanolamine, phosphatidylserine and phosphatidylinositol.

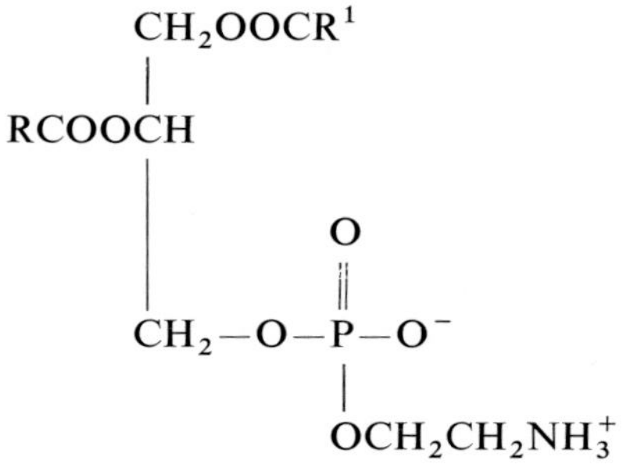

$$CH_2OOCR^1$$
$$|$$
$$RCOOCH$$
$$|$$
$$\qquad\qquad O$$
$$\qquad\qquad \|$$
$$CH_2-O-P-O^-$$
$$\qquad\qquad |$$
$$\qquad OCH_2CH_2NH_3^+$$

Phosphatidylethanolamine

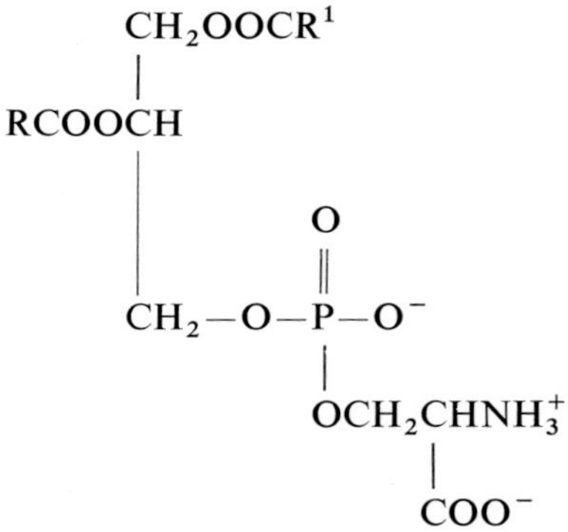

$$CH_2OOCR^1$$
$$|$$
$$RCOOCH$$
$$|$$
$$\qquad\qquad O$$
$$\qquad\qquad \|$$
$$CH_2-O-P-O^-$$
$$\qquad\qquad |$$
$$\qquad OCH_2CHNH_3^+$$
$$\qquad\qquad\qquad |$$
$$\qquad\qquad\qquad COO^-$$

Phosphatidylserine

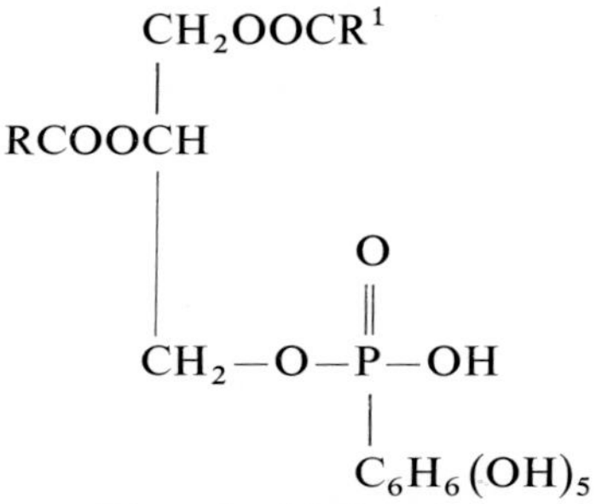

$$CH_2OOCR^1$$
$$|$$
$$RCOOCH$$
$$|$$
$$\qquad\qquad O$$
$$\qquad\qquad \|$$
$$CH_2-O-P-OH$$
$$\qquad\qquad |$$
$$\qquad\qquad C_6H_6(OH)_5$$

Phosphatidylinositol

Also to be included among the phospholipids is sphingomyelin, which is an important constituent of erythrocytes (Dawson et al. 1962; Kates and James 1961).

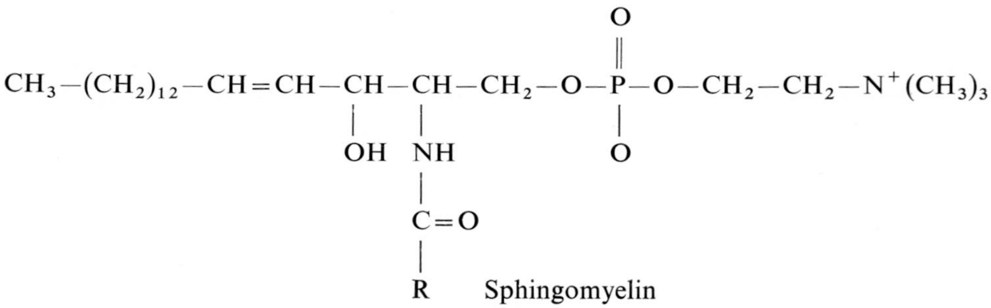

$$CH_3-(CH_2)_{12}-CH=CH-CH-CH-CH_2-O-\overset{\displaystyle \overset{O}{\|}}{P}-O-CH_2-CH_2-N^+(CH_3)_3$$
$$\qquad\qquad\qquad\qquad | \qquad | \qquad\qquad\qquad\qquad |$$
$$\qquad\qquad\qquad OH \quad NH \qquad\qquad\qquad\qquad O$$
$$\qquad\qquad\qquad\qquad\qquad |$$
$$\qquad\qquad\qquad\qquad\qquad C=O$$
$$\qquad\qquad\qquad\qquad\qquad |$$
$$\qquad\qquad\qquad\qquad\qquad R \qquad \text{Sphingomyelin}$$

Cardiolipin, or diphosphatidylglycerol (MacFarlane 1958), which is present in mitochondria, has not yet been identified in erythrocytes; however it should be included here because it is possibly present in the membranes of other cells.

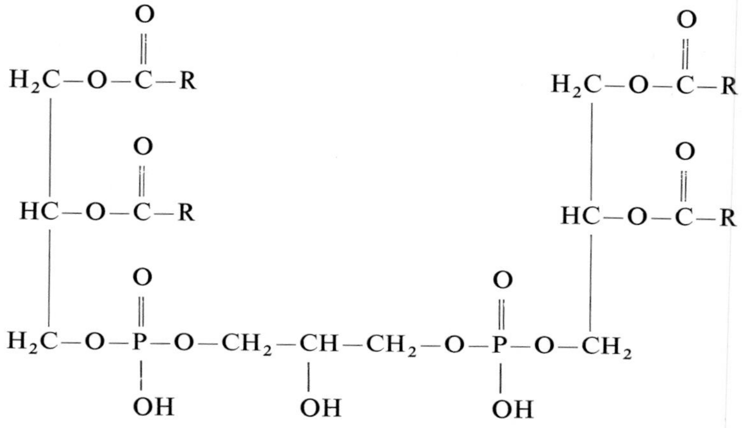

$$
\begin{array}{l}
\overset{\displaystyle O}{\underset{\displaystyle \|}{}} \\
H_2C-O-C-R \\[2pt]
\quad\quad\quad \overset{\displaystyle O}{\underset{\displaystyle \|}{}} \\
HC-O-C-R \\[2pt]
\quad\quad\quad \overset{\displaystyle O}{\underset{\displaystyle \|}{}} \\
H_2C-O-P-O-CH_2-CH-CH_2-O-P-O-CH_2 \\
\quad\quad\quad OH \quad\quad\quad OH \quad\quad\quad OH
\end{array}
$$

Cardiolipin

The plasmalogens were discovered by Feulgen and Voit (1924) and so named because they gave a positive 'plasmal' reaction for aldehydes with Schiff's reagent. These compounds are less confusingly known as the acetal phospholipids or phosphoglyceracetals. Thannhauser et al. (1951) prepared an acetal phosphatide from beef brain which had the structure shown, in which two of the hydroxyls of glycerylphosphorylethanolamine are bound with an acetal linkage. Farquhar (1962) has shown that 67% of the ethanolamine phospholipids from human erythrocytes are plasmalogens.

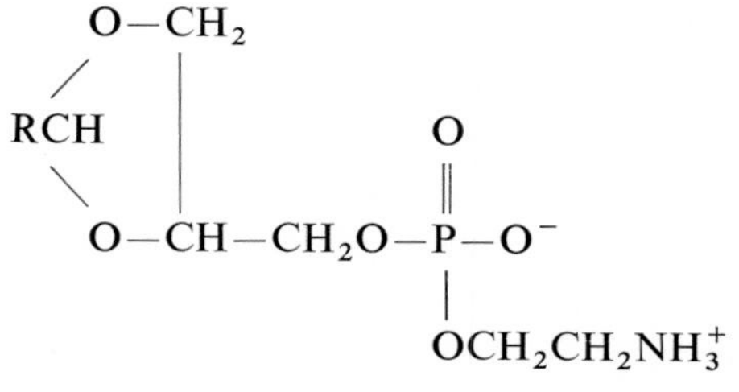

$$
\begin{array}{l}
\quad\quad O-CH_2 \\
\quad\; \diagup \\
RCH \\
\quad\; \diagdown \quad\quad\quad\quad\quad O \\
\quad\quad O-CH-CH_2O-P-O^- \\
\quad\quad\quad\quad\quad\quad\quad OCH_2CH_2NH_3^+
\end{array}
$$

Acetal phosphatide
(R is a long-chain aliphatic aldehyde)

It should be also mentioned that Klenk and Debuch (1954, 1955) have found
that some beef brain and heart cephalins and lecithins give aldehyde reactions. These substances are known as phosphatidalcholine, phosphatidale-
thanolamine or phosphatidalserine, depending on the nature of the base.
The distribution of phospholipids in whole human erythrocytes and ghosts
is given in table 1.3, which is taken from the data of Dawson et al. (1960).
It is seen that the figures for whole erythrocytes and ghosts agree.

TABLE 1.3

Phospholipids in whole human erythrocytes and ghosts, expressed as phospholipid
phosphorus as a percentage of the total lipid phosphorus. (After Dawson et al. 1960.)

	Ghosts	Whole cells
Lecithins	29.3	36.4
Phosphatidylethanolamine	14.4	17.6
Phosphatidylserine	11.7	5.1
Sphingomyelin	17.5	16.2
Choline plasmalogen	3.8	5.7
Ethanolamine plasmalogen	4.0	5.6
Serine plasmalogen	0.8	0.3
Monophosphoinositide	1.6	0
Phosphatidic acid	1.5	1.2
Unknown	3.3	2.6
Recovery	87.0	90.7

The average phosphorus content of phospholipids is about 4%, and
estimations of amount of phospholipid present in various preparations are
often made on lipid phosphorus values. As mentioned previously, comparison of the analytical data of a number of different workers in the field
is complicated by loss of lipid during washing procedures. However, in
spite of this, if the phospholipid content of human erythrocytes is calculated
on a 4% phosphorus basis and is considered as a percentage of total lipids,
this percentage is fairly constant at about 60% (table 1.4). As cholesterol
composes about 30% of the total lipids, it can be seen that quantitatively
cholesterol and phospholipids form about 85 to 90% of the total lipids.
Although many authors have stressed that these two components compose
most of the lipids present, it would appear pertinent to stress the point that
as much as 15% of the total lipids present are *not* phospholipids or cholesterol
in view of the tendency to regard the cholesterol/lecithin monolayer as a model
for cell membranes.

TABLE 1.4

Total and percentage of phospholipids in human erythrocytes (based on data collected by Van Deenen and De Gier, 1964).

	Phospholipid $(mg \times 10^{-10})$	Phospholipid as percent of total lipid
Erickson et al. (1938)	2.27	58 %
Reed et al. (1960)	2.88	58 %
Dodge et al. (1963)	3.15	60 %
Ways (1964; cited by Van Deenen and De Gier)	3.15	65 %
Van Deenen and De Gier (1964)	2.73	57 %

1.3.3 Fatty acids

Following the development of gas-liquid chromatography by James and Martin (1952), a great deal of work has been done in characterizing the fatty acid composition of lipids obtained from erythrocytes and their ghosts. It is not proposed to deal with this work here, and the reader is referred to the review of Van Deenen and De Gier (1964) for a very thorough discussion of such topics as the considerable species variations in fatty acid patterns, and the variations with diet and disease. The point is made by these authors that phospholipids compose 80–90% of the fatty acid-carrying lipids in erythrocytes.

1.4 Non-lipid constituents of the cell periphery

The tensions measured at the peripheries of a number of animal cells excluding eggs, vary between about 1–3 dynes per cm. These measurements represent not only the true surface tension in this region, but in addition the mechanical properties including the rheological elements, which in turn depend on intra- and intermolecular interactions (vide chapter 5). Part of the argument used by Harvey and Danielli in formulating their model for cell membranes was that these tensions of 1–3 dynes per cm are much less than would be expected for a lipid bilayer, where surface tensions at a water interface of the order of 10–20 dynes per cm would be expected. As observed, the tension at cell surfaces is much less than this expectation, and it was argued that the low value indicates that bare lipid is not present at the cell/environment interface. As a result of experiments showing that a number of different proteins adsorbed at an oil/water interface drastically reduced the interfacial tension (Danielli 1937), Danielli and Davson postulated their well-known model in which the lipid bilayer is shown covered with protein. More recent work by Thompson (1964) with artificial bilayer membranes formed from lecithin and *n*-tetradecane shows that these have a true surface tension (devoid of an elastic element) of only 1 dyne per cm at 36°C. Thompson reasonably concludes that as lipid bilayers have such low surface tension, (at least in his system), then measurements of the tension at cell peripheries cannot enable the investigator to decide whether bare lipid areas exist in this region or not. The best evidence that non-lipid constituents compose part of the cell periphery comes from various chemical analyses, immunochemical studies, staining reactions observed under the electron microscope, and consideration of the various interactions between proteins and lipids.

1.4.1 Some antigens of the cell periphery

It may be stated with confidence that antigens form part of the cell periphery on the evidence that many different antisera react with intact cells. Because of the well established inheritance patterns governing antigens, they are of particular interest in cell biology where they provide an accessible system with which to study the genetic control of the chemistry of the cell periphery. The genetic control of blood groups is reviewed in detail by Race and Sanger (1962), and the chemical basis of blood specificity is reviewed by Kabat (1956), Morgan (1960) and Watkins (1964).

Much data concerning the chemical nature of the blood group antigens on cells, particularly the erythrocyte, has come from study of the various secretions containing them. Fluid from ovarian cysts is rich in blood group substances A, B and H (Yosida, 1928) and Le^a and Le^b, and hydatid cyst fluid from sheep provides a source of P_1 blood group substances. Key references to the relevant literature and given by Watkins (1964).

The A and B blood group substances at the erythrocyte periphery cannot be extracted with water or salt solutions, and are to be contrasted with the water-soluble blood group substances found in the various secretions and tissue fluids. Although A and B group preparations were first extracted from erythrocytes with alcohol (Landsteiner and Van der Scheer 1925); the present-day approach is due to Yamakawa and Suzuki (1951, 1952) who extracted glycolipid 'globosides' from horse and human erythrocytes with methanol/ether. Chromatography of the globosides (Rodin 1957; Yamakawa et al. 1958; Yamakawa et al. 1960) shows them to be a heterogeneous entity. Of a series of six disaccharides isolated from human A substance by partial acid hydrolysis, only one, 0-α-N-acetyl-D-galactosaminoyl-(1→3)-D-galac-tose, inhibited antiserum to group A (Côté and Morgan 1956; Schiffman et al. 1962). Painter and Morgan (1961a and b) hydrolysed human B substance and obtained a number of disaccharides, one of which, 0-α-D-galactosyl-(1→3)-D-galactose (Painter et al. 1962) is a potent inhibitor in the group B-anti-B reaction, and therefore probably has the same terminal structure as blood group B antigen present at the erythrocyte periphery. Using a double diffusion test in agar gel and serological tests, Watkins and Morgan (1962b) showed that an α-N-acetylgalactosaminoyl grouping is present in the erythrocyte glycolipid carrying blood group A, and a non-reducing α-galactosyl group is present in B-group antigens. In general it may be stated that although the blood group substances on the erythrocyte are part of a glycolipid and those in the secretor substances are part of a mucopolysaccharide entity, the terminal units which determine the serological activity are similar.

Following the work of Thomsen (1926) and particularly Friedenrich (1927) it is known that some bacteria modify the agglutination of human erythrocytes by serum. Friedenrich (1928) showed that two groups of bacteria, diphtheroids and vibrio, produced the 'pan-agglutination' phenomena by a presumably enzymatic mechanism. Burnet et al. (1946) later showed that filtrates from *Vibrio cholerae* and *Clostridium welchii* in some way removed the receptor sites for influenza virus on the human red cell. Hanig (1948) noted that when erythrocytes adsorb PR8 virus, there is a decrease in their electrophoretic mobility, which he argued was due to loss of charged substance from the cells, or change in the spatial configuration of charged groups, or adsorption of charged elements from the virus. Ada and Stone (1950) showed that the *V. cholerae* receptor destroying enzyme (RDE) reduced the mobility of erythrocytes by some 87% and suggested that the 'liberated product itself contains acidic groups', and later showed (Stone and Ada 1952) that this loss in mobility was correlated with loss of virus receptors. In an electron microscopic study, Bayer (1964) has shown both influenza virus and RDE adsorb to receptor glycoprotein.

On the basis that sialic acids have been isolated in crystalline form from erythrocyte stroma of different animal species (Klenk and Lempfrid 1957), Klenk (1958) suggested that an acylated neuraminic acid could contribute to the charge on an erythrocyte. The identification of receptor destroying enzyme as neuraminidase; (vide Gottschalk 1960) its purification by Ada and French (1959) and determination of its specificity (Ada et al. 1961; Gottschalk 1957) which is the hydrolytic cleavage of the glycosidic bond joining the keto group of N-acetyl-neuraminic acid to a sugar or derivative

(D-galactosamine), have all enabled the relationship of the sialic acids to the cell periphery to be elucidated. Thus, Cook et al. (1960) showed that an 80% reduction in the electrophoretic mobility of human erythrocytes followed their incubation with neuraminidase, and further, free sialic acids could be chemically identified following such treatment (Cook et al. 1961).

Another approach to the position of N-acetylneuraminic acid in the erythrocyte ultrastructure comes through immunological techniques. Thus, treatment of erythrocytes with either RDE or influenza virus destroys their M and N antigenic activity (Springer and Ansell 1958; Mäkelä and Cantell 1958). Romanowska (1960) and Klenk and Uhlenbruck (1960) showed that treatment of isolated M and N substances with influenza virus or neuraminidase resulted in loss of M and N specificity, which was correlated in the latter case with liberation of N-acetylneuraminic acid. Although Mäkelä and Cantell and Uhlenbruck (1961a, b) reported that N-acetylneuraminic acid will weakly inhibit rabbit anti-M and anti-N sera, Springer et al. (1961) and Seaman and Uhlenbruck (1962) could not. It therefore appears at the moment that although N-acetylneuraminic acid forms part of the essential structure of M and N antigens, and that it has a terminal position in the antigenic molecules, M and N specificity is not to be correlated entirely with it alone.

Ponder (1951) showed that following incubation with trypsin, human erythrocytes lost some 20% of their net negative charge. This observation has been confirmed and extended to other proteolytic enzymes (Cook et al. 1960; Klenk and Uhlenbruck 1960; Mäkelä et al. 1960). Heard and Seaman (1960) concluded that the loss of charge resulted from bond fission with loss of carboxyl groups from the erythrocyte electrokinetic surface. Later work (Cook et al. 1960) showed that in fact a Sialomucopeptide was released from the cell due to the activity of trypsin on the arginine or lysine of proteins at the cell periphery. Sialic acid appears to form an a-ketosidic linkage with galactosamine (or an acyl derivative) which is linked to the carboxyl group of a dicarboxylic acid (e.g. the α-carboxyl of glutamic acid). This type of linkage has been elucidated in bovine submaxillary gland mucoprotein (Gottschalk and Graham 1959; Gottschalk 1960a; Murphy and Gottschalk 1961 and Gottschalk et al. 1962) and on the erythrocyte (Cook 1962) and is shown in fig. 1.2. The fact that the reduction in erythrocyte mobility produced by various proteolytic enzymes is much less than the reduction produced by neuraminidase, points to much of the sialic acid present not being directly linked to protein at the cell periphery.

Measurement of cellular electrophoretic mobilities before and after treat-

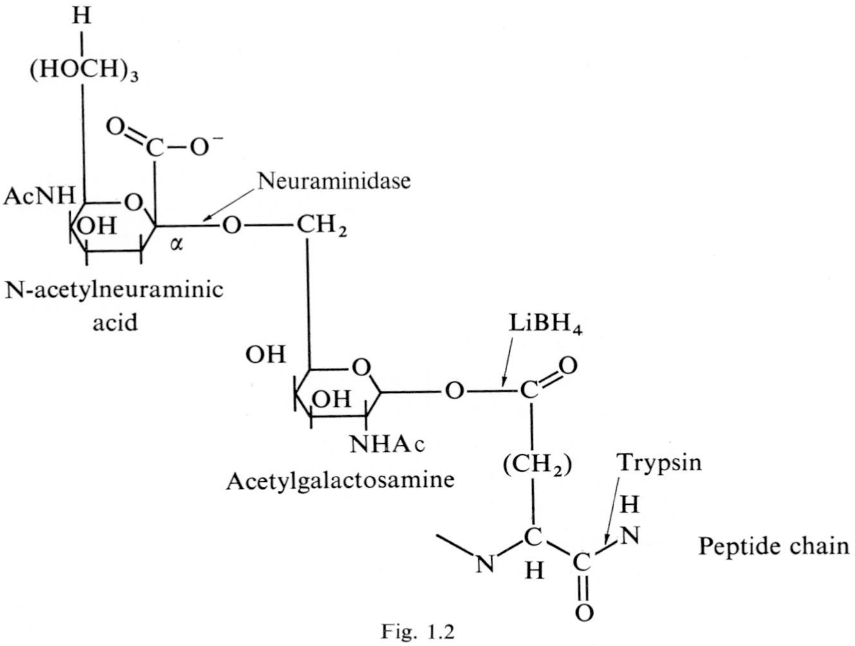

Fig. 1.2

ment with neuraminidase allows terminal N-acetylneuraminic acid to be easily and unequivocally detected at the cell periphery. An additional check can be provided by direct assay of liberated sialic acid using Warren's (1959) 2-thiobarbituric acid method. An indirect method utilizing cell detachment form glass following neuraminidase treatment has also been used by Weiss (1961a, 1963) to demonstrate sialic acids at the peripheries of various cultured cells. In many investigations so far recorded on normal and tumour cells, only the N-acetyl (Cook et al. 1962, 1963; Miller et al. 1963) and N-glycolyl (Miller et al. 1963) derivatives of sialic acid have been detected. The view that sialic acids are present only at the tumour 'tissue' cell periphery is probably erroneous and will be further discussed in chapter 6.

Morgan and Watkins (1951) showed that blood group receptors type P, were destroyed by treating the erythrocyte periphery with sodium periodate, which indicated that a key part of the receptor was carbohydrate. Of the seventy different simple sugars and polysaccharides later tested by them (Watkins and Morgan 1962a) for their capacity to inhibit the agglutination of P_1 cells by anti-P_1 serum, only two, 3-0-α and 4-0-α-digalactoside showed activity. In addition, the degradation of P_1 activity by enzymes (from *T.*

foetus) is specifically inhibited by D-galactose. It is therefore possible that an α-D-galactosyl unit is a 'specific' part of P_1 blood group antigen.

The serologically active substance in the secretions of individuals of blood group O is called H substance. Watkins and Morgan (1952) showed that simple fucose derivatives would inhibit agglutination of O-cells by eel anti-O (H). In reviewing the evidence, Kabat (1956) does not draw definite conclusions about the chemical groups responsible for specific activity.

According to Watkins (1964), the chemical nature of the Rhesus (Rh) blood group system is uncertain. Although attempts have been made to determine the nature of the antigenic groups by studying the inhibition of haemagglutination with chemically defined low molecular weight inhibitors (Boyd 1962), so many different compounds cause inhibition that, in the opinion of Watkins, judgement must be reserved at the present time. Although their chemical nature is obscure the numbers of Rh antigenic sites on cells have been determined by measuring the adsorption of isotopically labelled antibodies. Masouredis (1959, 1960) showed that homozygous (DD) erythrocytes bound 1.6 times as much anti-Rh_0 (anti-D) as heterozygous (Dd) cells; corresponding to 10,300 homozygous and 6,400 heterozygous sites per erythrocyte. This potentially valuable technique seems to have been used surprisingly little in quantitative studies on the cell periphery.

Over the last few years a great deal of work has been done on the genetic basis of tissue transplantation, particularly in mice; some of this work has been reviewed by Snell (1957), Gorer (1961) and Möller (1963) and is discussed in chapter 9. In mice the presence of cellular transplantation antigens, which determine the fate of 'grafts' is determined by at least 15 genetic loci, the best known and quantitatively most important of these is the H-2 or histocompatibility-2 locus. The present discussion will be concerned with the localization of the H-isoantigens in relation to the cell periphery, together with some comments on their chemical nature.

Although H-antigens were considered to be cytoplasmic by Medawar (1959), on the basis of techniques involving chemical extraction, Kandutsch and Reinert-Wenck (1957), Herzenberg and Herzenberg (1961), and Herberman and Stetson (1965) suggested that the H-2 antigens were confined to the membranes. Studies using a fluorescent antibody technique (Dumande et al. 1961; Möller 1963) have demonstrated the peripheral localization of H-2 isoantigens in leukaemic cells, and in a variety of normal and malignant cells.

Manson et al. (1963a, b) have also studied the histocompatibility antigens isolated from normal and malignant mouse tissues. Using material from cell suspensions, which were equilibrated at 1,500 pounds per square inch and then decompressed in a nitrogen bomb (Hunter and Commerford 1961), in tumour homograft sensitization tests, Manson and his colleagues concluded that all detectable transplantation antigens were in fact present in the microsomal lipoprotein fraction. These findings are not necessarily at variance with the 'surface' localization reported by others, since by means of the light microscope it is not possible to determine with absolute certainty whether an adsorbed fluorescent antibody is on or in a cell, and furthermore, pressure homogenization of tissues may well produce many microsome-like bodies which are formed from plasma membrane fragments. The chemical nature of the histocompatibility antigens up to 1961 was reviewed by Kandutsch (1961), and although work up to that time showed them to be composed largely of protein and lipid, it went little beyond this.

Haemagglutination can be induced by H-2 antibody in the presence of dextran (Gorer and Mikulska 1954), and inhibition of this haemagglutination has been used as a test of H-2 antigenic activity (Davies and Hutchison 1961). Davies (1962a) showed that cell-free ascitic fluid had specific antigenic activity which probably originates from cells which are lysed, and later Davies (1962b) chemically characterized the antigenic fraction as consisting of approximately 65% protein, 3.5% carbohydrate, 35% lipid, 1.4% hexosamine, 0.3% sialic acid. The nature of the specific determinant groups was not revealed by this work and there is always the possibility that inhibition of haemagglutination is in fact caused by a trace contaminant. As Davies' preparation was heterogeneous, this last possibility remains, and it is to be noted that Billingham et al. (1958) inactivated the so-called antigens by mild treatment with periodate, implicating sugars. Davies (1962b) noted that interference with the main lipid components of the H-2 antigen by means of various detergents, organic solvents, freeze-drying, sonication, etc. results in a loss of antigenic activity. This implies that the lipid itself is the antigen or that the lipid is responsible for maintaining the necessary spatial relationships of other components proteinaceous and/or carbohydrate constituents.

1.4.2 Water

Vandenheuvel (1965) has discussed the role of water in membranes in connection with tangential transference of enzymatically produced energy over the cell periphery, where protons or electrons would be much better energy carriers than bulky ions. Dry proteins conduct electricity poorly (Eley 1962; King and Medley 1949; Riehl 1957), but some, including keratin

(King and Medley) become more conductive when they adsorb water at their surfaces. Eley suggests that this conductivity effect is mediated by two or three times as many water molecules as polar groups, and Klotz (1962) visualizes structured water transporting electron and protons over long distances. Vandenheuvel has proposed an interesting membrane model in which a water monolayer, composing the outermost part, is hydrogen-bonded to polar groups of underlying extended proteins. The protein itself is adsorbed onto a water-cation monolayer, the cations of which are ionically linked to the underlying polar heads of the lipids by oxygen atoms. In this model, Vandenheuvel attempts to explain potassium selectivity of membranes in terms of the properties of the water-cation monolayer.

The possibility of biologically important water structures has been much discussed, and many of the relevant publications have been reviewed by Kavanau (1965). No attempt can be made here to review the field, since interpretative difficulties lead to the conclusion that efforts to relate water structure to cell membranes are premature. However, a few of what appear to be relevant points can be noted.

Three-dimensional structures are thought to exist in liquid water (Bernal and Fowler 1933) which may be due to partial retention of the tetrahedral hydrogen-bonded ice structure. Frank and Wen (1957) proposed that molecules such as quaternary ammonium ions have strong binding capacities for water and are there capable of acting as structure promoters. It might, therefore, be expected that around the head groups of some phospholipids, there is less randomness in the organization of the surrounding water than in the bulk aqueous phase. The structures are visualized as transcent' flickering clusters' of hydrogen-bonded water molecules with half lives of 10^{-11} to 10^{-10} sec. These short existences are meaningful physically, since they are 100 to 1,000 times as long as a molecular vibration period.

Pauling and Marsh (1952) suggested that water molecules can form structures which retain certain features of ice such as bond angle and intermolecular distance, but contain more cavity space. Pauling (1961) has advanced a molecular theory of general anaesthesis based on the interactions of anaesthetics with water molecules to form hydrate microcrystals. The stability of these crystals depends partly on the hydrogen-bonded water framework and partly on the Van der Waals interaction between the anaesthetic molecules and the water frameworks surrounding them.

Klotz (1958) has attempted to explain anomalous titration curves of many proteins which differ from predictions based on electrostatic theory in terms of surrounding structured water, which could mask both naturally occurring and artificially introduced functional groups. The term 'iceberg' used by Klotz in this paper is rather misleading as nuclear magnetic resonance spectroscopy of proteins indicates that their associated water does not have the structure of ice (Bovey 1961). The term 'soft ice' refers not strictly to ice-like structure but rather to imply water in association with – and oriented by – polar interactions.

The fact that water molecules are small enough to fit into small spaces in proteins (Coulson 1957), within a water lattice itself (Pauling 1959) and within a lipid-protein interface (Kavanau 1965), and can form hydrogen-bonds in all of these regions, suggests that many structural arrangements in membranes are probably affected by water. Warner (1961, 1962) has considered the relationships of carbohydrates (using a scylloinositol model) and proteins with water structures, and concludes that water may affect the interactions of carbohydrates with peptides, and impose a hexagonal conformation on polypeptides in the aqueous phase. Good (1961) has attempted to correlate lysis of erythrocytes by various reagents, with their ability to disrupt water lattice structure; although he has obtained a positive correlation, he has by no means established a causal relationship.

Although it is to be expected that water will materially affect membrane structure and function, the experimental proof of this is lacking. On the negative side however, it may be suggested that data obtained from studies on dehydrated material must be taken very cautiously in terms of molecular arrangements.

1.4.3 Proteins

The nature of the proteins associated with cell membranes is not well known. Some work has been done on extracting proteins from erythrocytes, and more precise work has been carried out on the nature and localization of enzymes associated with the cell periphery and mitochondrial membranes.

Attempts made to extract the protein from erythrocytes include those of Dandliker et al. (1950), Moscovitch et al. (1950), and Moscovitch and Calvin (1952). These workers lysed erythrocytes in distilled water and then washed them at pH 9, to yield a proteinaceous material known as 'reticulin' or 'stromin', and ether extraction of this yielded 'elenin', which under the electron microscope is seen to consist of rods having the dimensions 5 to 11μ by 0.3 to 1.3μ. When the elenin is extracted with ether, a protein is obtained which is said to resemble the 'stromatin' previously described by Jorpes (1932) and Boehm (1935), and which is depicted as forming an inner layer of the erythrocyte membrane by Winkler and Bungenberg de Jong (1941). 'Stromatin' is not a protein, and Furchgott (1940) showed that it is a suspension of myelin forms. After 'elenin' is precipitated from reticulin with ether, the so-called S-protein may be precipitated from the supernate.

Ponder (1961) has remarked on the paucity of physicochemical data on these 'protein' fractions from erythrocyte ghosts, and concludes that present knowledge of them tells us virtually nothing about their state in the intact cell.

1.4.4 Enzymes

Other proteins located in membrane systems include enzymes. Data are available on enzymes present at the peripheries of erythrocytes which include a diglyceride kinase (Hokin and Hokin 1961). Other enzymes present in the erythrocyte stroma include a phosphoribose isomerase (Micheli and Grabar 1961) and Cathepsins I, II and III (Morrison and Newrath 1953); other data are discussed by Kleinzeller and Kotyk (1960). Wenkstern and Engelhardt (1955, 1959) have demonstrated different 'ectopyrases' in a variety of vertebrate erythrocytes, which split adenosine mono-, di- and tri-phosphates. ATP-ase activity, which is linked to sodium transport has been demonstrated in the peripheries of human erythrocytes (Skou 1957); liver cells (Essner et al. 1958); rat hepatomata (Novikoff 1957; Kaplan and Novikoff 1959); and in Ehrlich murine ascites carcinoma cells (Acs et al. 1954). The ATP-ases located at the cell periphery by Novikoff and his associates hydrolyse other nucleosidetriphosphates in addition to ATP and are therefore better named nucleosidetriphosphatases (Novikoff et al. 1962). Fernández-Morán (1964) advances the thesis that all cell membrane systems contain particles analogous to the mitochondrial elementary particles described by them; this is discussed further in reviews by Green (1964).

1.5 Molecular organization of the cell periphery

1.5.1 Molecular arrangements in model systems

Before going into the possible molecular arrangements of membrane lipids in the cell, it is necessary to consider the comparatively simple arrangement of lipids at an air/water interface. Although in 1765, Benjamin Franklin observed that oil would spread out to form very thin films on the surface of the pond at Clapham Common, quantitative, indoor measurements were apparently first made by Pockels in 1891. Using a water-filled trough, she was able to confine insoluble films at the air/water interface, between barriers extending across the whole width of the trough. By moving one of the barriers towards the other, the relationship between surface tension and area could be determined. Lord Rayleigh (1899) showed that 'judged by surface tension, the effect of contamination comes on suddenly' and 'the first drop in tension corresponds to a complete layer one molecule thick', Hardy (1913) suggested that when monolayers are formed at an air/water interface from molecules which are hydrophilic at one end, and hydrophobic at the other, it would be expected that they would be oriented with their hydrophilic ends in the water and their hydrophobic parts in the air. Langmuir (1917) provided experimental support for Hardy's hypothesis by showing that the compressed area of monolayers of fatty acids is, within limits, independent of the length of their hydrophobic tails. Much of the work on monolayers is described and discussed by Adam (1941) and more recently by Davies and Rideal (1961). Although the early workers on monolayers were aware of the interactions of the polar parts of molecular with the underlying aqueous phase, these interactions are seldom discussed in more recent papers.

Danielli (1958) makes the point that any membrane model should take note of the inherent property of lipoidal molecules to form highly oriented structures. If phospholipids at an air/water interface are oriented with their polar groups in the aqueous phase and their hydrocarbon chains in the air, then the ratio of contra-oriented groups can be calculated as follows (Weiss 1962);

$$\frac{\text{Phospholipids with polar groups in aqueous phase}}{\text{Phospholipids with hydrocarbon groups in aqueous phase}} = \frac{e^{\Delta G/RT}}{1}$$

where e is an exponential, R is the gas constant per gramme molecule, T is the absolute temperature and ΔG is the free energy change resulting when a given molecule changes its orientation from one position to the other. ΔG may be approximately computed, assuming that in the rearrangement of one phospholipid molecule, eight $CH_{2(3)}$ groups (i.e. a double hydrocarbon chain of four segments) are transferred from a predominantly non-aqueous medium to a predominantly aqueous region around the polar head groups of adjacent phospholipid molecules. The energy change for this process, assuming 600 calories per CH_2 group (Rideal and Taylor 1957) is $8 \times 600 = 4,800$ cal. In addition the polar head group of the involved molecule is transferred in the reverse direction to the hydrocarbon change, for which the energy requirements are probably in excess of the 5,000 cal required to transfer a carboxyl group under similar circumstances (Haydon, personal communication), ΔG is therefore assumed to be approximately 9,800 calories, and

$$e^{\Delta G/RT} \cdot 5.6 \times 10^8.$$

Therefore, from this calculation the expected number of contra-oriented phospholipid molecules in an 'oriented' array is very small indeed.

When a lipid film spreads on water and is compressed by a movable barrier, a point is reached where the film resists further compression. At this point, where the film itself is exerting a lateral pressure, the molecules composing it are coherent. Measured pressure may be applied to a film to produce a measured decrease in area, and a pressure/area curve may be obtained. Such pressure area relationships fall into two main categories: (1) The condensed film, which has the properties of a two-dimensional solid in which beyond the pressure of 'solidification', application of increased pressure produces little change in surface area, and in which the molecules preserve fixed positions.
(2) The expanded film which has the properties of a two-dimensional liquid in which the constituent molecules do not have fixed positions.

The behaviour of phospholipid monolayers is reviewed by Kavanau (1965). Apparently in both monolayers and micelles, although the choline and ethanolamine moieties of the phospholipids do not leave the aqueous phase, they may well be orientated at various angles with the interface on account of their polar interactions with each other and with the phosphoryl groups present in the molecule. The proposed J-shaped molecule suggested by Finean (1953a), Few (1955) and Finean and Millington (1955) seems rather unlikely, as will shortly be discussed.

It was pointed out by Gorter and Grendel (1926) that cephalin and lecithin form expanded, liquid films, and this appears true of most natural phospholipids at an air/water interface (Leathes 1923, 1925; Turner and Watson 1930; Adam 1941; De Bernard 1958; Van Deenen et al. 1962). In contrast to the phospholipids, cholesterol and sphingomyelin form more solid condensed films. Collet (1922) examined a series of binary mixtures of solid and liquid triglycerides and made the important observation that the area of the mixtures often differed considerably from what would be expected from simple addition of the areas occupied by films of the separate constituents, suggesting the existence of molecular associations in such monolayers. In view of the fairly constant proportion of cholesterol in the total lipids present in the erythrocyte (membrane), it is of interest that Leathes (1925) studied the behaviour of films composed of mixtures of lecithin and cholesterol and discovered that the cholesterol apparently caused a diminution in the areas of lecithin films. Later studies of the 'condensing' effect of cholesterol were made by Adam and Jessop (1928) and Schulman and Hughes (1935). Leathes, Adam and Jessop, and De Bernard all concluded that the effect of cholesterol can only be interpreted in terms of an actual decrease in the surface area of the lecithin. The actual nature of the cholesterol/lecithin associations is reviewed by Dervichian (1958), but is is clear to the present author that there is still not complete agreement. The different types of molecular interactions between cholesterol and lecithin have been discussed by Schulman and Rideal (1937), Schulman and Stenhagen (1938) and Kavanau in terms of Van der Waals attractions between the hydrocarbon parts of the molecules, and interaction between their polar heads.

Fowkes (1963) has criticized the interpretations given to associations in mixed monolayers and thinks that the experimental evidence is in favour of a random association of both types of molecules rather than a complex of fixed molecular proportions.

In an important paper on the interactions of membrane lipids, Pethica (1966) has proposed on the basis of measurements of surface potential on synthetic phospholipid films, that phospholipid zwitterions are arranged tangentially to the surface. Calculations suggest that coulombic interactions are of major importance in forming and stabilizing phospholipid sheets. In bimolecular lipid leaves, the cohesion between the two layers of the leaflet is stabilized by the energetically unfavourable interaction of the paraffin chains with water. When cholesterol is introduced into phospholipid sheets, coulombic and possibly Van der Waals' stability is diminished. Pethica also cites unpublished data of Standish and himself showing that the surface potentials of mixed cholesterol cephalin monolayers at an air/water interface are close to the proportionate mean for separate monolayers of the pure substances, which suggest that the phospholipid zwitterions and dipoles of cholesterol are not mutually distorted in the mixed monolayer, as proposed by Finean (1953c). Positive interaction with cholesterol is only obtained with those phospholipids containing double bonds (oleyl).

Although attempts have been made to correlate the penetrating activities of various reagents on cell membranes with their activity on lipid monolayers at air/water interfaces (Schulman and Rideal 1937; Rideal and Schulman

1939; Pethica and Schulman 1953; Pethica 1958; Bangham et al. 1962; Bangham 1963), as pointed by Haydon and Taylor (1963), and as realized by those doing the actual experiments, there are limitations to this model system. One of the objections is that the pressures in monomolecular layers may be too low to provide an entirely meaningful model. The effect of film surface area on the number of available adsorbing sites, and the effect of surface pressure on the adsorption energy, lead Haydon and Taylor to conclude that there are quantitative deficiencies in the monomolecular film when compared to the bimolecular layer, which is often considered a better biological model.

Other lipid configurations in addition to the monolayer are the subject of a review by Bangham, who traces the evolution of structures formed by amphipathic lipid molecules as a function of lipid concentration relative to water. At an oil/water interface, which is the situation of most biological relevance, phospholipids, for example, will adsorb until the interfacial space is fully occupied. If, at this stage, the concentration of lipid is increased, the lipid molecules aggregate when the so-called critical micelle concentration (CMC) is reached and form micelles, which usually consist of spherical structures, which in water have their constituent lipids oriented with their polar heads on the water and their hydrophobic tails in the centre of the micelle. As the lipid concentration increases still further, the previously isotropic system becomes anisotropic, the viscosity increases, optical birefringence is noted, and phase changes occur; the new phases may coexist in equilibrium with the interfacial film and micelles. One of the newly emerging phases, the liquid crystalline, smectic phase, consists of bimolecular lipid sheets, separated from each other by water, and demonstrable with the polarizing microscope. It seems possible that other phases may exist at these lipid concentrations (around 50% lipid w/v) as suggested by X-ray diffraction studies on soap and water systems (Luzzati and Husson 1962). These consist of cylinders with the polar heads arranged at their peripheries and the hydrophobic tails innermost. They are of apparently indefinite length, and are arranged in groups of seven, having hexagonal cross-section. The shapes suggested by these X-ray studies has been confirmed with electron micrographs, by Stoeckenius (1962). Finally, as the concentration of lipid exceeds 95% crystalline solids are formed, consisting of multiple banks of bimolecular layers. However, it should be remembered that not all amphipathic molecules undergo these phase-transitions at similar concentrations.

On the evidence of light-scattering experiments (Robinson 1960) pure lecithin(s) in concentrations down to 10^{-5} g/ml, form micellar lamellae, having a 'micellar' molecular weight of about 20 millions, diameters of approximately 900Å, and a thickness of 69Å, which is equivalent to a bimolecular layer of phospholipid. Such bimolecular layers can incorporate other lipids, phospholipids, and sterols without change of phase (Saunders et al. 1962). The tendency for phospholipids to form bimolecular leaflets in water is a reflection of the fact that such bilayers are the lowest free energy configuration for undissolved phospholipids in water (Haydon and Taylor 1963).

Another aspect of lipid configuration is brought out in the studies of Lawrence and his associates (Lawrence 1961; Hyde et al. 1954) on ternary systems of soap/water/cholesterol. These systems are physico-chemically similar to phospholipid/water/cholesterol systems, which previously mentioned analytical data indicate may be relevant to cell membranes. These workers have shown that, depending on concentration of any of the three components, marked phase changes can occur, which are associated with variations in electrical conductivity, viscosity and other rheological parameters, and surface tension. Weiss (1962) has raised the question of whether local quantitative variations (within the physiological range) in concentrations of constituents such as cholesterol-like steroids and water, of possible ternary systems within cell membranes, could initiate physical heterogeneities of biological importance.

Attempts have been made to study artificial (lipoidal) bimolecular layers separating two aqueous phases. Langmuir and Waugh (1938) described films made from lecithin dissolved in benzene and in contact with aqueous solutions of egg albumin which were thin (i.e. grey or black; <500Å, see Overbeek 1960; Vašiček 1960) and stable for some minutes. They also pointed out the possibility of carrying out electrical and permeability measurements on such films.

A more workable system has been described by Mueller et al. (1962a, b; 1963) and Mueller and Rudin (1963) have described a technique for making such black films from lipids and lipid-protein brain extracts, in which the film covers a small hole, and is stable for more than 24 hours. The work has been extended by Thompson and his associates (Thompson 1964; Huang et al. 1964) to films of lecithin and tetradecane which are 61Å thick, and therefore presumably bimolecular. Their experiments show that in order to form bimolecular layers of phospholipids under these conditions, the presence of a neutral lipid is required. The phospholipid must carry a zero net charge, and the phospholipid must contain unsaturated fatty acids which cannot be appreciably oxidized. Thompson notes that it is of considerable interest that of a large group of neutral lipids studied, only cholestrol formed stable bilayers (in a 1:1 mole ratio) with his lecithin/tetradecane system.

Hanai et al. (1964, 1965) have also studied black films of lecithin in *n*-heptane, *n*-decane and *n*-hexadecane in an attempt to perform measurements on pure systems. From their capacitance and interfacial tension measurements, they calculate that their films were also bimolecular.

An important observation has been made by Tien (1966a) on black films, as used in these experiments. Freshly recrystallized cholesterol apparently does not form stable membranes, however its oxidation products such as 7-dehydrocholesterol do, thereby indicating that the presence of phospholipids is not indispensable for the formation of black membranes. Tien considers that the fact that a cholesterol derivate alone can form a stable bimbolecular membrane may necessitate a revaluation of those theories requiring a phospholipid/cholesterol combination.

Tien (1966b) has reported observations on the thickness of bimolecular lipid membranes in aqueous media, and notes discrepancies between his results and those of Huang and Thompson (1965), which he attributes to an error in these authors' calculations. Tien also notes that in the case of membranes studied in saline solutions, the electrical methods used by Hanai et al. are inapplicable. Tien's estimate of 69Å for a bimolecular lecithin layer is incompatible with two fully extended and perpendicularly aligned layers, which would measure some 74Å (Vandenheuvel 1963b), and may be explained either in terms of interaction of the polar heads of the phospholipids with the aqueous phase and/or the hydration of the polar heads so affecting the refractive index that optical measurements of film thickness are rendered insensitive. Tien does not regard significant interdigitation of the hydrocarbon chains as likely.

In spite of the obvious difficulties, this technique of studying artificial lipid membranes appears promising, although its relevance to cell membranes is speculative.

Some interesting studies of model lipid systems have been made on so-called negatively-stained material under the electron microscope. Negative staining was described by Hall (1955), Huxley (1956) and Brenner and Horne (1959) and has been recently discussed by Horne (1965) and Glauert (1965). The technique consists of suspending the specimen in phosphotungstate, depositing it on a carbon film, and then examining by electron microscopy those areas lying over holes in the film. Although the mechanisms involved in the technique are not well understood, fine structural details of some biological specimens may be visualized directly because of the considerable enhancement of contrast due to heterogeneous penetration of the specimen. The requirements of the ideal negative stain have been discussed by Valentine and Horne (1962) who state that it should have a high electron density and not react with the specimen. Van Bruggen et al. (1960) have also drawn attention to the dangers of electrostatic interactions between the negatively charged phosphotungstate ions and the specimen. Although Glauert, in defending the 'mildness' of the technique, pointed to the maintenance of infectivity in viruses (Horne and Wildy 1964) and to activity in enzymes (Watson 1962) after exposure to phosphotungstate, these data are probably more relevant to protein structures and cannot be extrapolated to the lipid elements of membrane structures.

As a result of electron microscopic studies of negatively-stained saponin/ cholesterol/lecithin model systems, Lucy and Glauert (1964) suggested that lamellar structures usually visualized in terms of bimolecular lipid leaflets may actually be formed by the association of lipid micelles containing lecithin and cholesterol, having a diameter of about 40 Å. Mixtures of lecithin/ cholesterol and saponin/cholesterol micelles appear to aggregate spontaneously to form helices, built up of an outer helix of lecithin/cholesterol micelles, around an inner helix of saponin/cholesterol micelles. Sjöstrand (1963b, c) has also reported the presence of globular units in ultra-thin sections of some membranes after freeze-drying, and also suggests that they may represent regular arrays of lipid micelles.

Lucy (1964) has suggested that if micellar structures are actually present in membranes in dynamic equilibrium with bimolecular structures, they could form aqueous pores of 8 Å diameter extending through the thickness of the bilayer. This suggested arrangement is expected to be difficult to demonstrate experimentally, since of the total lipid present, only a small amount need be present in the micellar phase to be of considerable physiological importance.

Bangham and Horne (1964) have made a critical study on the effect of negative staining with phosphotungstate on the electron microscopic appearance of phospholipids. They note that the bimolecular leaflet conformation of lecithin and similar amphipathic lipid is dependent partly on the free energy relationships of the polar head groups with the aqueous and lipid phases, and partly on the lack of repulsion between the electrostatically neutral (i.e. zero net charge) head groups. They discuss the conformational charges which would result if this balance of electrostatic and interfacial forces are disturbed, for example by altering the charge on the head groups with polyions or by altering the environmental pH; or by penetrating the leaflet with wedge-shaped molecules. Experimental evidence in favour of the disturbing effect of a wedge-shaped molecule is shown by the break-up of an equimolar system of lecithin and cholesterol in water treated with lyso-lecithin. It is suggested that during the drying process, associated with negative staining with phosphotungstate, the phosphotungstate ions may become concentrated at the lipid surface and induce a sufficiently large charge in net negative charge on the polar head groups to make them electro-statically wedge-shaped, producing micellization. Evidence in favour of potassium phosphotungstate altering the net charge on lecithin head groups is provided by the change in electrophoretic mobility of lecithin dispersions in its presence (Bangham and Haydon; unpublished data cited by Glauert 1965). Bangham and Horne also comment on the fact that due to the great difference in valency between the phosphotungstate and potassium ions, an electrostatic stress may be set up at a lipid/water interface, producing phase changes. Bangham and Horne (cited by Glauert) failed to observe micellar subunits, after staining with calcium phosphotungstate, where the electrostatic stress and consequent likelihood of phase changes are less. In absolute contradiction however, Lucy and Glauert (1964) state that helices built of micellar subunits are in fact seen after staining with calcium phosphotung-state, and therefore phosphotungstate ions per se are not required for helix formation. These conflicting statements are probably as confusing to the reader as the writer! Other possible artifacts associated with the potassium phosphotungstate staining technique have been discussed by Finean and Rumsby (1963), who argue that as the phase structure of phospholipids depends on water concentration, as suggested by low-angle X-ray diffraction studies on nerve myelin (Finean 1961), the various structures seen may be formed only in the terminal phases of dehydration. It would appear that in the case of micelle formation, in addition to the balance between the elec-trostatic repulsion between charged head groups and the Van der Waals attraction between non-polar parts (Debye 1949a, b), the nature of the solvent must also be considered. The statistical thermodynamic treatment of water developed by Nemethy and Scheraga (1962a, 1964) has been considered in connection with hydrocarbon aggregation (Nemethy and Scheraga 1962b, c, 1963). Poland and Scheraga (1965a, b) have suggested that in the case of non-ionic systems, solvent effects are of the first order in accounting for micelle stability. In a later communication, Poland (1966) has also argued that there must be considerable solvent effects around the charged heads which contribute a negative enthalpy change when a monomer enters a micelle.

The overall evidence would suggest that negative staining with potassium phosphotungstate is inherently a bad method for demonstrating pre-existing micellar structures in membranes. Although Glauert (1965) states that if micellar structures were already present, they would not be affected by negative staining, this really begs the question of whether or not they really exist in cell membranes.

1.5.2 *Molecular arrangements of lipids in the cell periphery*

The classical experiments leading to many current concepts of the ultrastructure of the cell membrane were made by Gorter and Grendel (1925, 1926), who extracted the lipids of chromocytes (erythrocytes) with large quantities of acetone. After evaporation of the acetone, the residue was redissolved in a small quantity of benzene and spread as a thin film at the air/water interface of a Langmuir trough. The monomolecular film was compressed until resistance to further compression was observed, and its area was measured. The surface area of the chromocytes from which the lipids were extracted was computed, and on the assumption that the lipids in them were arranged as in the Langmuir trough at an air/water interface, enough lipids were considered to be present to form a bimolecular film over the cells. In an interesting review on this topic, Davson (1962) quotes examples of similar measurements made on erythrocytes of the rabbit, guinea pig and man, where the ratios of the surface areas of spread films of lipids to the computed surface areas of the erythrocytes from which they were extracted, are respectively 2, 1.9 and 2.

Winkler and Bungenberg de Jong (1941) considered that Gorter and Grendel's estimates of the erythrocyte surface area are too low by some 50% and Hoffman (1962) has made the same point, and suggests that using Gorter and Grendel's data, the ratio of total lipid surface area to cell surface area is nearer to 1 than 2. However, as acetone is now known to extract only about two-thirds of the total lipid present, the ratio might well *in vivo*, tend towards 2. It must be emphasized however that the interpretation of surface area measurements in troughs, of mixed lipid films is difficult, and that as stated earlier, the assumption is made that, in the cell, the lipids are arranged as in the trough. Whether or not Gorter and Grendel's estimate of a lipid layer two molecules thick around cells is absolutely correct in the light of present-day refinements in technique, seems of less importance than the fact that the concept acted as a direct stimulus to so much later work; and the concept that the main underlying structural element of membranes is a bimolecular lipid leaflet stems from their suggestion made in 1925.

1.5.2.1 Membrane dimensions
Some of the evidence relating to the dimensions of cellular membranes will now be examined with a view to determining the feasibility of the bimolecular lipid leaflet constituting the basic membrane skeleton. Before the advent of electron microscopy attempts were made to determine the thickness of cell membranes by various other indirect methods which are discussed by Danielli (1935), Ponder (1961) and Davson (1962).

1.5.2.2 Conductivity studies
Höber's (1910, 1912) studies on the conductivities of cell suspensions showed that electrically, the cell could be regarded as consisting of a conducting cytoplasm, separated from the surrounding medium by a non-conducting membrane. Later Fricke (1923, 1924, 1925a, b) developed a theory relating measurements of the capacity of cell suspensions to the static capacity per square centimeter of their surfaces, which numerically approximated to $0.8\,\mu F$ per cm^2. By substituting this value (C_0) in the formula:

$$\text{membrane thickness} = \frac{C_0}{3/4\pi \cdot 9 \times 10^5} \quad \text{(Davson 1962)},$$

the membrane is calculated to be $33\,\text{Å}$ thick, which approximates to more than a monolayer and less than a bilayer of lipid. In view of the approximations made in ascribing a value of 3 for the dielectric constant of the lipids, and of difficulties in extrapolating measurement made of dieletric constant with alternating current to the conditions pertaining in the membrane (vide Danielli 1935), it is surprising that Fricke's value of $0.8\,\mu F/cm^2$ should agree so well with the result of approximately $1\,\mu F/cm^2$ obtained for the equivalent static capacity of squid nerve fibres by Curtis and Cole (1938) and Cole (1940), where the membrane thickness was calculated at about $50\,\text{Å}$. These estimates are concerned only with the lipid constituents of the membranes.

Hanai et al. (1965) have measured the capacitance of artificial bimolecular layers of lecithin (vide p. 44) into which varying ratios of cholesterol have been incorporated. They calculated that the upper limit of capacitance of these bilayers is $0.55\,\mu F/cm^2$. The lower value obtained for artificial bilayers when compared with natural membranes is not likely to be due to either variation of the molecular length of the various lipids, which would make the membrane thinner, or sandwiching layers of protein. However, Hanai et al. remark that if only 1% of the membrane were made up of polar pores, containing material of dielectric constant 80 (water), then the capacitance would be increased to 0.16 μF, and the general electrical properties of the cell membrane could be accounted for in terms of a perforated lipid bilayer.

1.5.2.3 Leptoscopic studies

Waugh and Schmitt (1940) attempted to measure the thickness of the cell membrane lipids by comparing the intensities of the light reflected from the two thicknesses of opposing membrane of collapsed dried erythrocyte ghosts, with an optical wedge coated with barium stearate in known thickness by repeated dipping. Davson and Danielli (1952) note that as cytoplasmic and other non-lipid constituents may be present in the ghost, and as the apparent thickness varies with the pH of lyzing solution, leptoscopic measurements should be made on ghosts prepared at different pH's, and before and after treatment with lipid solvents. When this is done, the lipid-extracted ghosts are consistently thinner than their untreated counterparts over the range of pH 4 to 8, by an amount corresponding to 100Å for each thickness of membrane. This corresponds to about four layers of lipid, again if this is how the lipid is arranged.

1.5.2.4 Electron microscope and X-ray diffraction

The various observations made by electron microscopy on cell membranes up to 1960 are reviewed by Robertson (1960), who discusses how development in techniques suggest that the basic unit seen, particularly after permanganate fixation, but also after osmium fixation, consists of a pair of electron dense lines, each about 20Å across, separated by 35Å. The whole assembly being designated a '75Å unit', and considered to be the basic membrane unit.

Sjöstrand (1963c) has compared the ultrastructural features of plasma membranes, mitochrondrial and other cytomembranes. His evidence which is based on recent improved techniques is in agreement with the observations of Freeman (1959), Karrer (1960), Smith (1961), Zetterqvist (1956) and Yamoto (1963) that there are significant deviations in dimensions of various membranes from the '75%Å unit'. Thus, in mouse kidney and pancreas, mitochondrial membranes and the α-cytomembranes measure 50Å in osmium-fixed material and 60Å in material fixed with permanganate. In the same material, the 'smooth' cytomembranes measure 60Å in osmium-fixed and 70–80Å in permanganate-fixed preparations, whereas plasma membranes and the membranes surrounding zymogen granules measure 90–100Å. As Sjöstrand's measurements were all made on adjacent membranes in the same specimens, they cannot be attributed to technical artefacts, and Sjöstrand quite rightly questions the usefulness of the unit membrane hypothesis. The validity of measurements of membranes made under the electron microscope must clearly be examined before the data can be elaborated into membrane models. As an important method of testing these data involves the use of X-ray diffraction, further discussion will be postponed until after consideration of the X-ray diffraction data.

1.5.2.5 X-ray diffraction and related studies
Most of the relevant X-ray diffraction studies have been done on myelin sheath material. Although Geren (1954), Maturana (1960) and Peters (1960) showed that the myelin sheath is formed by a rolling-up of the plasma membrane of Schwann cells, the general impression is that the myelin sheath is so specialized in its function as an insulator, that it may at best be a poor model dimensionally for anything but a myelin sheath. In spite of this qualifying objection, the myelin sheath data are considered to be relevant to the present discussion not only because they lead to probably the most accurate picture of any biological membrane so far studied, but also because the X-ray diffraction data can be directly compared with that obtained with the electron microscope and with fresh material by means of the polarizing microscope. Much of the relevant literature is surveyed by Engstrom and Finean (1958), and Finean (1962).

Finean's work has clarified the position which may be summarized by stating that the myelin sheath contains a membrane some 80 to 90Å in thickness and that the distance separating the phosphatic polar heads of incorporated phospholipid is 51Å (Finean 1962). The model put forward by Finean and his various colleagues based on X-ray diffraction of fresh material therefore is strongly in support of the majority of lipids being arranged in a bimolecular leaf, in the myelin sheath and possibly the plasma membrane of Schwann cells.

As stated above, the data obtained by X-ray diffraction on fresh material provide an invaluable basis for determining the validity of the electron microscopic image. Changes in X-diffraction patterns in myelin occur after freezing, thawing and drying (Finean 1953b). The changes occurring after osmium fixation have been considered by Fernández-Morán and Finean (1957) starting with myelin with a 171Å repeat unit. Initially there is a shrinkage reducing the repeat period to 150–160Å. After alcohol dehydration there is a further reduction to about 130Å, but on methacrylate embedding there is an expansion to about 150Å. Electron microscopy of myelin after both permanganate and osmium fixation reveals a repeating density pattern of about 120 Å, and it seems reasonable to assume that this 120 Å pattern represents the periodicity observed in fresh myelin by X-ray diffraction if allowance is made for shrinkage (Robertson 1956b; Finean 1958). It is of interest to note here that Schmidt showed changes of birefringence with polarization microscopy after treatment of myelin with potassium permanganate (1936) and osmium tetroxide (1938) and that whatever precise interpretation is given to his data, it is clear that these two reagents alter the membrane properties. On a less pessimistic note, Finean and Rumsby (1963) comment that fixatives such as osmium tetroxide and potassium permanganate prevent the separation of independently diffracting units during drying. The hydrocarbon chains of lipid molecules in lamellar liquid/ crystalline phases, are identified by a broad band in the 4.5 Å region in X-ray diffraction diagrams (Luzzati and Husson 1962). Stoeckenius et al. (1960) showed that after such lamellar phase systems reacted with osmium tetroxide, although the 4.5 Å band disappears completely, the repeat pattern indicates that the lamellar structure is preserved. These authors therefore assume that after fixation the lamellae are held together by relatively few cross-links which are formed between fatty acid chains on opposite sides of the bimolecular lipid layers, but that the packing of the remaining fatty acid chains must be 'severely disturbed'. These various artefacts have been minimized as far as membranes are concerned, by the introduction of permanganate fixation in place of osmium (Luft 1957), better embedding techniques using epoxy resins in place of methacrylate (Glauert et al. 1956; Maalöe and Birch-Anderson 1956), and reduction of the distortion caused by sublimation of embedding medium by the use of Vestopal (Kellenberger et al. 1958). Other possible sources of error in electron micrographic measurements are the alterations occurring in thin sections during bombardment with the electron beam (Robertson 1957), due to loss of mass in the specimen which Reimer (1959) ascribes as due to loss of the lighter atoms (hydrogen, oxygen, nitrogen). Cosslett (1960) has measured the loss of mass in thin sections exposed to electron beams by microscopic interferometry, and notes that methacrylate becomes thinner by 20–50% and expoxy resins by 20–30%. Another difficulty which arises in comparing sets of electron micrographs is due to inexactitude in focussing and magnification, as discussed by Sjöstrand (1963c).

So far, this discussion has not touched on the important point of which chemical groups are visualized in electron microscopic preparations. Following the demonstration by Palade (1952) of cellular fine structure after osmium fixation, the chemistry of this process has received a good deal of attention (Wolman 1955; Baker 1958; Gunstone 1960) and it was concluded that osmium reacts with double bonds. In apparent disagreement with this conclusion were the observations of Stoeckenius (1962), that when osmium reacted with sodium linolenate in the hexagonal phase, the stain appeared to concentrate around the peripheries of the cylinders which according to Luzzati and Husson (1962), contained polar head groups. On the other hand, in preparations of brain phospholipids which were fixed with osmium after they had undergone phase reversal, the osmium appears in the aqueous centres of the cylinders, again where the polar groups are expected. The position has been clarified in a paper by Stoeckenius and Mahr (1965), who have observed the reaction of osmium tetroxide with lipids and related compounds. They note the reaction of 1 gramme atom of osmium per mole of $C=C$ double bond of starting material; and that, except in the case of phosphatidyl serine, no direct reaction of osmium tetroxide with hydrophilic groups of lipid could be demonstrated. However, spectroscopic measurements made in the infra-red region strongly indicate that secondary reactions involving hydrophilic groups do, in fact, take place. As far as the electron microscope image is concerned, the tendency to correlate the position of sites of double bonds with sites of deposition of osmium has led to difficulties in interpretation in the past. Ornstein (1957) has pointed out that metals need not necessarily be deposited at the exact site of the initial chemical reaction. The resulting osmium-containing compounds apparently do not nucleate in the hydrocarbon region. The same type of consideration would presumably also apply to the reduction products after reaction with permanganate. The combined evidence (Robertson 1960) would suggest that the site of deposition of osmium in electron micrographs can cautiously be used to localize the position of polar groups which, in the case of artificial phospholipid systems, will correspond to their head groups. In the case of biological membranes, electron microscopic data based on osmium and permanganate fixation, can be related only to polar groups which may be predominantly part of phospholipid or protein and/or carbohydrate molecules.

Korn and Weisman (1966) have studied the loss of lipids during the preparation of amoebae for electron microscopy. After fixation in glutaraldehyde the lipids themselves were unchanged, but they were almost completely extracted by ethanol during dehydration. Permanganate fixation and ethanol treatment resulted in extraction of all of the neutral lipids and about 25% of the phospholipids. Following fixation in osmium tetroxide, most of the neutral lipid and some of the phospholipid were extracted by ethanol, and osmium tetroxide 'destroyed' the unsaturated fatty acids. Sabatini et al.

(1963) showed that there was conspicuous absence of membrane structures in electron mircographs of rat tissues fixed in glutaraldehyde. Thus, although it appears that the demonstration of membranous structures requires the presence of lipid (except possibly in the case of mitochondrial cristae), it is clear that the standard electron microscopic techniques may give a false impression of the lipid constitution of membranes.

It may be reasonably concluded at this stage of the discussion that the various measurements of membrane thickness do not detract from the concept of the bimolecular lipid leaf as applied to cell membranes, but it should be clearly emphasized that, except in the possible case of the myelin sheath, they certainly do not prove its existence. Quantitatively small deviations from the bimolecular layer may produce disproportionately large effects in terms of cell physiology, and it is to be questioned whether such deviations can be detected by existing techniques. In the case of myelin sheath structures, the combined approach of X-ray diffraction and electron microscopy have given a model which can be viewed with considerable confidence, however it seems doubtful whether the myelin sheath is necessarily a good model for other membranes.

1.5.3 Protein/lipid associations

An early experimental attempt to clarify the modes of association of protein with lipids in the cell periphery was made by Parpart and Ballentine (1952) who determined the ease with which various lipids could be extracted from the dried ghosts of beef erythrocytes, and thereby obtained a measure of binding. All of the cholesterol and comparatively small quantities of the phospholipids were extracted with dry ether, implying that this fraction which consisted mainly of cephalins, was loosely bound. More of the phospholipids containing more cephalins than in the previous fraction were removed by wet ether, and these were termed 'weakly bound'. Most of the phospholipids and the remaining 50% of the cephalins were removed only by polar solvents and were termed 'strongly bound'. Further experiments of this type were carried out by De Gier et al. (1960) and Van Deenen et al. (1961, 1962) on erythrocyte ghosts from various species. These workers essentially confirmed the observations of Parpart and Ballentine in showing that all of the cholesterol was extracted by ether together with a variable amount of phospholipids ranging from 6% from cow, 21% from human and 26% from rabbit erythrocytes. As the major part of the phospholipids are not extracted by non-polar solvents such as ether, but are extracted by polar solvents such as ethanolether, it was concluded that the major part is associated with non-lipid membrane constituents. Further experiments showed that, once extracted, the major fraction is readily soluble in ether. Hence, the differences in the liberation of the major and minor lipid fractions from erythrocyte ghosts are due to their extractability or binding, as distinct from their solubility.

The extraction data led Parpart and Ballentine to suggest that the minor lipid fraction which is extracted by non-polar solvents are bound to the fatty acid chains of the major fraction which itself is strongly bound to proteins.

The model proposed by these authors, of a proteinaceous framework in which spaces are filled with lipid, is not incompatible with the electron microscopic data. If it is taken that very little can be assumed about the reaction sites of double bonds of lipids from electron micrographs, and that the constituent amino acids of structural proteins show a wide range of reaction with various stains, then the familiar trilaminar structure seen under the electron microscope can at most be taken as evidence of the sites of part of the proteins. The same appearance could be given presumably by the Davson–Danielli model, or by other models in which the additive effects of the deposition sites of migrant reactants with lipids and the variable reactions with proteins combined to give a trilaminar image which had a patchy appearance at high resolution.

This arrangement of a proteinaceous stroma stabilizing lipid structures received temporary support from the observations of Dourmashkin et al. (1962). These workers examined saponin-treated erythrocytes and tumour cells under the electron microscope after staining with potassium phosphotungstate. Such material showed a remarkably uniform structure consisting of dark circles approximately 80Å in diameter. The centres of adjacent 'circles' were separated by about 150Å and each circular region was surrounded by hexagonal band approximately 30Å wide. It was inferred from this data that the dark circles possibly indicated the sites of holes or pits normally occupied by lipids, within a proteinaceous membrane stroma. This view is reminiscent of the model put forward on the basis of early electron microscopy by Wolpers (1941), who suggested that the proteins of the cell membranes are arranged in a lattice, the holes of which are filled with lipids which can be removed with suitable solvents.

Schulman and Rideal (1937) had shown that saponin could penetrate from an aqueous phase, and form insoluble complexes with lipid films, including cholesterol. This suggested that the electron micrographs of

Dourmashkin and his colleagues represented the molecular rearrangements subsequent to adding saponin to a lipid membrane, rather than those due to removing lipid from the membrane. Bangham and Horne (1962) took electron micrographs of saponin-treated negatively stained (sodium phosphotungstate) films of lecithin, cholesterol and lecithin plus cholesterol mixtures, and Glauert et al. (1962) did essentially the same with cholesterol films. Both of these groups found that the dimensions of the hexagonal structures in their artificial saponin/cholesterol complexes agreed closely with those of Dourmashkin and his colleagues. Bangham and Horne also noted that the hexagonal structures were not seen after treating lecithin alone with saponin; here typical lamellar structures were seen. It was concluded that although the observations of Dourmashkin and his associates were of interest in connection with the interactions of saponin and like substances with membranes, the observation cannot be taken as evidence of a pre-existing structure.

The association of proteins with lipids is dependent on the nature of their side chains, of which, in many proteins, some $35 - 50\%$ are non-polar (Tristam 1953; Waugh 1954). Normally, in the absence of strong interactions with surrounding molecules, proteins tend to maintain a globular state, because, in an aqueous environment, the non-polar side chains are driven to the 'interior' of the molecule, where they are held together by hydrophobic interactions (Langmuir 1939; Cheesman and Davies 1954; Klotz 1958).

Some of the newer studies on protein structure, up to the end of 1962, have been reviewed by Richards (1963). The work of Kendrew et al. (1960), on the structure of myoglobin, provides direct evidence for the structure of an α-helix in globular proteins. Kendrew (1962) has pointed out that in the case of myoglobin in the globular form, apart from less than five single water molecules, there is no solvent inside the molecule, and that the non-polar residues are concentrated in the interior, where they bound hydrophobically. In this native state, structure is maintained by about eight times as many hydrophobic bonds, as hydrogen bonds and salt linkages combined. The X-ray diffraction data also show that all of the visualized surface polar groups have bound water molecules associated with them. It would also appear that a number of non-polar groups, mainly glycyl and alanyl residues, are also at the surface. This observation is of considerable importance, as myoglobin and possibly other proteins would therefore be capable of forming both polar and hydrophobic associations with lipids for example, without necessarily unfolding from the globular state.

   As with the lipids discussed earlier, the question has to be raised of the relevance of protein structure as determined by X-ray diffraction of crystals, to the structure of proteins in the cell periphery. Although it can be said that there is good correlation between X-ray diffraction data and electron micrographic data on collagen (Hodge and Schmitt 1958; Engstrom and Finean 1958) and myelin (vide supra) for example, Low (1960) has pointed out that the question is not really answered. Richards (1963) reviews some of the evidence related to studies of crystal density, composition and unit cell dimensions during controlled drying processes, which permit the partial specific volumes of the protein and the associated water to be calculated. The mercury dimer of serum albumin apparently has the same structural dimensions in both crystals and in aqueous solution (Low and Richards 1954) and insulin citrate crystals appear to have similar dimensions as in dilute solution (Low and Berger 1961). However, in the case of β-lactoglobulin (McMeekin et al. 1954), differences exist between the crystal state and that in aqueous solution. It would appear that a possible source of discrepancy is that in crystals (including the 'wet' crystals used in X-ray diffraction studies), contact occurs between neighboring molecules (Kendrew 1962) which may produce structural changes, whereas the frequency of such contacts will be less in dilute solution. Even in crystals the contacts must be relatively few, since large molecules such as p-phenyl isocyanide can diffuse into crystalline myoglobin and interact with its iron, without changing its unit cell dimensions (Kendrew). Richards (1963) concludes that although gross artefactual changes in protein structure are unlikely to result from examining proteins in the crystalline state, small structural alterations cannot be excluded, and these will become progressively more important as the resolution of X-ray analysis improves.

   At a lipid/water interface when a lipid monolayer is closely packed at pressures greater than 30 dynes per cm, the interactions between lipids and proteins are complex in that they may depend on interactions between both their polar and non-polar groups. Interaction between polar groups of the proteins and lipids may occur, resulting in adsorption of the protein without denaturation (Doty and Schulman 1949; Matalon and Schulman 1949). However, the proteins may also uncoil, and non-polar side chains may penetrate between the polar head groups and participate in hydrophobic bonding with the non-polar hydrocarbon chains (Matalon and Schulman; Schulman 1951) resulting in either an increase of surface area, or increase of surface pressure, if the area of the spread lipid is kept constant in a Langmuir trough. The amount of penetration of the lipid monolayer which takes place will depend on its surface pressure. At lipid pressures much above about 30 dynes per cm, proteins apparently will not unfold and penetrate (Schulmann and Rideal 1937; Payens 1960; Biswas et al. 1962). However, at lower surface pressures, penetration of both ionized and un-ionized lipid monolayers by the non-polar side chains of proteins occurs (Matalon and Schulman; Eley and Hedge 1956, 1957).

Vandenheuvel (1965) draws attention to the multiplicity of function in natural membranes which mitigates against the acceptance of a simple liquid crystal state of the lipids, and that association of lipids with structural protein would reduce the degree of freedom below that found in smectic liquid crystals or in monolayers. Associations expected within the cell periphery correspond to the molecular configurations associated with low energy levels. Methods used for the calculation of the high intermolecular cohesion forces making for stability of structure have been described by Vandenheuvel (1963a) and Jackson and Vandenheuvel (1964) and will not be considered in detail here. It must be remembered that such approximations indicate probable equilibrium states only, and models derived from them are subject to continuous modification by ionic and thermal variations quite apart from other physiologically induced changes.

Vandenheuvel (1965) has attempted to build up a model showing the detailed interaction between the proteins and lipids in myelin, based on the analysis of amino acids in myelin protein carried out by Hulcher (1963), and the protein to lipid class ratios obtained by Norton and Autilio (1964) and Terry (1964). Taken together the data suggest that $32.5 Å^2$ of lipid are in association with each amino acid (Vandenheuvel 1964). 'Pure' dry myelin consists of 77.7% lipid and 22% protein, and Vandenheuvel has considered various arrangements which would allow the whole underlying lipid surface to be covered by protein. Assuming that the lipids are present in bimolecular leaf, it is noted that only the chain arrangement as in the β-keratin model described by Marsh et al. (1955) would fulfil the areal requirements of each amino acid occupying $32.5 Å^2$ of underlying lipid. With this arrangement, the protein forms a layer about $10 Å$ thick. This proposed model fits the X-ray diffraction data obtained on both fresh and dry myelin when allowances are made for hydration. Vandenheuvel's model differs from some of those discussed in that the lipid/protein interactions are described in terms of the hydrophobic attractions between adjacent lipids; coulombic attractions between proteins and lipids; hydrogen-bonding via water bridges between susceptible groups, and ion-binding between negatively charged groups by calcium. Bangham et al. (1965) have noted that in model systems phospholipids appear to bind cations. They note that the amount of cation trapped is expected to vary with the charge density of lipid head groups and the ionic strength of a postulated aqueous phase lying between bimolecular lipid leaflets. No mention is made by Vandenheuvel of hydrophobic bonding between the apolar amino acid groups of proteins and the hydrocarbon chains of the underlying lipid. Discrepancies between functional aspects of this model and experimental data according to Vandenheuvel, may be accounted for by consideration of the properties of associated water molecules.

(a) *Mitochondrial membranes.* Studies on mitochondria indicate that proteins form a basic structural component of their membranes. This change of emphasis to proteins from lipids, with regard to membrane structure, may obviously be of relevance to the structure of corresponding parts of the peripheral zone of cells. The mitochondrial proteins may be broadly divided in those having electron carrier properties such as the cytochromes; enzymes such as dehydrogenases and adenosinetriphosphatases, and proteins for which no carrier or enzymatic activity has yet been demonstrated, including the 'structural' proteins described by Richardson et al. (1963) and the 'Fo' of Racker et al. (1966).

Mitochondria contain two membrane systems, inner and outer, which differ from each other both in morphology and carrier activity. The inner membrane has projecting sub-units known either as 'elementary particles' (Fernández-Morán 1962; Fernández-Morán et al. 1964) or 'inner membrane subunits' (Parsons 1963, 1965b). Although it was at first thought that these projecting subunits contain cytochrome (Fernández-Morán et al. 1964), later work has shown that they do not (Chance and Parsons 1963; Chance et al. 1964; Stasny and Crane 1964). Evidence presented by Kagawa and Racker (1966) strongly suggests that much of the spherical structures associated with the inner membrane is in fact adenosine triphosphatase. The mesozone which comprises the structural framework of the mitochondrion contains some 70% of the total mitochondrial lipids, of which over 90% are phospholipid, and about 60% of the total mitochondrial protein. Green and Fleischer (1963) suggest that lipid/protein bonds are mainly responsible for holding together not only the elementary particles, but also holding the elementary particles to the mesozone. Although specific details of the association of proteins with lipids are not well known, two main types of binding may be considered, namely ionic binding between basic proteins and phospholipids having acidic polar head groups (Fleischer et al. 1963) non-ionic, hydrophobic binding between non-polar side chains of the protein and the hydrocarbon tails of the phospholipid. In the latter type of interaction the net charge on the polar heads of the lipids are of little ultimate importance (Green and Fleischer).

Green and Fleischer take as an example of the ionic interactions, those between phospholipids and the basic protein, cytochrome C, and note that the molecular proportions of phospholipid and cytochrome C in complexes are apparently determined by charge neutralization. Thus at pH 7.4 cyto-chrome C contains 21 positively charged groups (19 lysine and 2 arginine) and 13 negatively charged groups (9 glutamic acids, 3 aspartic acids and one additional carboxyl group) giving a net positive charge of 8 per molecule. This protein combines with the acidic phospholipids, cardiolipin and phos-phatidylinositol which each have one negative charge per phosphorus, to form complexes containing 8 to 9 moles of phospholipid phosphorus per mole of cytochrome C. On the other hand, lecithin which has a zero net charge does not react with cytochrome C at all, and in an intermediate position is phosphatidylethanolamine, which is less acidic than either cardiolipin or phosphatidylinositol, and which interacts to a limited extent (Das et al.). When the basic groups of cytochrome C are succinylated or acetylated then it no longer forms complexes with lipids (Takemori et al. 1962). Further evidence of the ionic nature of the interaction is provided by the observation that neutral or acidic cytochromes obtained from plants will not form com-plexes with phospholipids.

A number of other basic compounds react with micelles of acidic phos-pholipid micelles in water, including histones, protamine, ribonuclease and lysozyme (Green and Fleischer). It is not understood why protein/phos-pholipid complex formation is determined by the net charge on the protein as distinct from its total charge.

Amino acid analyses of structural protein from mitochondria show the presence of more positively charged (lysine, arginine and histidine) than negatively charged residues (glutamic and aspartic acids) after the loss of ionized carboxyl group by amide formation is accounted for. The mitochon-drial proteins also contain relatively high proportions of amino acids with hydrophobic side chains (isoleucine, leucine, methionine, valine, phenyla-lanine, tyrosine) (Criddle et al. 1962) and hydrophobic bonding between phospholipids and protein is suggested on the evidence that complexes may be formed between mitochondrial structural protein and phospholipid micelles regardless of the net charge on the polar head groups of the phos-pholipids, and that the interaction is unaffected by salt concentration (Fleischer et al. 1963; Green and Fleischer). The fact that polar groups are not demonstrably involved in interactions of the type described, leaves them free to make the protein/phospholipid complex hydrophilic; and Green and Fleischer have suggested that the predominantly hydrophobic proteins of the electron transfer chain utilize this interaction as a 'bridge' to the aqueous phase.

When mitochondria are extracted with aqueous acetone some 85% of the phosolipid is removed, without change in the basic trilaminar structure of the mitochondrial membrane, as viewed by electron microscopy after fixation with osmium tetroxide. The structural pattern of the membrane is thus not dependent on the presence of the majority of the lipids, which can be reinserted to restore enzymatic function. Green and Fleischer have proposed a model which would allow for the failure to observe shrinkage after lipid extraction, in which a stack of proteinaceous rings form a tubular structure, the cavity of which is filled with lipids. Korn and Weisman (1966), quoted earlier, showed that in the amoeba, following massive loss of lipids, the trilaminar structure is still observed under the electron microscope. This surely shows that lipids are not necessary for much of the trilaminar structures seen, and also that the presence of trilaminar structures indicates neither the molecular arrangement or even the presence of lipids.

Benson (1966) has proposed a very interesting model for chloroplast and cell membranes, in which the hydrophobic amino acid residues of the peripheral proteins determine the sites where the lipids will be most firmly bound by their hydrocarbon tails. This leads to a mixed protein/lipid aggregate, instead of the usual laminar structure.

(b) *Other data.* The various evidence discussed so far would suggest that proteins may associate with lipids in either the unfolded β-conformation and/or in the globular form. The suggestion that globular proteins may be associated with membrane-structures has been made by Danielli (1938, 1951), Furchgott and Ponder (1941) and Davson and Danielli (1943), among others. Association in the globular form might be expected to favour the release of the protein from the associated lipid. However, it should be remembered that, in either conformation, the non-polar side chains of proteins can be squeezed out from between the hydrocarbon tails of a phospholipid film when the pressure is raised.

It is known that when oil droplets are injected into cells, they adsorb protein with consequent drop of surface tension (Scarth 1942; Davson and Danielli) and that this adsorption need not invariably be associated with denaturation of the protein (Kopac 1950). When oil is removed from the interior of the injected droplet, the adsorbed protein does not collapse (Chambers and Kopac 1940) but the adsorbed protein is apparently released from its association with the oil and goes back into solution (Goldacre 1958).

Haydon and Taylor (1963) have suggested that many mechanical properties of membranes would have to be conferred on lipid structures by proteins and carbohydrates, and this suggestion has received experimental support from the observation of Weiss (1965) that removal of sialic acids from the periphery of ascites tumour cells enables them to be more easily deformed.

Work done on monolayers of lipids indicates that when these are exposed to globular proteins, adsorption and penetration take place. On further exposure, a second 'layer' of proteins is adsorbed, which are thought to remain in the globular state and do not penetrate and hence produce little change in surface pressure (Matalon and Schulman 1949; Eley and Hedge 1956; Eley and Miller 1960). This concept is further supported by work done on enzymes adsorbed on lipids where molecular unfolding is associated with loss of enzymatic activity (Cheesman and Davies 1954), and Ray and Augenstine (1956) suggest that the first molecules adsorbed unfold and so modify the lipid surface pressure that additional enzyme molecules do not unfold, and retain observable activity. This whole question of protein conformation in membrane is exhaustively reviewed by Kavanau (1965), who appears to favour a β-conformation.

Maddy and Malcolm (1965) have made attempts to study protein conformations in the plasma membranes of dried ox erythrocyte ghosts, by means of infra-red spectroscopy. This technique enables β-protein to be recognized by amide I and II bands present at 1,630 and 1,520 cm^{-1}, as distinct from 1,660 and 1,540 cm^{-1} in the α-helix or random coil conformation (Elliott et al. 1962). They found no evidence to support the view that a monolayer of protein in the β-conformation is present as would be required adjacent to the membrane lipids in the Harvey–Danielli model, although proteins extracted from ghosts with n-butanol could be converted to a form giving the spectrum of β-conformation, by heating with 50% ethanol for 3 min at 70 °C. They suggest that very approximately 17% of the globular protein present is in the α-helical form, but are unable to suggest how the protein interacts with the lipid.

When the electron microscopic data on lipids were considered, the point was made that it must not be assumed that the sites of interaction between chemical groups of the lipids and osmium tetroxide or potassium permanganate are the same as the visualized sites of deposition of the reduced osmium compound(s) or of the manganese dioxide; the same qualification holds for proteins. Bahr (1954) noted a wide variation in the abilities of different amino acids to reduce osmium tetroxide, and that leucine, isoleucine and alamine for example, were almost non-reactive. This reduction of OsO_4 is quite separate from its binding reactions. Eddy and Johns (1965) have reported detailed studies on the reactions of amino acids and membrane proteins and lipids with potassium permanganate in the concentrations used in electron microscopy. They found that in the erythrocyte ghosts, on a weight basis, the membrane lipids are about as reactive as the proteins. They also demonstrated that considerable differences exist between amino acids in their ability to reduce potassium permanganate. These differences are illustrated in table 1.5, and suggest that reactivity of $KMnO_4$ with amino acids is not directly correlated with either side chain charge or hydrophilia.

Eddy and Johns (1965) also compared the observed reactivity of proteins of known amino acid composition with $KMnO_4$ with the calculated reactivity obtained by the addition of the values of the individual amino acids. Lysozyme gave 79% of the calculated values, bovine globulin 72%, and casein 80%. This amount of agreement suggests that the side chains of the amino

TABLE 1.5

The oxidation of individual amino acids by potassium permanganate (from Eddy and Johns 1965). The values show the number of moles of potassium permanganate reduced per mole of amino acid after 5 or 60 min reaction at about 20 °C.

	5 min	60 min
Tryptophane	7.0	10.3
Tyrosine	2.6	6.0
Hydroxyproline	1.5	5.5
Methionine	2.5	4.4
Cysteine	2.8	4.0
Histidine	2.6	3.7
Serine	1.8	3.1
Threonine	0.8	3.1
Glycine	0.1	2.2
Lysine	1.9	2.1
Arginine	1.1	1.5
Phenylalanine	0.3	1.4
Proline	0.2	1.2
Isoleucine	0.04	0.3
Valine	0.04	0.3
Leucine	0.03	0.3
Alanine	0.05	0.25
Aspartic acid	0	0.03
Glutamic acid	0	0.06

acids were the quantitatively important sites of reaction and that the peptide bonds are relatively unimportant. The data also suggest that as the amino acids are arranged in a complex way in native proteins, and as the observed results are remarkably close to calculated results, the permanganate was in fact reacting with nearly all the side chains and might therefore be producing marked structural changes in the proteins themselves during oxidation. Eddy and Johns have calculated that the manganese dioxide formed by reduction of potassium permanganate would occupy about one fifth of the volume of the oxidized protein, and that newly formed hydrophilic groups in the region of the oxidation reaction might well coordinate with a possible compact manganese dioxide lattice. Thus, in contrast to lipids, where the reaction product probably migrates away from the reaction site, there is a case for suggesting that with proteins, the reaction product, manganese dioxide, may be deposited near to the reaction site.

When proteins are stained with either osmium tetroxide or potassium permanganate and then examined with electron microscopy, Hake's (1965) studies would suggest that both reagents exhibit only weak staining properties, and that whereas osmium produces good preservation of the proteins, potassium permanganate produces a good deal of structural damage. Parsons (1965) has reviewed some effects of preparative procedures of the resulting electron micrographic image which seem relevant to proteins, and draws attention to the possibility of doing away with heavy metal staining altogether in the future, either by observing freeze dried preparations in which electron optical contrast is enhanced with a velocity analyser (Watanabe and Uyeda 1962), or by phase-contrast electron microscopy (Fert et al. 1962). In the meantime it is to be noted that Levin (1963) has compared the electron microscopic data on bovine cytochrome C, haemoglobin and myoglobin with hydrodynamic data, and reports good agreement.

As the emphasis in so much current research on membranes is conducted on lipid models, and the concept of a lipid 'back bone' seems to have been generally accepted on what seems suggestive evidence at most; it is to be questioned whether the whole idea of a membrane based primarily on lipids could not be dropped for one based on proteins. It seems distinctly possible that the 'essential' part of the structure may well be a proteinaceous framework on which various functional properties are conferred, by its association with lipids as well as other components.

In addition to the more static structural requirements for the cell periphery, it must also be remembered that the very many observations on transport across the cell periphery impose certain functional requirements. Thus, although Overton (1895) noted that the permeability of cells to a number of compounds depended on their lipid solubility, the permeability to many other compounds does not. Some thermodynamic considerations of molecules crossing such a barrier are given by Danielli (1952). Other transport processes have fitted in with the concept of polar pores in which discontinuities in lipids are lined by hydrophilic groups belonging to protein (Danielli 1958), and the blanket term 'active transport' has been used to cover specific metabolically (enzymatically) linked transport processes. The whole field is covered up to that time in the monograph by Harris (1960). Other evidence of heterogeneity at the periphery of the erythrocyte comes from the observation of scintillatory movements in this region which have been likened to wind blowing across a field of wheat (Browicz 1890; Cabot 1901; Pulvertaft 1949). In any scheme put forward for the cell periphery, heterogeneity must be taken into account. Obviously, many feasible models can be put forward which invoke heterogeneity and which doubtless account for the experimental evidence, but which in many cases, are only tenable because of the lack of it.

So far this discussion has been limited to single cells. When tissues are considered, in many of which cells are separated by more or less intercellular connective tissue, the question arises of where the cell periphery ends and where the connective tissue begins. In the next chapter, the point will be discussed that the connective tissue and microenvironment can regulate important functions and structures in the region of the cell periphery. It has been suggested (Weiss 1962) that this arbitrary boundary of the cell is better defined by the interests of the experimentalist than by semantics.

I am in entire agreement with Ponder (1961) who in a critical review of the erythrocyte membrane states: 'If the reader of this chapter has concluded that the author is not convinced about the structure, or even the necessary existence, of the cell membrane as it is generally described, he will not be far wrong'.

References

Acs, G., Ostrowski, W., and Straub, F. B. (1954). Acta Physiol. Hung. **6**, 261

Ada, G. L., and French, E. L. (1959). Nature **183**, 1740

Ada, G. L., French, E. L., and Lind, P. E. (1961). J. Gen. Microbiol. **24**, 409

Ada, G. L. and Stone, J. D. (1950). Brit. J. Exptl. Pathol. **31**, 263

Adam, N. K. (1941). The physics and chemistry of surfaces. 3rd ed. Oxford Univ. Press, London

Adam, N. K. and Jessop, G. (1928). Proc. Roy. Soc. A. **120**, 473

Allfrey, V. G. (1959). In, J. Brachet and A. E. Mirsky, eds., The cell, **1**. Academic Press, Inc., New York, p. 200

Baer, E., and Kates, M. (1950). J. Biol. Chem. **185**, 615

Bahr, G. F. (1954). Exptl. Cell Res. **7**, 457

Bairati, A., and Lehman, F. E. (1954). Exptl. Cell Res. **5**, 220

Baker, J. R. (1958). Principles of biological microtechnique: a study of fixation and dyeing. Methuen, London

Bangham, A. D. (1963). Advan. Lipid Res. **1**, 65

Bangham, A. D., and Horne, R. W. (1962). Nature **196**, 952

Bangham, A. D., and Horne, R. W. (1964). J. Mol. Biol. **8**, 660

Bangham, A. D., Rees, K. R., and Shotlander, V. (1962). Nature **193**, 754

Bangham, A. D., Standish, M. M., and Watkins, J. C. (1965). J. Mol. Biol. **13**, 238

Bayer, M. E. (1964). Trans. N. Y. Acad. Sci. **26**, 1103

Benson, A. A. (1966). J. Am. Oil Chemists' Soc. **43**, 265

Bernal, J. D., and Fowler, R. H. (1933). J. Chem. Phys. **1**, 515

Billingham, R. E., Brent, L., and Medawar, P. B. (1958). Transplant. Bull. **5**, 377

Biswas, B., Taylor, J., and Haydon, D. A. (1962). Cited by Weiss (1962).

Boehm, G. (1935). Biochem. Z. **282**, 222

Boell, E. J., and Nachmansohn, D. (1940). Science **92**, 513

Borgström, B. (1952). Acta Physiol. Scand. **25**, 10

Bovey, F. A. (1961). Nature **192**, 324

Boyd, W. C. (1962). Introduction to immunochemical specificity. John Wiley & Sons, Inc., New York

Brenner, S., and Horne, R. W. (1959). Biochem. Biophys. Acta **34**, 103

Browicz, E. (1890). Zentr. Med. Wiss. **28**, 625

Burnet, F. M., McCrea, J. F., and Stone, J. D. (1946). Brit. J. Exptl. Pathol. **27**, 228

Cabot, R. C. (1901). A guide to the clinical examination of the blood. 4th ed., Longmans, Green and Co., London

Chambers, R., and Kopac, M. J. (1940). Cited by Needham, J. (1950), in, Biochemistry and morphogenesis. Cambridge University Press, London, p. 657

Chance, B. and Parsons, D. F. (1963). Science **142**, 1176

Chance, B., Parsons, D. F. and Williams, G. R. (1964). Science **143**, 136

Cheesman, D. F. and Davies, J. T. (1954). Advan. Protein Chem. **9**, 439

Cole, K. S. (1940). Cold Spring Harbor Symp. **8**, 110

Collet, P. (1922). J. Phys. Radium **3**, 128

Colmer, W. D., and Carter, H. E. (1952). Physiol. Rev. **32**, 167

Cook, G. M. W. (1962). Nature **195**, 159

Cook, G. M. W., Heard, D. H., and Seaman, G. V. F. (1960). Nature **188**, 1011
Cook, G. M. W., Heard, D. H., and Seaman, G. V. F. (1961). Nature **191**, 44
Cook, G. M. W., Heard, D. H., and Seaman, G. V. F. (1962). Exptl. Cell Res. **28**, 27
Cook, G. M. W., Seaman, G. V. F., and Weiss, L. (1963). Cancer Res., **23**, 1813
Cosslett, A. (1960). Proc. Europ. Regional Conf. Electron Microscopy, Delft **2**, 678
Côté, R. H., and Morgan, W. T. J. (1956). Nature **178**, 1171
Coulson, C. A. (1957). Research **10**, 149
Criddle, R. S., Bock, R. M., Green, D. E., and Tisdale, H. D. (1962). Biochem. **1**, 827
Curtis, H. J., and Cole, K. S. (1938). J. Gen. Physiol. **21**, 757
Dandliker, W. B., Moscovitch, M., Zimm, B., and Calvin, M. (1950). J. Am. Chem. Soc. **72**, 5587
Danielli, J. F. (1935). J. Gen. Physiol. **19**, 19
Danielli, J. F. (1937). Proc. Roy. Soc. B **122**, 155
Danielli, J. F. (1938). Cold Spring Harbor Symp. Quant. Biol. **6**, 190
Danielli, J. F. (1951). In, G. H. Bourne, ed., Cytology and cell physiology. Clarendon Press, Oxford
Danielli, J. F. (1952). Symp. Soc. Exptl. Biol. **6**, 1
Danielli, J. F. (1958). In, Danielli, J. F., Pankhurst, K. G. A. and Riddiford A. C., eds., Surface phenomena in chemistry and biology. Pergamon Press, London–New York, p. 246 ff.
Das, H. L., Hiratsuka, H., Machinist, J. M., and Crane, F. L. (1962). Biochem. Biophys. Acta **60**, 633
Davies, D. A. L. (1962a). Nature **193**, 34
Davies, D. A. L. (1962b). Biochem. J. **84**, 307
Davies, D. A. L., and Hutchison, A. M. (1961). Brit. J. Exptl. Pathol. **42**, 587
Davies, J. T., and Rideal, E. K. (1961). Interfacial phenomena. Academic Press, London
Davson, H. (1962). Circulation **26**, 1022
Davson, H., and Danielli, J. F. (1943). The permeability of natural membranes. MacMillan, London–New York
Davson, H. and Danielli, J. F. (1952). The permeability of natural membranes. 2nd ed. Cambridge University Press, London
Dawson, R. M. C., Hemington, N., and Davenport, J. B. (1962). Biochem. J. **84**, 497
Dawson, R. M. C., Hemington, N. and Lindsay, D. B. (1960). Biochem. J. **77**, 226
De Bernard, L. (1958). Bull. Soc. Chem. Biol. **40**, 161
Debye, P. (1949a). J. Phys. Chem. **53**, 1
Debye, P. (1949b). Ann. N. Y. Acad. Sci. **51**, 575
De Duve, G., Pressman, B. D., Gianetto, R., Wattiaux, R., and Appelmans, F. (1955). Biochem. J. **60**, 604
De Gier, J., Mulder, I., and van Deenen, L. L. M. (1961). Naturwissenschaften **48**, 54
Dervichian, D. G. (1958). In, Danielli, J. F., Pankhurst, K. G. A., and Riddiford, A. C., eds., Surface phenomena in chemistry and biology. Pergamon Press, London-New York, p. 70 ff.
De Vries, H. (1884). Jahrb. Wiss. Botan. **14**, 427
Dodge, J. T., Mitchell, C., and Hanahan, D. J. (1963). Arch. Biochem. Biophys. **180**, 119
Doty, P., and Schulman, J. H. (1949). Discussions Faraday Soc. **6**, 21
Dourmashkin, R. R., Dougherty, R. M., and Harris, R. J. E. (1962). Nature **194**, 1116

Dumande, D. C., Walter, C. M., Bitensky, L., Cunningham, C. J., and Chayen, J. (1961). Nature **192**, 1302

Dutrochet, R. J. H. (1827). Ann. Chim. et Phys. **35**, 393

Eddy, A. A., and Johns, P. (1965). Soc. Chem. Ind. Monograph **19**, 24 (London)

Eley, D. D. (1962). In, M. Kasha and B. Pullman, eds., Horizons in biochemistry. Academic Press, London

Eley, D. D., and Hedge, D. G. (1956). Discussions Faraday Soc. **21**, 221

Eley, D. D., and Hedge, D. G. (1957). J. Colloid. Sci. **12**, 419

Eley, D. D., and Miller, G. (1960). Third Intern. Congr. Surface Activity **2**, 157

Elliott, A., Bradbury, E. M., Downie, A. R., and Hanby, W. E. (1962). In, M. A. Stahlmann, ed., Polyamino acids, polypeptides and proteins. Univ. Wisconsin Press, Madison, p. 255

Emmelot, P., Bos, C. J., Benedetti, E. L., and Rumke, P. (1964). Biochim. Biophys. Acta **90**, 126

Engstrom, A., and Finean, J. B. (1958). Biological ultrastructure. Academic Press, New York

Erickson, B. N., Williams, H. H., Bernstein, S. S., Arvin, I., Jones, R. L. and Macy, I. G. (1938). J. Biol. Chem. **122**, 515

Essner, E., Novikoff, A. B., and Masek, B. (1958). J. Biophys. Biochem. Cytol. **4**, 711

Farquhar, J. W. (1962). Biochim. Biophys. Acta **60**, 80

Fernández-Morán, H. (1962). Circulation **26**, 1039

Fernández-Morán, H., and Finean, J. B. (1957). J. Biophys. Biochem. Cytol. **3**, 725

Fernández-Morán, H., Oda, T., Blair, P. V., and Green, D. E. (1964). J. Cell Biol. **22**, 63

Fert, C., Foget, J., Fagot, M. and Ferre, J. (1962). J. Phys. Soc. Japan **17** (Suppl. B11), 186

Feulgen, R., and Voit, K. (1924). Arch. Ges. Physiol. **206**, 389

Few, A. V., (1955). Biochim. Biophys. Acta **16**, 144

Finean, J. B. (1953a). Biochim. Biophys. Acta **10**, 371

Finean, J. B. (1953b). Exptl. Cell Res. **5**, 202

Finean, J. B. (1953c). Experientia **9**, 17

Finean, J. B. (1958). Exptl. Cell Res. Suppl. **5**, 18

Finean, J. B. (1961). Intern. Rev. Cytol. **12**, 303

Finean, J. B. (1962). Circulation **2**, 1151

Finean, J. B., and Millington, P. F. (1955). Trans. Faraday Soc. **51**, 1008

Finean, J. B., and Rumsby, M. G. (1963). Nature 197, 1326

Fleischer, S., Richardson, S. H., Chapman, A., Fleischer, B., and Hultin, H. O. (1963) Federation Proc. **22**, 2186

Fowkes, F. (1963). J. Phys. Chem. **67**, 1982

Frank, H. S., and Wen, W–Y. (1957). Discussions Faraday Soc. **24**, 133

Freeman, J. A. (1959). J. Biophys. Biochem. Cytol. **2**, 353

Fricke, H. (1923). Phys. Rev. **21**, 708

Fricke, H. (1924). Phys. Rev. **24**, 575

Fricke, H. (1925a). Phys. Rev. **26**, 678

Fricke, H. (1925b) J. Gen. Physiol. **9**, 137

Friedenrich, V. (1927). C. R. Soc. Biol., Paris **96**, 1079

Friedenrich, V. (1928). C. R. Soc. Biol., Paris **98**, 894

Furchgott, R. F. (1940). Cold Spring Harbor Symp. Quant. Biol. **8**, 224

Furchgott, R. F., and Ponder, E. (1941). J. Gen. Physiol. **24**, 447

Geren, B. B. (1954). Exptl. Cell Res. **7**, 558

Glauert, A. M. (1965). Lab. Invest, **14**, 331

Glauert, A. M., Dingle, J. T., and Lucy, J. A. (1962). Nature **196**, 953

Glauert, A. M., Rogers, G. E., and Glauert, R. H. (1956). Nature **178**, 803

Goldacre, R. J. (1958). In, J. F. Danielli, K. G. A. Pankhurst and A. C. Riddiford, eds., Surface phenomena in chemistry and biology. Academic Press, London, p. 278

Good, W. (1961). Biochim. Biophys. Acta. **52**, 545

Gorer, P. A. (1961). Advan. Immunol. **1**, 345

Gorer, P. A., and Mikulska, Z. B. (1954). Cancer Res. **14**, 651

Gorter, E., and Grendel, F. (1925). J. Exptl. Med. **41**, 439

Gorter, E., and Grendel, F. (1926). Koninkl. Ned. Akad. Wetenschap. **29**, 315

Gottschalk, A. (1957). Biochem. Biophys. Acta **23**, 654

Gottschalk, A. (1960a). The chemistry and biology of sialic acids and related substances. Cambridge University Press, London–New York

Gottschalk, A. (1960b). Nature **186**, 949

Gottschalk, A., and Graham, E. R. (1959). Biochim. Biophys. Acta **34**, 380

Gottschalk, A., Murphy, W. H., and Graham, E. R. B. (1962). Nature **194**, 1051

Green, D. E. (1964). Sci. Am. **210**, 63

Green, D. E., and Fleischer, S. (1963). Biochim. Biophys. Acta **70**, 554

Gunstone, F. D. (1960). Advan. Org. Chem. **1**, 103

Hakomori, S. I., and Jeanloz, R. W. (1961), J. Biol. Chem. **236**, 2827

Hake, T. (1965). Lab. Invest. **14**, 470

Hall, C. E. (1955). J. Biophys. Biochem. Cytol. **1**, 1

Hanahan, D. J. (1954) J. Biol. Chem. **211**, 313, 321

Hanahan, D. J., Watts, R. M., and Pappajohn, D. (1960). J. Lipid Res. **1**, 412

Hanai, T., Haydon, D. A., and Taylor, J. (1964). Proc. Roy. Soc. A. **281**, 377

Hanai, T., Haydon, D. A., and Taylor, J. (1965). J. Gen. Physiol. **48**, 59

Hanig, M. (1948), Proc. Soc. Exptl. Biol., N. Y., **68**, 585

Hardy, W. (1913). Proc. Roy. Soc. A. **88**, 303

Harris, E. J. (1956). Transport and accumulation in biological systems. Academic Press, Inc., New York, p. 1

Haydon, D. A., and Taylor, J. (1963), J. Theoret. Biol. **4**, 281

Heard, D. H., and Seaman, G. V. F. (1960). J. Gen. Physiol. **43**, 635

Herberman, R., and Stetson, C. A. (1965). J. Exptl. Med. **121**, 533

Herzenberg, L. A., and Herzenberg, L. A. (1961a). J. Exptl. Med. **121**, 533

Herzenberg, L. A., and Herzenberg, L. A. (1961b). Natl. Acad. Sci. **47**, 762

Höber, R. (1910). Arch. Ges. Physiol. **133**, 237

Höber, R. (1912). Arch. Ges. Physiol. **148**, 189

Hodge, A. J., and Schmitt, F. O. (1958). Proc. 4th Intern. Conf. Electron Micros., Berlin

Hoffman, J. F. (1962). Circulation **26**, 1073

Hokin, L. E., and Hokin, H. R. (1961). Nature **189**, 836

Horne, R. W. (1965). Lab. Invest. **14**, 316

Horne, R. W., and Wildy, P. (1964). Virus Research **10**, 101

Huang, C. and Thompson, T. E. (1965). J. Mol. Biol. **13**, 183

Huang, C., Wheeldon, L. and Thompson, T. E. (1964). J. Mol. Biol. **8**, 148

Hulcher, F. H. (1963). Arch. Biochem. Biophys. **100**, 237

Hunter, M. J., and Commerford, S. L. (1961). Biochim. Biophys. Acta **47**, 580

Huxley, H. E. (1956). Proc. 1st Reg. Conf. Electron-Microscopy (Stockholm). Almqvist & Wiksells, Stockholm, p. 260

Hyde, A. J., Langbridge, D. M., and Lawrence, A. S. C. (1954). Discussions Faraday Soc. **18**, 239

Irie, R., Iwanaga, M., and Yamakawa, T. (1961). J. Biochem. (Torio) **50**, 122

Jackson, H. R., and Vandenheuvel, F. A. (1964). J. Phot. Sci. 12, 134

James, A. T., and Martin, A. J. P. (1952). Biochem. J. **50**, 679

Jorpes, E. (1932). Biochem. J. **26**, 1488

Kabat, E. A. (1956). Blood group substances; their chemistry and immunochemistry. Academic Press, New York

Kagawa, Y., and Racker, E. (1966). J. Biol. Chem. **241, 2**475

Kandutsch, A. A. (1961). Transplant. Bull. **27**, 135

Kandutsch, A. A., and Reinert-Wenck, U. (1957). J. Exptl. Med. **105**, 125

Kaplan, S. E., and Novikoff, A. B. (1959). J. Histochem. Cytochem. **7**, 295

Karrer, H. E. (1960). J. Biophys. Biochem. Cytol. **7**, 357

Kates, M., and James, A. T. (1961). Biochim. Biophys. Acta **50**, 477

Kavanau, J. L. (1965). Structure and function in biological membranes. Vol. 1, Holden-Day, Inc., San Francisco–London–Amsterdam p. 102 ff

Kellenberger, E., Ryter, A., and Sechaud, J. (1958). J. Biophys. Biochem. Cytol. **4**, 671

Kendrew, J. C. (1962). Brookhaven Symp. Biol. **15**, 216

Kendrew, J. C., Dickerson, R. E., Stranberg, B. E., Hart, R. G., and Davies, D. R. (1960), Nature **185**, 422

King, G., and Medley, J. A. (1949). J. Colloid Sci. **4**, 1

Kleinzeller, A., and Kotyk, A. (1960). Membrane transport and metabolism. Prague

Klenk, E. (1958). In, Chemistry and biology of mucopolysaccharides. Ciba Foundation Symposium. J. and A. Churchill Ltd., London, p. 311

Klenk, E., and Debuch, H. (1954). Z. Physiol. Chem. **296**, 179

Klenk, E., and Debuch, H. (1955). Z. Physiol. Chem. **299**, 66

Klenk, E., and Gielen, W. (1962). Z. Physiol. Chem. **326**, 9

Klenk, E., and Lauenstein, K. (1953). Z. Physiol. Chem. **295**, 164

Klenk, E., and Lempfrid, H. (1957). Z. Physiol. Chem. **307**, 278

Klenk, E., and Padberg, G. (1962). Z. Physiol. Chem. 327, 249

Klenk, E., and Uhlenbruck, G. (1960). Z. Physiol. Chem. **319**, 151

Klenk, E., and Wolter, H. (1952). Z. Physiol. Chem. **291**, 259

Klotz, I. M. (1958). Science **128**, 815

Klotz, I. M. (1962). In, M. Kasha, and B. Pullman, eds., Horizons in biochemistry. Academic Press, London

Kopac, M. J. (1950). Ann. N. Y. Acad. Sci. **50**, 870

Korn, E. D., and Weisman, R. A. (1966). Biochim. Biophys. Acta, **116**, 309

Landsteiner, K., and Van der Scheer, J. (1925). J. Exptl. Med. **41**, 427

Langmuir, I. (1917). J. Am. Chem. Soc. **39**, 1948

Langmuir, I. (1939). Proc. Roy. Soc. A. **170**, 1

Langmuir, I., and Waugh, D. F. (1938). J. Gen. Physiol. **21**, 745

Lawrence, A. S. C. (1961). In, A. Kleinzeller and A. Kotyk, eds., Symposium on membrane transport and metabolism. Czech. Acad. Sci., Prague, p. 35

Leathes, J. B. (1923). Z. Physiol. Chem. **130**, 113

Leathes, J. B. (1925). Lancet **208**, 853

Ledeen, R. (1966). J. Am. Oil Chemists' Soc. **43**, 57

Levin, O. (1963). J. Mol. Biol. **6**, 137, 158

Low, B. W. (1960). J. Polymer Sci. 49, 153

Low, B. W., and Berger, J. E. (1961). Acta Cryst. **14**, 82

Low, B. W., and Richards, F. M. (1954). J. Am. Chem. Soc. **76**, 2511

Lucy, J. A. (1964). J. Theoret. Biol. **7**, 360

Lucy, J. A., and Glauert, A. M. (1964). J. Mol. Biol. **8**, 727

Luft, J. H. (1957). J. Biophys. Biochem. Cytol. **2**, 799

Luzzati, V., and Husson, F. (1962). J. Cell Biol. **12**, 207

Maalöe, O., and Birch-Anderson, A. (1956). Symp. Soc. Gen. Microbiol. **6**, 268

Macfarlane, M. G. (1958). Nature **182**, 946

Maclean, H., and Smedley-Maclean, J. (1927). Lecithin and allied substances. Longmans, Green & Co. Ltd., London

Maddy, A. H., and Malcolm, B. R. (1965). Science **150**, 1616

Mäkelä, O., and Cantell, K. (1958). Ann. Med. Exptl. Biol. Fenn. **36**, 366

Mäkelä, O., Miettinen, T., and Pesola, R. (1960). Vox Sanguinis **5**, 492

Manson, L. A., Foschi, G. V., and Palm, J. (1963a). Proc. Natl. Acad. Sci. **48**, 1816

Manson, L. A., Foschi, G. V., and Palm, J. (1963b). J. Cellular Comp. Physiol. **61**, 109

Marsh, R. E., Pauling, L., and Corey, R. B. (1955). Biochim. Biophys. Acta **16**, 1

Masouredis, S. P. (1959). J. Clin. Invest. **38**, 279

Masouredis, S. P. (1960). Science **131**, 1442

Matalon, R., and Schulman, J. H. (1949). Discussions Faraday Soc. **6**, 27

Maturana, H. R. (1960). J. Biophys. Biochem. Cytol. **7**, 107

McMeekin, T. L., Groves, M. L., and Hipp, N. J. (1954). J. Polymer Sci. **12**, 309

Medawar, P. B. (1959). In, Biological problems of grafting. Congr. Colloq. Univ. Liège, **12**, 6

Micheli, A., and Grabar, P. (1961). Ann. Inst. Pasteur **100**, 569

Miller, A., Sullivan, J. F., and Katz, J. H. (1963). Cancer Res., **23**, 485

Möller, G. (1963). On the role of iso-immune reactions in tissue transplantation. Tryckeri Balder AB, Stockholm

Moore, J. H., and Williams, D. L. (1965). Biochim. Biophys. Acta **98**, 137–150

Morgan, W. T. J. (1960). Proc. Roy. Soc. B **151**, 308

Morgan, W. T. J., and Watkins, W. M. (1951). Brit, J. Exptl. Pathol. **29**, 159

Morrison, W. L., and Neurath, H. (1953). J. Biol. Chem. **200**, 39

Moscovitch, M., and Calvin, M. (1952). Exptl. Cell Res. **3**, 33

Moscovitch, M., Dandliker, W. B., Calvin, M., and Evans, R. S. (1950). J. Immunol. **65**, 383

Mueller, P., and Rudin, D. O. (1963). J. Theoret. Biol. **4**, 268

Mueller, P., Rudin, D. O. Titien, H., and Wescott, W. C. (1962a). Nature **194**, 979

Mueller, P., Rudin, D. O., Titien, H. and Wescott, W. C. (1962b). Circulation **26**, 1167

Mueller, P., Rudin, D. O., Titien, H., and Wescott, W. C. (1963). J. Phys. Chem. **67**, 534

Murphy, W. H., and Gottschalk, A. (1961). Biochim. Biophys. Acta **52**, 349

Nemethy, G., and Scheraga, H. A. (1962a). J. Chem. Phys. **36**, 3382

Nemethy, G., and Scheraga, H. A. (1962b). J. Chem. Phys. **36**, 3401

Nemethy, G., and Scheraga, H. A. (1962c). J. Phys. Chem. **66**, 1773

Nemethy, G., and Scheraga, H. A. (1963). J. Phys. Chem. **67**, 2888

Nemethy, G., and Scheraga, H. A. (1964). J. Chem. Phys. **41**, 680

Neville, D. M. (1960). J. Biophys. Biochem. Cytol. **8**, 413

Norton, W. T., and Autilio, L. A. (1964). Ann. N. Y. Acad. Sci. **122**, 77

Novikoff, A. B. (1957). Cancer Res. **17**, 1010

Novikoff, A. B., Essner, E., Goldfischer, S., and Heus, M. (1962). Interpretation of ultrastructure. Vol. 1, Academic Press, New York–London, p. 149

O'Neill, C. H. (1964). Exptl. Cell Res. **35**, 477

Ornstein, L. (1957). J. Biochem. Biophys. Cytol. **3**, 809

Overbeek, J. Th. G. (1960). J. Phys. Chem. **64**, 1178

Overton, E. (1895). Vierteljahresschr. Naturforsch. Ges. Zürich **40**, 159

Painter, T. J., and Morgan, W. T. J. (1961a). Nature **191**, 39

Painter, T. J., and Morgan, W. T. J. (1961b). Chem. Ind. (London) 437

Painter, T. J., Watkins, W. M., and Morgan, W. T. J. (1962). Nature **193**, 1042

Palade, G. E. (1952). J. Exptl. Med. **95**, 285

Parpart, A. K. (1942). J. Cell. Comp. Physiol. **19**, 248

Parpart, A. K., and Ballentine, R. (1952). In, E. S. G. Barron, ed., Modern trends in physiology and biochemistry. Academic Press, New York–London, p. 135

Parsons, D. F. (1963). Science **140**, 985

Parsons, D. F. (1965a). Lab. Invest. **14**, 431

Parsons, D. F. (1965b). Intern. Rev. Exptl. Pathol.

Pauling, L. (1959). In, D. Hadzi and H. W. Thompson, eds., Hydrogen bonding. Pergamon Press, London–New York

Pauling, L. (1961). Science **134**, 15

Pauling, L., and Marsh, R. E. (1952). Proc. Natl. Acad. Sci. **38**, 112

Payens, Th. A. J. (1960). Biochim. Biophys. Acta **38**, 539

Peters, A. (1960). J. Biophys. Biochem. Cytol. **7**, 121

Pethica, B. A. (1958). J. Gen. Microbiol. **18**, 473

Pethica, B. A. (1966). In, Surface activity and the microbial cell, p. 85

Pethica, B. A., and Schulman, J. H. (1953). Biochem. J. **53**, 177

Pfeffer, W. (1877). Osmotische Untersuchungen: Studien zur Zellmechanik. W. Englemann, Leipzig

Pockels, A. (1891). Nature **43**, 437

Poland, D. C. (1966). J. Colloid Interface Sci. **21**, 273

Poland, D. C., and Scheraga, H. A. (1965a). J. Phys. Chem. **69**, 2431

Poland, D. C., and Scheraga, H. A. (1965b). J. Phys. Chem. **69**, 4425

Ponder, E. (1948). Hemolysis and related phenomena. Grune and Stratton, New York

Ponder, E. (1951). Blood **6**, 350

Ponder, E. (1955). Protoplasmatologia X, 2. Red cell structure and its breakdown. Springer, Vienna

Ponder, E. (1961). In, Brachet, J. and Mirsky, A. E., eds., The cell, 2,1. Academic Press, New York and London

Ponder, E., and Barreto, D. (1953). Acta Haematol. **12**, 393

Ponder, E., and Barreto, D. (1957). Blood **12**, 1016

Prankerd, T. A. J. (1961). The red cell. Blackwell, Oxford

Pulvertaft, R. J. V. (1949). J. Clin. Pathol. **2**, 281

Race, R. R., and Sanger, R., (1962). Blood groups in man. Blackwell Sci. Pub., Oxford

Racker, E., Tyler, D. D., Estabrook, R. W., Connover, T. E., Parsons, D. F., and Chance, B. (1966). In, T. E. King, H. S. Mason and M. Morrison, eds., Oxidases and related redox systems. John Wiley & Sons, Inc., New York

Rajam, P. C., and Jackson, A. L. (1958). Nature **181**, 1670

Ray, B. R., and Augenstine, L. G. (1956). J. Phys. Chem. **60**, 1193

Rayleigh, Lord (1899). Phil. Mag. **48**, 321

Reed, C. F., Swisher, S. N., Marinett, G. V., and Eden, E. G. (1960). J. Lab. Clin. Med. **56**, 281

Reimer, L. (1959). Z. Naturforsch. **146**, 566

Richards, F. M. (1963). Ann. Rev. Biochem. **32**, 269

Richardson, S. H., Hultin, H. O., and Green, D. E. (1963). Proc. Natl. Acad. Sci. (Wash.) **50**, 821

Rideal, E., and Taylor, F. H. (1957). Proc. Roy. Soc. B **148**, 450

Rideal, E. K., and Schulman, J. H. (1939). Nature **144**, 100

Riehl, N. V. (1957). Kolloid-Z. **151**, 66

Robertson, J. D. (1956a). J. Biophys. Biochem. Cytol. **2**, 381

Robertson, J. D. (1956b). In, H. Waelsch, ed., Ultrastructure and chemistry of neural tissue. Cassel, London, p. 1

Robertson, J. D. (1957). Progr. Neurobiol. **2**, 1

Robertson, J. D. (1960). Progr. Biophys. Biophys. Chem. **10**, 343

Robinson, N. (1960). Trans. Faraday Soc. **56**, 1260

Rodin, N. S. (1957). Federation Proc. **16**, 825

Romanowska, E. (1960). Naturwissenschaften **47**, 66

Sabatini, D. D., Bensch, K. and Barnett, R. J. (1963). J. Cell. Biol. **17**, 19

Saunders, L., Perrin, J., and Gammack, D. (1962). J. Pharm. Pharmacol. **14**, 567

Scarth, G. W. (1942). In, W. Seifriz, ed., The structure of protoplasm. Iowa State College Press, Ames, Iowa

Schiffman, G., Kabat, E. A., and Leskowitz, S. (1962). J. Am. Chem. Soc. **84**, 73

Schmidt, W. J. (1936). Z. Zellforsch. Mikroskop. Anat. **23**, 261

Schmidt, W. J. (1938). Kolloid-Z. **84**, 137

Schulman, J. H. (1951). In, G. H. Bourne, ed., Cytology and cell physiology. Clarendon Press, Oxford

Schulman, J. H., and Hughes, A. H. (1935). Biochem. J. **29**, 1243

Schulman, J. H., and Rideal, E. K. (1937). Proc. Roy. Soc. B **122**, 29, 46

Schulman, J. H., and Stenhagen, E. (1938). Proc. Roy. Soc. B **126**, 356

Seaman, G. V. F., and Uhlenbruck, G. (1962). Z. Ärztl. Fortbild (Jena) **56**, 739

Sjöstrand, F. S. (1963a). Nature **199**, 1262

Sjöstrand, F. S. (1963b). J. Ultrastructure Res. **9**, 340

Sjöstrand, F. S. (1963c). J. Ultrastructure Res. **9**, 561

Skipski, V. P., Barclay, M., Archibald, F. M., Terebus-Kekish, O., Reichman, E. S., and Good, J. J. (1965). Life Sciences **4**, 1673

Skou, J. C. (1957). Biochim. Biophys. Acta **23**, 394

Smith, D. S. (1961). J. Biophys. Biochem. Cytol. **10**, 123

Smith, H. W. (1962). Circulation **26**, 987–1011

Snell, G. D. (1957). Ann. Rev. Microbiol. **11**, 439

Springer, G. F., and Ansell, N. J. (1958). Proc. Nat. Acad. Sci. (Wash.) **441**, 182

Springer, G. F., Williamson, P., and Brandes, W. C. (1961). J. Exptl. Med. **113**, 1077

Stasny, J. T., and Crane, F. L. (1964). Exptl. Cell Res. **34**, 423

Stern, H., and Mirsky, A. E. (1953). J. Gen. Physiol. **37**, 177

Stoeckenius, W. (1962). J. Cell Biol. **12**, 221

Stoeckenius, W., and Mahr, S. C. (1965). Lab. Invest. **14**, 458

Stoeckenius, W., Schulman, J. H., and Prince, L. M. (1960). Kolloid–Z. **169**, 170

Stone, J. D., and Ada, G. L. (1952). Brit. J. Exptl. Pathol. **33**, 428

Takemori, S., Wada, K., Sekuzu, I., and Okunuki, K. (1962). Nature **195**, 456

Takeuchi, M., and Terayama, H. (1965). Exptl. Cell Res. **40**, 32

Terry, R. D. (1964). Ann. N. Y. Acad. Sci. **122**, 3

Thannhauser, S. J., Boncoddo, N. F., and Schmidt, G. (1951). J. Biol. Chem. **188**, 417

Thierfelder, H., and Klenk, E. (1930). Chemie der Cerebroside und Phosphastide. Springer
  Verlag, Berlin

Thompson, T. E. (1964). In, M. Locke, ed., Cellular membranes in development. Academic
  Press, New York–London, p. 83

Thomsen, O. (1926). Z. Immunol. Forsch. **52**, 85

Tien, H. T. (1966a). Personal communication

Tien, H. T. (1966b). J. Mol. Biol. **16**, 577

Tria, E., and Barnabei, O. (1963). Nature **197**, 598

Tristam, G. R. (1953). In, Neurath, H., and K. Bailey, eds., The proteins, Vol. 1A.
  Academic Press, New York

Turner, K., and Watson, M. M. (1930). Biochem. J. **24**, 113

Uhlenbruck, G. (1961a). Nature **190**, 181

Uhlenbruck, G. (1961b). Sonderdruck aus Hippokrates **14**, 537

Vacca, J. B., Waring, P. P., and Nims, R. M. (1960). Proc. Soc. Exptl. Biol. Med. **105**, 100

Valentine, R. C., and Horne, R. W. (1962). In, R. J. E. Harris, ed., Interpretation of
  ultrastructure. Academic Press, New York, p. 262

Van Bruggen, E. F. J., Wiebenga, E. H., and Gruber, M. (1960). Biochim. Biophys.
  Acta **42**, 171

Van Deenen, L. L. M., and De Gier, J. (1964). In, C. Bishop and D. M. Surgenor, eds.,
  The red blood cell. Academic Press, New York, p. 243

Van Deenen, L. L. M., De Gier, J., Houtsmuller, U. T. M., and Mulder, E. (1962).
  Biochem. Problems Lipids; Proc. 6th Internat. Conf., Birmingham, Elsevier, Amsterdam,
  413

Van Deenen, L. L. M., De Gier, J., and Veerkamp, J. H. (1961) Biochem. Probl. Lipids,
  Proc. 5th Intern. Conf. Marseilles, 32

Van Deenen, L. L., Houtsmuller, U. M., De Haas, G. H., and Mulder, E. (1962). J
  Pharm. Pharmacol. **14**, 429

Vandenheuvel, F. A. (1963a). J. Am. Oil Chem. Soc. **40**, 455

Vandenheuvel, F. A. (1963b). J. Am. Oil Chem. Soc. **40**, 1

Vandenheuvel, F. A. (1964). Ann. N. Y. Acad. Sci. **122**, 57

Vandenheuvel, F. A. (1965). J. Am. Oil Chem. Soc. **42**, 481

Vašiček, A. (1960). Optics of thin films. North-Holland Publishing Co., Amsterdam

Warner, D. T. (1961). J. Theoret. Biol. **1**, 514

Warner, D. T. (1962). Nature **196**, 1055

Warren, L. (1959). J. Biol. Chem. **234**, 1971

Warren, L., Glick, M. C., and Nass, M. K. (1966). J. Cell Physiol. **68**, 269

Watanabe, H., and Uyeda, R. (1962). J. Phys. Soc. Japan **17**, 569

Watkins, W. M. (1964). In, C. Bishop and D. M. Surgenor, eds., The red blood cell.
  Academic Press, New York–London, p. 359

Watkins, W. M., and Morgan, W. T. J. (1952). Nature **169**, 852

Watkins, W. M., and Morgan, W. T. J. (1962a). Proc. 9th Intern. Congr. Blood Transfusion, Karger, Basel–New York, p. 230

Watkins, W. M., and Morgan, W. T. J. (1962b). Vox Sanguinis 7, 129

Watson, D. H. (1962). Biochim. Biophys. Acta 61, 321

Waugh, D. F. (1954). Advan. Protein Chem. 9, 326

Waugh, D. F., and Schmitt, F. O. (1940). Cold Spring Harbor Symposia Quant. Biol. 8, 17

Weiss, L. (1961). Nature 191, 1108

Weiss, L. (1962). Biochem. Soc. Symp. 22, 32

Weiss, L. (1963). Exptl. Cell Res. 30, 509

Weiss, L. (1965). J. Cell Biol. 30, 39

Weiss, L., and Armstrong, J. A. (1960). J. Biophys. Biochem. Cytol. 7, 673

Wenkstern, T. V., and Engelhardt, V. A. (1955). C. R. Acad. Sci. U. R. S. S. 102, 133

Wenkstern, T. V., and Engelhardt, V. A. (1959). Folia Haematol., Lpz. 76, 3

Williams, H. H., Erikson, B. N., Avrin, J., Bernstein, S. S., and Macy, I. G. (1938). J. Biol. Chem. 123, 111

Winkler, K. C., and Bungenberg de Jong, H. G. (1941). Arch. Neerl. Physiol. 25, 431, 467

Witcoff, H. (1951). The phosphatides. Reinhold, New York

Wolman, M. (1955). Intern. Rev. Cytol. 4, 79

Wolpers, C. (1941). Naturwissenschaften 29, 416

Yamakawa, T., Irie, R., and Iwanaga, M. (1960). J. Biochem. (Tokyo) 48, 490

Yamakawa, T., Matsumoto, M., and Suzuki, S. (1956). J. Biochem. (Tokyo) 43, 63

Yamakawa, T., Matsumoto, M., Suzuki, S., and Iida, T. (1965). Proc. Intern. Genet. Symp. Nahkodo, 616

Yamakawa, T., and Suzuki, S. (1951). J. Biochem. (Tokyo) 38, 199

Yamakawa, T., and Suzuki, S. (1952). J. Biochem. (Tokyo) 39, 393

Yamakawa, T., Yokoyama, S., and Kiso, N. (1962). J. Biochem. (Tokyo) 52, 228

Yamoto, T. (1963). J. Cell Biol. 17, 413

Yosida, K. (1928). Z. Ges. Exptl. Med. 63, 331

Zetterqvist, H. (1956). The ultrastructural organization of the columnar absorbing cells of the mouse intestine. Godvil, Stockholm

CHAPTER 2

The dynamic nature of the cell periphery

The cell as a whole is in a state of dynamic equilibrium, and the same appears true of its periphery. Some aspects of this dynamism which touch directly on peripheral constitution and contact reactions will be discussed here, but the treatment will be limited. Thus, such important topics as the exchange of lipids between the cell periphery and its environment, as demonstrated for example by cholesterol movements between plasma and the erythrocyte periphery will not be dealt with in detail. The biosynthesis of the many constituents of the cell periphery, some of which were described in the preceding chapter, are the subjects of separate monographs, and cannot usefully be covered here in biochemical detail and, by the same token, no attempt will be made to comment in detail on transport phenomena. However, emphasis will be placed on the modification of those peripheral properties of cells which are thought to affect both structures described in the first chapter, and the cellular interactions described in following chapters.

2.1 Cytodifferentiation

The various expressions of recognition seen in the coordinated cell movements occurring in morphogenesis, and the possible altered contact reactions of malignant cells, in part at least, reflect differences in macromolecular constitution, and may result from a changed emphasis in biosynthesis. Structural and functional changes associated with changed biosynthetic activity are seen in cytodifferentiation (e.g. Spiegelman 1948; Ebert 1955; Markert 1956, 1960; Grobstein 1963). For the purposes of the present discussion, Jacob and Monod's (1963) definition of differentiation is useful as: ...'two cells are differentiated with respect to each other if, while they harbor the same genome, the pattern of proteins which they synthesize is different'. Although this definition refers only to proteins, it does not exclude low-protein components, since synthesis of these is mediated through enzymes, which are themselves proteins. However, as so eloquently stated by P. Weiss (1963), '...suppose we do know how genes beget proteins – and surely this knowledge is a spectacular achievement – how do we get from these to the knowledge, let alone the synthesis, of a living cell? In principle, by just more of the same? The standard affirmative answer, that after all, proteins in the form of enzymes do hold the key to the synthesis of all other, non-protein compounds in the cell, begs the question; for it still leads only to a random bag of compounds, instead of the highly coordinated chemical machinery that is the cell.'

Grobstein (1963) also stresses the point that the differentiative process also includes the assembly of various defined sequences of amino acid sub-units into physiologically active units. As examples of variation on this scale, he quotes the case of the isozymes of lactic dehydrogenase (Markert 1963) and the controlled alterations in collagen as the basis for ultrastructural variations (Gross et al. 1963) which, in themselves, control other differentiative processes. Grobstein raises the point that in addition to acting as an assembly point in the formation of macromolecular units, the cell periphery may also have important controlling functions in biosynthesis by linking synthetic sites to the environment.

As an initial working hypothesis, it may be taken that almost all processes going on within cells are capable of being expressed in one way or another at their peripheries, in the form of heterogeneity. 'The transformations by which heterogeneity arises or increases, make up the process of differentiation' (Grobstein 1959); and in this section it is proposed to consider a few aspects of differentiation and related phenomena as they are reflected in the cell pheriphery.

It is known that a number of components of the cell periphery are under genetic control, such as the blood groups of the ABO systems, the appearance of which correlates with the presence of one of a number of allelic genes. On the other hand, in the case of the immobilising antigen system of *Paramecium aurelia* (Beale 1957, 1958) the expression of the antigen-determining genes is apparently controlled by non-genetic factors.

The use of the term 'genetic' in this context can be misleading since it should, in the light of recent advances, be used to include both replication and transcription along the lines suggested by Jacob and Monod (1961) for the synthesis of proteins in bacteria, where the structural genes are thought to determine the molecular organization of the protein, while they are under the control of operator genes. Units of structural and operator genes are known as 'operons' which are 'units of transcriptive activity'. The 'operon' is susceptible to regulation through the agency of regulatory genes, which respond to 'signals' from cytoplasmic regulatory metabolites to produce 'repressors'. If the repressors are inactivated, 'induction' occurs; if they are activated, 'repression' occurs. The fascinating chain of events whereby parts of the genome (which is built up of operons) are transcribed into RNA and then translated into ordered amino acid sequences determined by messenger RNA cannot be described in detail here. However, the point can be made that differentiation in terms of protein (enzyme) synthesis is to be considered both in terms of genetic material and repressive control which may be linked to the cellular environment by metabolic regulators.

Specific examples of enzyme 'induction' by the presence of substrates in the cellular environment are well-known in bacteria, where it has been shown that the synthesis really represents an increase in the amount of pre-existing enzymes rather than *de novo* production (Pollock 1959). Knox et al. (1956) have reviewed the various experiments carried out *in vivo*, in which enzymatic substrates have been presented to whole animals, where the situation is probably too complex to permit detailed analysis of mechanisms. However, studies have been made on enzyme induction in animal cells in cell and tissue culture. Burkhalter et al. (1957) showed that the amount of acetylcholine esterase in chick embryo explants increased following the addition of acetylcholine; and Kato and Moog (1958) described and increase of alkaline phosphatase in duodenal explants following exposure to phenylphosphate. Klein (1960, 1961), working on substrate-induced enzyme synthesis on cell cultures, observed that in the case of a variety of cell strains, addition of the relevant substrates did not cause increased synthesis of alkaline and acid phosphatases, acetylcholine esterase, *d*-amino acid oxidase, adenosine deaminase, asparaginase or tryptophane peroxidase; however, a slight increase in arginase production could be induced in HeLa cells, but not in other strains. She observed that when yeast RNA was added to the culture medium, exposure to arginine resulted in a 7- to 10-fold increase in arginase production in all of the seven varieties of cells examined, except Earle's L-strain. For further discussion of this problem, which is related to the question of the development of drug resistance, the reader is referred to Harris' monograph (1964).

As discussed by Grobstein (1959a), recent concepts about differentiation have been dependent on a number of assumptions which must be considered cautiously. Thus, the assumption that the differentiated state is transmitted by replication from one cell division to the next has been questioned by

Trinkaus (1956) and by Grobstein (1959a). From the viewpoint of experimentation, it would be of obvious help if it could be assumed that there is a general differentiating mechanism used by all cell types. While there is a great deal in common between mechanisms of protein synthesis in, for example, bacteria on the one hand, and mammalian cells on the other; at a higher level of structural organization, differences become apparent. It is generally appreciated that in addition to the purely chemical aspects of macromolecular synthesis, the questions of controlling mechanisms and spatial and temporal locations of the synthesized complexes allow a good deal of variation. Grobstein remarks that differentiation generally appears to come about as a result of interaction of both intrinsic and extrinsic determinants, and that in different types of cells, the relative importance of the two determinants may be quite different. Thus, in the case of free living organisms, in which considerable variability of their environment is a common occurrence, it is to be expected that intrinsic determinants will be emphasized. On the other hand, in the case of metazoal cells, it might be expected that extrinsic determinants will be emphasized, since events taking place in any one cell must relate to its integration within the animal as a whole. The role of extrinsic factors in terms of 'microenvironment' has been repeatedly emphasized by P. Weiss in respect to effects of intercellular materials (P. Weiss 1933) and other cells (P. Weiss 1947, 1950, 1953, 1959a).

An indication of cell membrane changes in development comes from studies of sodium and potassium movements in the developing chick heart. R. L. Klein (1960) showed that during early embryogenesis, the ventricular and atrial potassium content increased to reach a plateau at 13 days, and then decreased to the time of hatching. The potassium influx and efflux in isolated ventricles fell from a relatively high level after 7 days, to a minimum at 13 days, and then increased shortly after hatching; the sodium content of the developing heart was high at 2 days, fell sharply by 7 days, and then more gradually until hatching. Intracellular potassium exchangeability was relatively constant throughout development at about 70%, however, sodium exchange rose from 7% at 7 days to 73% after hatching. These results suggested the presence of an active transport mechanism by the second day of development. The fact that both acetylcholinesterase (Dianzani 1951; Sippel 1955) and adenylpyrophosphatase (Moog 1947) increase during the early stages of myocardial development, reach a peak at 12 to 16 days and then decrease about the time of hatching, suggested to Klein that the same might also hold for ATP-ase and that this might correlate with the reported permeability changes.

A more direct correlation between ATP-ase activity and the sodium content of the chick heart was suggested by later experiments made by R. L. Klein (1961) in which Mg and Ca-ATP-ase activity was measured in different cell fractions at various stages of embryonic development. A marked increase in Mg-ATP-ase was observed between 4 and 7 days incubation, with a lesser increase just before hatching. Although contractile elements are not seen in electron micrographs until the third day of development (Hibbs 1956), myosin has been detected with immunofluorescent techniques as early as the first to second days (Ebert 1953; Holtzer et al. 1959); the formation of the myofibril may act as a inducer for Mg-ATP-ase.

The permeability of chick embryo heart cells has also been studied by Guidotti et al. (1961). The 5-day chick embryo heart is permeable to glucose *in vitro*, and its uptake is limited by the rate of intracellular phosphorylation involving a hexokinase system. During the seventh day an insulin-sensitive mechanism regulating glucose uptake begins to develop, which requires the presence of an intact membrane, suggesting that this is the site of insulin action and it is of interest that β-granules first appear in the pancreas on the seventh day. Later work by Guidotti and Foà (1961) tends to confirm the suggestion that changes in the cell membranes of the developing chick heart regulate the transport of glucose and sorbitol.

Grobstein (1963) has reviewed a number of current concepts of differentiation as they apply to metazoal cells, and has looked into the key questions of whether repressors have been identified in these cells and, if so, whether or not they react with factors known to control cytodifferentiation. Grobstein considered that there was at that time scanty evidence in favour of the presence of repressors in metazoal cells. Evidence relevant to the interaction between differentiating factors and the regulator/operon complex comes from experiments made on embryonic induction.

2.2 Embryonic induction

Browne (1909) grafted pieces of tissue from the region surrounding the hypostomes of Hydra to the flanks of others, and noted that new buds would arise in the recipients at the site of the grafts, indicating that a specific region of Hydra induced the formation of new hydra. Later Spemann (see Spemann 1938 for review) extended this basic type of experiment to amphibians and showed that the dorsal lip of the blastopore could be transplanted to other regions and induce the formation of second embryos.

Bautzmann et al. (1932) showed that the inducing tissue or organizer, retained its activity after it had been killed by a variety of methods. In addition to inductor activity, the potentialities of the reacting tissue are of obvious importance, and the term 'competence' (Waddington 1932; 'Reaktionsfähigkeit' of Mangold 1929) is used to define the '…physiological state of a tissue which permits it to react in a morphogenetically specific way to determinative stimuli' (Holtfreter and Hamburger 1955). In their monograph, Saxén and Toivonen (1962) present and discuss the evidence that in the embryo, at the early gastrula stage, part of the ectoderm is competent to react to a variety of stimuli by differentiations, corresponding to those seen during primary induction. This competence decreases during gastrulation, and disappears altogether by the early neurula stage. Thus the repertoire of differentiation in the ectodermal cells becomes progressively limited during development. Many studies carried out on the interactions between mesenchyme and epithelium indicate that the mesenchyme affects the subsequent growth and differentiation of salivary gland (Grobstein 1954), mammary gland (Lasfargues 1957), pancreas (Golosow and Grobstein 1962), skin (McLoughlin 1963; Wessels 1962; Dodson 1963), feather germs (Sengel 1958), enamel organ (Szabó 1962), anterior pituitary (Sobel 1958), gonads (Haffen 1961) and prostate (Franks 1963). It has also been shown by morphological studies that induction may cause the formation of tubules in metanephric anlagen (Grobstein 1954), cartilage in somite explants (Holtzer 1959, 1961) and lymphocyte production in explants of thymus (Auerbach 1961a,b). Other examples are given by Saxén and Toivonen, and by Needham (1942).

The criteria of cytodifferentiation discussed by Grobstein include morphological, behavioural, chemical and developmental categories. The simpler type of observation on cell shape and consequent classification into epithelioid, fibroblastic etc. is probably unjustified, since experiments carried out *in vitro* have shown cell shape to be dependent on many environmental factors (Willmer 1965) and capable of reversible change. Avery et al. (1956) described how the differentiation of chick somite cells into cartilage cells *in vitro* is dependent on the inductive action of embryonic spinal cord or notochord. In the absence of an inducer, the somitic cells differentiate into mesenchyme or immature muscle cells; furthermore, the inducing capacity is quite specific. Lash et al. (1960) showed by use of isotopes that chondroitin sulphates could only be extracted from cultures containing a distinguishable cartilaginous matrix, but not from somites grown in the absence of an inducer. Later experiments (Glick et al. 1964) showed that induction of cartilage was associated with the appearance of enzyme(s) capable of forming 3'-phos-phoadenosine-5'-phosphosulphate from ATP, Mg^{2+} and $^{35}SO_4^{2-}$. This type of chemical marker will be of great value on following differentiation.

Another technique for a potentially more rapid and quantitative approach to differentiation is due to Vainio et al. (1963a,b), who studied viral resistance in differentiating embryonic mouse kidney rudiments. Tubules were induced in metanephrogenic mesenchyme with spinal chord, and the distribution of applied SE polyoma virus was followed by means of an immunofluorescent technique. Mesenchyme not induced to form tubules, synthesized polyoma virus, whereas that induced to form tubules did not. These authors have not demonstrated whether the entry of viruses into the cells was affected, indicating a change in their peripheries associated with differentiation, or whether viruses enter both induced and non-induced cells and merely fail to replicate in the former. However, the technique has potentialities as a tool to correlate other parameters of differentiation.

Immunological studies carried out in connection with differentiating cells have demonstrated the synthesis of new antigens during development (Cooper 1948; Flickinger and Nace 1952; Perlmann 1953), and here it seems quite clear that changes in antigenicity are occurring at the cell periphery. It should perhaps be emphasized that mere possession of antigenic properties, by peripheral components, should not be taken to mean that the normal function of these components is 'immunological'.

The early studies on induction, and the demonstration that in at least some cases, dead tissues retain their inductive capacity led to the hypothesis that induction was mediated through chemical agents. Mangold (1932), Dalcq (1941), Needham (1942) and others, suggested that the inductive substances diffused from one tissue to the other. Brachet (1960, review) has long suggested that the inducing agent is transferred between tissues in the form of particles the size of microsomes. However, as pointed out by Holt-freter (1955), the fact that the same inductive event can be brought about by a variety of agents raises the question of whether these substances act in an indirect way, by killing or producing a sublethal release of inductive material from reactive cells, or cells nearby, as seen in neuralization of ectoderm (Holtfreter 1945, 1947; Yamada 1950). On the basis of experiments with the amphibian neural tube, in which development was induced by protein-denaturing agents and inhibited by substances 'stabilizing' protein molecules, Ranzi (1963) discussed the desolvation of organized water around peripheral proteins leading to the unmasking of 'specific structures'. This attractive suggestion is feasible but almost impossible to test directly. In contrast to the variants of diffusion-promoted induction, Lewis (1904) and P. Weiss (1947, 1949) have proposed that induction was mediated through cell contact.

Mangold (1932) demonstrated the feasibility of induction by diffusion, by inducing the formation of a neural tube with pieces of agar which had previously been in contact with medullary plate, which is known to be an active inducer. Holtfreter (1955) demonstrated induction when he separated the inducing tissue from the reacting tissue with either agar or cellophane. However, these experiments are very difficult to interpret, not only because of the diffusibility of cytolytic products which can cause induction, but also because cellular contact could occur through small defects in either the agar or the cellophane.

Many studies have since been carried out in which the interacting tissues have been separated by membranes with defined pore size and thickness. Much of this work has been critically reviewed by Grobstein (1961a) and Saxén and Toivonen (1962). It appears that although it is unwise to generalize, the situation *in vitro* at least, is well covered by experiments of Grobstein (1956, 1957) and Grobstein and Dalton (1957) in which spinal cord/metanephrogenic mesenchyme interactions were allowed to proceed across 'millipore' filters. At mean pore diameters of about $100\,m\mu$, some induction occured in the absence of penetration of the membrane by cellular processes identifiable under the phase contrast and electron microscopes. Much more induction occurred across filters with $500\,m\mu$ pores, which permitted recognizable cellular penetration. However, even with the $500\,m\mu$ membranes, inductive activity decreases when the membrane thickness is increased to 30 to $40\,\mu$, and ceases altogether at 60 to $80\,\mu$ thickness. Autoradiographic studies (Grobstein 1959b, 1961b) of spinal cord isotopically labelled with amino acids demonstrate the presence of radioactive material in the 'millipore' membrane in those parts over which tubule induction occurs. Grobstein (1961) takes the view that the inductive effects are associated with a proteinaceous material which is closely associated with 'cytoplasmic boundaries'.

Other experiments on the problem of transmission in primary embryonic induction have been made by Vainio et al. (1962) using *Triturus vulgaris* ectoderm as the reacting tissue (this system has been described by Toivonen (1954)). A fluorescent antiserum against the inductor was used to detect and localize antigenic material transferred to the ectoderm. After 3 to 6 hours contact between the two tissues, antigenic granules were observed inside the ectodermal cells. This was taken to show that large molecular antigenic material is transferred in the inductive process. Although inductive information could be transmitted in a similar way, no definite evidence could be presented at the time that these granules in fact carried it. Studies by Yamada (1962) on the induction produced in the isolated prospective ectoderm of the early gastrula of *Triturus pyrrhogaster* by a protein fraction separated from guinea pig bone marrow, suggest an uptake of the protein by pinocytosis, and also suggest, but do not prove, that this antigenic material is the inducer.

Electron microscopic studies have raised some interesting points in connection with the problem of the mediation of induction through cell contact. Studies of the fine structure of the junctions between chordamesoderm and ectoderm in the gastrulae of Xenopus show definite cell contacts between trilaminar membranous structures (Eakin 1957; Eakin and Lehmann 1957). During lens induction, similar intimacy between cells is observed (Nieuwkoop 1959; P. Weiss 1959b). On the other hand, Bellairs (1959) notes a space of some 200 to 1.000 Å between trilaminar structures at the peripheries of the cell of the mesoderm and presumptive neural plate, during neural induction in the chick embryo. Hunt (1961) also noted a space of 1 to 3μ between the cells of the optic vesicle and the epidermal cells of the lens placode in the chick embryo.

As observed by L. Weiss (1960), in reviewing some of the literature, the diffusion and contact hypotheses in induction do not have to be mutually exclusive. P. Weiss (1960) has also invoked both a preliminary molecular reorientation at the cell periphery, followed by a transfer of substances by some sort of diffusive mechanism. This combination of hypotheses is to some extent supported by the study of P. Weiss and Jackson (1961) of the changes in fine structure of retinal and presumptive lens (i.e. epidermis) during lens induction in chick embryos. They observed that throughout the preliminary stage of the inductive period, the interacting cells were 'separated' by an 'interlayer'. During the following stage, this interlayer was narrowed, and filamentous structures appeared in the cells, oriented at right angles to the interlayer. Discontinuities next appeared in the 'membranes', of the opposing retinal and epidermal cells, which were apparently penetrated by the radially oriented fibres running across the interlayer. These authors are not inclined to regard the breaches in membrane integrity as artifacts, as possibly suggested by Hunt's work. Weiss and Jackson concluded that the inductive interaction was associated with a reorientation of cellular material to link the interacting cells, and tentatively suggested that the reoriented structures could serve as channels for transfer of inducing substances, although their results do not demonstrate the existence of these substances.

The question of whether or not induction is to be regarded as a cell contact reaction obviously cannot be discussed unless 'contact' is defined. In my opinion, the most useful operational definition of contact to date is that given by P. Weiss (1958), namely: '... a cell (is) in contact with another body not only if the two surfaces are in direct apposition, but also if they are separated by a narrow space occupied by a molecular population whose free mobility is restrained'. It will be appreciated that this definition avoids the semantic difficulties inherent in describing the spatial limits of the cell as discussed in chapter 1, and also permits a very wide interpretation of contact.

Within this deliberately vague concept of contact, it appears that induction resulting in differentiative changes in cells which are partially reflected in their peripheries can be brought about by both diffusion and contact with other cells. It also appears dangerous to generalize on the data available, or to suggest that because induction can be mediated through diffusion *in vitro*, that this is the normal mechanism. Whether one or both mechanisms occur *in vivo*, is of less importance within the present context, than the undisputed fact that environmental influences can bring about permanent changes in cells, and that as suggested by Trinkaus (1956), the assumption that the differentiated state is 'simply' transmitted by replication must be taken cautiously.

2.3 Modulation

Modulation is discussed in two important papers by Lacey (1960, 1961) not only in connection with his own experiments on *Bordetella pertussis*, but also in a wide biological context. The term 'modulation' was introduced by P. Weiss (see Bloom, 1937) to denote reversible changes in cellular appearance and behaviour under different environmental conditions. Lacey uses the term in the sense of 'change of phenotype occurring in all, or almost all, members of a population as the expression of a reversible and continuously environmentally-dependent change in metabolism'. Although in the light of recent advances in molecular biology, the differences between 'modulation' and 'differentiation' need not be as sharp as previously supposed, the reversible nature of this phenomenon is stressed. In this section, modulatory changes in a few different types of cells will be considered.

In the case of bacteria and viruses, Lacey observes that in general three types of change in surface antigenicity can occur. In the first, the amount of antigen varies continuously with the environmental change. Under this heading are the changes in O, capsular, slime and Vi antigens. The second type is one in which the changes are an all-or-none response to environmental variation, as exemplified by flagellar antigens. Lacey considers that this type of change may not be really different from the first type because either quantities of antigen below a critical level may not be retained at the periphery or the environmental conditions so far tested have not permitted the formation of intermediate states. In the third type the antigenic and environmental changes are discontinuous, and are seen in viruses.

Lacey's (1960) own experiments made on *Bordetella pertussis* showed that the antigenic structure of this organism varies continuously with environmental conditions and that three 'modes' with different surface antigens may develop. High incubation temperatures, the presence of sodium, potassium, halides, formate and/or nitrate favour the antigenically distinct 'X mode'; low temperatures, magnesium and sulphate ions, and mono- and di-carboxylic acids favour development of a distinct 'C mode'; and intermediate temperatures and ionic ratios favour the formation of the 'I mode'. The effect of the various ions is in some way related to their species and ratios, but is not a function of their absolute concentrations or total ionic strength. Lacey showed that the modulation process in *B. pertussis* is not due to a selective process, but reflects altered rates of synthesis of at least three antigens.

Jollos (1921) described 'dauermodification' in paramecia treated with high environmental temperatures, increasing concentrations of calcium ions and arsenious oxide. The changes persisted after removal of the abnormal environmental factor, but eventually reverted; however, it is not clear whether these changes were due to selection or modulation. Margolin (1956) has observed modulation involving quantitative change in surface antigens D and M in *Paramecium aurelia*. For more details of antigens in these organisms, reference should be made to Beale's (1954) monograph.

Another example of environmentally induced reversible change involving structure of the cell periphery is seen in the soil amoeba, *Naegleria gruberi*, which modulates into a flagellate form when its normal culture medium is diluted with distilled water. This observation of Schaudinn (1896) and Schardinger (1899) has been extensively studied by Willmer (1956, 1958, 1961a). Some two hours after amoeboid forms are transferred from their 'normal' culture medium containing meat extract to distilled water, they change into flagellates. This change is associated with the development of polarity, during which lobopodia are confined to the front end of the organism, and the periphery in general becomes tenuous, as evidenced by the observation that if two organisms undergoing modulation make contact and then move apart, they remain connected by long, thin filamentous processes.

Willmer considers that the biological function of this modulation may be to aid the dispersal of the organisms when their natural environment, the soil water, is diluted by rainfall. Flagellates rarely occur in the presence of sodium chloride in concentrations greater than 50 mM (Hollande 1942) and magnesium chloride (in the absence of calcium) in concentrations of 6 mM will also maintain the amoeboid form. Of the anions, bicarbonate, lactate and phosphate favour the flagellate form, but sulphate favours the amoeboid. Willmer (1961a) makes the general observation that when the cation concentration is below a critical point, alkalinity favours the flagellate form, and aciditiy the amoeboid. Willmer further suggests that in media with salt concentrations higher than 25 mM, the emphasis in amoebae is on ion excretion and/or water retention, whereas below this level of salinity the flagellate cells are mainly concerned with ion-retention and/or water excretion. This change may reflect changes in plasma membranes in the two forms. It is of interest that deoxycorticosterone, which is expected to partition in the membrane lipids favours the flagellar to amoeboid modulation, and Willmer (1961b) uses this to support his ideas on the direct interaction of steroids with cell membranes, the result of which is presumed to depend on the inserted steroid presenting different end groups to the aqueous phase. There is little direct evidence in support of this interesting hypothesis.

A fascinating example of modulation in simple metazoa as distinct from cultures of single cells comes from experiments on the environmental control of sexual differentiation in Hydra. Kerschner (1880, cited by Loomis) was one of the first to observe that cultures of hydra turn sexual if left for a few weeks, and Loomis (1961, 1964) has done much analytical work on this phenomenon to identify the chemical substances involved. Differentiation depends on the nature of the aqueous environment immediately surrounding the organism, and occurs as a result of accumulation of metabolites excreted from the organism's ectodermal cells into their own microenvironment. If Hydra are kept in a flowing stream of fresh water they will not show sexuality because the inducing substances are continuously removed from the microenvironment. These substances have not been identified chemically, although Loomis (1964) has shown that they appear to include the dicarboxyllic acids of Krebs' citric acid cycle and possibly carbon dioxide, and that they will withstand heating to 100 °C. Although sexual differentiation in Hydra is not known to be associated with changes in the peripheries of their constituent cells, it is considered to be of interest in that it is an example of a reversible change induced in an organism by its *microenvironment* as distinct from its environment at large. This distinction must be borne in mind when modulation is studied in vertebrates, where so little is known of the nature of cellular microenvironment within organs, and where it is probable that it will not be revealed by examination of 'bulk' tissue fluids.

The term modulation has been used in connection with metazoan cells by P. Weiss (1939, 1947, 1953), Waddington (1948) and Fell (1954).

Fell observed that in organ cultures, the allantoic endoderm of embryonic chicks displayed a variety of histological responses to different environmental conditions. Under normal conditions *in vivo*, the allantoic endoderm develops into a flattened granular layer. However, when the intact sac is cultured in plasma clot the cells lining it are seen as columnar epithelium, which contains many goblet cells which secrete mucus. If the sac is everted and grown in a 'stiff' clot, the endoderm formed a tall columnar epithelium with conspicuously few goblet cells. If the everted allantoic sac was grown in a 'soft' clot, it became cystic and distended, and the endoderm developed into a membrane of normal appearance. Some parts of the everted endoderm, in both consistency clots, form a papillomatous, secreting outgrowth. Although Fell regarded these responses to environmental conditions as modulations, rather than metaplasia or irreversible transformation, in this paper at least, she offers no evidence of the reversibility of these changes.

Lasnitzki (1953) studied changes occurring in the (solid) subcutaneous and ascitic forms of Sarcoma 37 and the T2146 tumour in mice, with a view to determining whether the reversible changes from one form to another were due to a selective or an adaptive process. On the basis of morphological evidence, mitotic counts and viability tests *in vivo* and *in vitro*, Lasnitzki concluded that the change from one cell type to another is not a selective process, but is a reversible adaptation to environment, and therefore may be considered a modulation. The problem in the case of Sarcoma 37 was taken a step further by Cook et al. (1963) who showed that there was a significant difference in the electrophoretic mobilities of cells derived from the ascitic and solid (subcutaneous) forms of the tumour. Treatment of cells from both forms with neuranimidase showed a highly significant reduction in mobility for the ascites type, whereas no measurable change in mobility occurred for the solid type. Sialic acids were released from both the ascites and 'solid' cells by neuraminidase. Cells were obtained from the solid tumours by mincing and the constituent cells were torn apart from each other.

It was therefore not possible to state whether the cells of the solid tumours had less terminal sialic acids at their peripheries than the corresponding ascites cells, or whether they were bound together strongly through their carboxyl groups, which were not unmasked electrokinetically by the separation procedures. Either way, the evidence showed that in the reversible change from ascitic to solid form of tumour, the constituent cells lost charged groups reflected in electrophoretic mobility. Consideration of the mitotic rate of the cells suggested that if the electrokinetic change reported by these authors was a selective one, there should have been evidence of a bimodal distribution of mobilities, since at least 10% of any one form of cell would have to be present in the population. This was not observed, and it was concluded that some physicochemical differences of the cell periphery associated with the process of modulation had been demonstrated.

2.4 Possible effects of viruses

The effect of viruses on the nature of the cell periphery has been explored in bacteria. Although it is useful to briefly consider some aspects of this work here because the concepts are of interest to the present discussion, it cannot necessarily be assumed that the bacterial cell is a model for animal cells in this respect.

Although many bacteriophages are bacteriocidal, some are not, and lead a symbiotic existence with their bacterial hosts, and are replicated as part of the hereditary apparatus of the host during normal growth. Lwoff and Guttman (1950) and Stent (1963) have reviewed the various experimental evidence which indicates that each bacterium of a lysogenic strain maintains within itself non-infective prophage, which confers on the bacterium the ability to produce infective phage particles. These infective particles may be released following lethal lysis of their bacterial hosts; however, in any population of 'healthy' lysogenic bacteria, induction of the prophage to produce phage only occurs in a small fraction. The emergence of 'new' lysogenic strains of bacteria from the survivors of infected non-lysogenic strains, as demonstrated by Bail (1925) and Bordet (1925), was regarded by Lwoff (1953) as 'the first example of a specific hereditary property being conferred on an organism by a specific extrinsic particle'. Once bacteria become lysogenic, this property is as stable as any of their other hereditary properties. Stent and Fuerst (1956) suggested that although the viral genome is attached to some specific site on the chromosome of its host, the DNA of the infecting phage is not directly incorporated into the bacterial DNA, since very few of the phosphorus atoms of the phage DNA appear in the prophage to which it gives rise. Jacob and Wollman (1959) reviewed the evidence and concluded that following infection, in the lysogenic response, the phage genome is added to a segment of the bacterial chromosome, as distinct from substituting for a segment of the chromosome of the previously non-lysogenic cell.

Following the lysogenic response, the bacterial cell may acquire new traits which are classified as 'conversion', and the reader is referred to Stent's (1963) monograph for a full discussion of the many aspects of conversion. An example which is of immediate interest of the finding of Uetake et al. (1955) that the development of lysogeny in various Salmonellae is followed by the appearance of new surface antigens. Uetake et al. (1958) showed that Salmonella anatum developed new surface antigens within 15 minutes of infection of non-lysogenic host with C^{15} phage. In addition to these antigenic changes, other surface changes occur in the host as manifest by the development of receptors for phage C^{34}, which are not apparently present before conversion. After infection with phage C^{15}, the survivors eventually segregrate into a non-lysogenic variant which loses the new antigen after a few generations and reverts to its original preinfected antigenic state, and a lysogenic variant which permanently retains the new surface antigen. Thus, the nature of the bacteria surface is changed in an hereditable way, following conversion induced by the genome of phage C^{15} in both its vegetative and prophage forms.

The question of whether or not animal cells and tissues are infected with virus is of obvious importance in studies of malignancy, and possibly of importance in embryogenesis, particularly as viruses may affect the properties of the cell periphery. A class of phage mutants, the so-called 'defective' strains can only be studied in the prophage state and their characteristic property is that they are unable to give rise to infective virus particles. Nevertheless their lysogenic association with their bacterial host manifests itself in the conference of immunity on the host against super-infection by exogenous, temperate phage particles of the original lysogenic strain. Replication of the defectives proceeds only while their own viral genome is associated with the genome of the bacterial host, but will not replicate autonomously. In other words, the viral genome is very much under control of the host cell. The immunity of lysogenic bacteria to infection by exogenous phage appears to be due to a cytoplasmic 'immunity substance' (Bertani 1958) which not only prevents vegetative multiplication of any penetrating

exogenous phage genome, but which also controls the replication of the
endogenous prophage (Jacob 1960). The cytoplasmic substance may be
classified as a 'repressor' according to the scheme advanced by Jacob and
Monod (1961) for the genetic regulation of protein synthesis, and is itself
formed under the influence of prophage, thereby constituting a negative
feed-back mechanism. Stent (1963) notes that probably many defective
lysogenic strains exist without their lysogenic nature being recognized, since
in these cases the chief manifestation of the presence of prophage, which
is specific cellular immunity against infection by exogenous phage, might
well not be noticed. As pointed out by Jacob such defective prophages may
thus be considered as intermediates between virus particles and cellular
organelles. If this disturbing concept is in any way applicable to animal
cells, one wonders how many properties or changes in properties in the
peripheral zone and elsewhere are due to genomic or other expression
of unrecognized defective virus. A discussion of oncogenic viruses which
is relevant here, will be deferred until the malignant cell is considered in
chapter 6.

Multinucleated cells, giant cells or polykaryocytes have been known to
pathologists for many years. An excellent review of their appearance in
many sites under various physiological and pathological conditions is given
by Roizman (1962), who covers the literature from Langhans' paper of
1868, in which it was suggested that they were formed in tuberculosis by
cell fusion of division nuclei. Polykaryocytes are well known in infectious
and non-infectious granulomata, in various lesions caused by viruses including tumours, and in many different types of tumours not as yet ascribed to
oncogenic viruses. They were described as occurring in the Rous sarcoma
(Rous 1910), in polyomas (Eddy et al. 1961) and in transplants of tumour
cells from animals inoculated with the friend leukemia virus (Buffet and
Furth 1959). In the case of *in vitro* systems, direct observation has shown
that fusion, not fission, of mononuclear cells is responsible for the formation
of polykaryocytes after infection with the viruses of mumps (Henle et al.
1954) para-influenza (Marston 1958) and measles (Aoyama 1959). Appearance of multinucleate cells too soon after infection for fission to be responsible for their genesis has been used in support of fusion by Ross and Orlans
(1958), Stoker (1958), Wildy et al. (1959), Stoker and Newton (1959) and
Roizman (1961). It was shown by Okada et al. (1957) that fusion required
viable cells and Okada (1962) showed that when Ehrlich ascites tumour
cells aggregated following infection with the Z strain of HVJ myxovirus,
degenerate cells were rejected from the cell aggregates just before fusion

began, after some 30 min incubation *in vitro* at 37 °C. Giant cell formation in measles-infected cultured LLC-MK$_2$ cells has been observed by light microscopy in some detail by Klöne et al. (1963) who remarked that it is initiated by 'disappearance of contacting borders of two cells'. After some hours a cytoplasmic 'bridge' was observed connecting the nuclear regions of both cells; the nucleus of one cell of a pair migrated along this bridge at maximum speeds of 2 μ per min and, several hours after the migrating nucleus reaches the nuclear region of the other, the 'bridge' fragments. Bungay and Watkins (1964) observed polykaryocytosis in HeLa cells infected with herpes simplex virus in the presence and absence of 5-iodo-2'-deoxyuridine, which inhibits viral synthesis, and noted that cell fusion was also inhibited for a period indicating a delay of an hour between the completion of DNA synthesis and fusion, suggesting that fusion can take place in the absence of 'mature' virus. They also concluded that giant cells arise by fusion between infected and uninfected cells. The actual mechanisms of fusion are obscure, although on the negative side, Okada and Tadokoro's (1962) work on the Ehrlich ascites cell/HVJ virus system indicates that the fusing activity of HVJ virus is different from its infectivity, haemagglutinating and haemolytic activity and is unconnected with its sialidase activity. In the case of a number of stable cell lines of human and animal origin, with two variants of parainfluenza virus, Ho and Gorbunova (1962) also noted that fusion activity, which occurred with most cell types examined, and varied in amount with the different viruses, parallelled haemagglutinating activity but was not identical with it. More recently Okada and Murayama (1965) have observed fusion between cells of different strains, and Harris and Watkins (1965) have observed interspecies fusion between human (HeLa) and mouse (Ehrlich ascites) cells infected with Sendai virus. Artificial heterokaryons of animals cells from different species are also described and discussed by Harris et al. (1966). Roizman (1962) suggested that, although the mechanisms of fusion were unknown, viruses might alter the structure of the cell periphery initially by binding to it, and in the course of replication alter the proportions of its varying constituents by genetic or epigenetic mechanisms. These changes might well be expected to be reflected in abnormal cellular behaviour.

Abercrombie (1962) has briefly considered some virus-induced changes in connection with contact-dependent cell behaviour, and notes that as the cell periphery reflects much of cellular organization, changes in it due to virus are not expected to be unique, and that 'the virus merely elects' ordinary stereotyped developmental mechanisms which in normal ontogeny or in other experimental circumstances are switched on or quantitatively controlled by quite different means, and to go outside this repertoire invites another standard response, cell degeneration'. In view of the work on virus infected bacteria, and other work on oncogenic viruses which will be discussed later, virus induced changes may well be unique, contrary to Abercrombie's opinion. The simple point can be made, that by one method or another, viruses can alter the peripheries of cells and might therefore produce behavioural changes which might well be attributed to other causal entities. It is well known that viruses are very widely distributed in nature, and it seems reasonable therefore to assume that unless we are aware of and on the lookout for viral effects, it is unlikely that they will be correctly ascribed.

2.5 Sublethal autolysis

In 1952 Fell and Mellanby showed that when the cartilaginous limb-bone rudiments of chick embryos were cultured in the presence of excess vitamin A (10–15 I.U. per ml), they stopped increasing in size and the cartilaginous matrix became gelatinous and tended to disappear with corresponding loss of metachromasia on staining with toluidine blue. The cells themselves remained viable as evidenced by continuing mitosis. Further experiments made on cartilage from foetal mice showed that vitamin A is without effect on explants previously killed by heating at 45 °C for 15 min. Fell et al. (1956) later showed that synthesis of new cartilaginous matrix is inhibited by excess vitamin A. On the basis of this and previous observations, they suggested that under the influence of excess vitamin A, cartilage cells possibly produced an enzyme which degraded sulphated mucopolysaccharide with the resulting observed dissolution of cartilage.

Support for the effect of vitamin A being mediated through enzymatic activity was provided by the observations of Thomas et al. (1960) and Fell and Thomas (1960) that a histological picture similar to that produced by excess of vitamin A could be produced by the action of papain. Lucy et al. (1961) made experiments to determine whether normal cartilage contains an enzyme that is capable of producing an effect on the matrix like that of vitamin A. Cartilaginous rudiments were first immersed in distilled water to disrupt the cells and their organelles, and then incubated in buffers covering the pH range of 1 to 8 units, after which they were stained for metachromasia. There was great reduction in metachromasia in the rudiments incubated between pH 3 to 5, but little effect on the matrix outside this narrow range. It was also shown that a fraction rich in cytoplasmic particles had maximum proteolytic activity at *p*H 3. These workers concluded that normal chondrocytes contain an enzyme system capable of producing an effect on the cartilaginous matrix, which resembles that produced by vitamin A. L. Weiss (1962b) showed that pretreatment of cultured cells with vitamin A facilitates their detachment from glass surfaces to which they adhere *in vitro*. One possible interpretation of this observation is that enzymes released in a manner analogous to that seen in cartilaginous rudiments weakened the peripheral zone of the cells by autolysis, thus making their detachment from glass easier. Dingle (1961) made a significant contribution to an understanding of these effects of vitamin A by showing that the enzymes involved are the lysosomal hydrolases. It thus appeared that sublethal autolysis was possible, not only of the intercellular matrix, but also of what might be more usually regarded as the peripheral zone of cells, through the activity of lysosomal acid hydrolases.

Much of our knowledge of the lysosomes and their enzymes and the acid hydrolases has been reviewed by De Duve (1959), Novikoff (1961) and Weissmann (1965) and is the subject of a published symposium edited by Reuck and Cameron (1963). In 1955, De Duve et al. proposed the name 'lysosome' for a group of cytoplasmic particles with which were associated a number of acid hydrolases. The lysosomes of rat liver are associated with acid ribonuclease and desoxyribonuclease (De Duve et al. 1955), acid phosphatase, phosphoproteinase, phosphatase (Paigen and Griffiths 1959), cathepsin(s) (Finkelstaedt 1957), collagenase (Frankland and Wynn 1962), α-glucosidase (Lejeune et al. 1963), β-N-acetylglucosaminidase, β-glucuronidase (De Duve et al. 1955). Within the cell, the lysosomal particles are bound by single membranes as viewed with the electron microscope (Novikoff 1961), which constitute some sort of osmotic barrier (Berthet et al. 1951). It is not known at present whether all of the identified enzymes are present in each lysosome, or whether there are several types of lysosome, each differing qualitatively and quantitatively in its associated enzymes. It should also be noted that all of the cellular acid hydrolases are not associated with the lysosomes, as for example the non-lysosomal β-glucuronidase in the liver (De Duve et al. 1955; Paigen 1961). Lysosomal acid phosphatase may be localized within the cell by application of various modifications of the Gomori technique to frozen sections of liver (Holt 1959; Novikoff 1959, 1950; Daems 1962) or to cells cultured on coverslips (Weiss and Dingle 1964) and by examination of preparations under the electron microscope (Essner and Novikoff 1961; Holt and Hicks 1961; Daems 1962). However, as pointed out by De Duve (1963), among others, the term lysosome should not be given indiscriminately to any intracellular structure giving a positive staining reaction for acid phosphatase, even though up to the present time acid phosphatase staining has been invaluable as a marker for other less easily located acid hydrolases.

The lysosomes are associated with four types of biological activity (De Duve 1964), which may be summarized as follows:

(1) 'Heterolysis', or digestion of exogenous material, which may be intracellular and follow ingestion of cells and subcellular fragments; or extracellular and follow liberation of lysosomal enzymes from the cell.

(2) So-called 'digestive dysfunctions' of cells which follow either lysosomal insufficiency or inability of the enzymes present to degrade ingested material. This cellular indigestion may result in inability of the cell to excrete the material, leading to cellular constipation.

(3) Cellular 'autophagy' which possibly represents a response to adverse conditions during which cells presumably digest parts of themselves. This is not necessarily a lethal process, since regeneration can occur.

(4) 'Generalized autolysis' which may precede, follow and/or cause cell death.

As far as the cell periphery is concerned, its alteration by enzymes is of immediate concern, and the next problems to be considered are the conditions favoring the release of lysosomal enzymes, and the regulation of their activity.

It is usually considered that in the intact cells, within intact lysosomes, the acid hydrolases are in a 'bound and inaccessible state'. A variety of stimuli may act on the lysosomes rendering the enzymes 'soluble and accessible' (De Duve 1963). At the moment no definite statements can be made on what is really meant by 'bound and inaccessible state'. Berthet et al. (1951) took a sac composed of a semi-permeable membrane containing enzymes as a simple model for lysosomes, and considered that any agent breaching the sac would release the enzymes; certainly a wide variety of agents including mechanical and sonic homogenization, osmotic imbalance of suspending solutions, freezing and thawing, the action of lecithinase and various proteases, fat solvents, detergents and excess vitamin A all cause 'activation' and release of acid hydrolases. Beaufay and De Duve (1959) and De Duve and Beaufay (1959) have suggested that the cathepsins within the lysosomes may cause autolytic breakdown of the particle when the immediate environmental pH is acid enough to coincide with enzyme activity. The main point of this and similar arguments is that as a low pH (3–5) is required for appreciable activity, autodigestion of the lysosomal enzymes does not occur within the intact particle. De Duve (1963) has pointed out that the sac model for lysosomes is a conceptual rather than a morphological entity. Koenig (1962) has suggested that the various enzymes are maintained in an inactive state within a solid as distinct from a saccular lysosome, by forming ionic bonds with acidic glycolipids. In support of this suggestion Koenig and Jibril (1962) note that lysosomes resemble solid structures in electron micrographs, and that enzymes can be released from them after exposure to various concentrations of cations, in a manner compatible with ionic bounds. The electron micrographic appearances of lysosomes are compatible with either view, and, as De Duve has pointed out, ionic bonds may be involved in holding the limiting membranes together without linking to the enzymes at all, and the parameter of enzyme release on the presence if substances weakening ionic bonds would not enable a distinction to be drawn between the two views. Another view proposed by myself is that the activity of acid hydrolases could well be controlled if they were bound to a charged membrane in such a way that their active centres were outside a zone some 5–8 Å from the plane of the charged groups. This view which is concerned with hydrogen ion concentrations near to surfaces, will be developed below, but it will be noted here that it invokes both pH -control of autolytic activity and enzyme binding.

Much of the work of the group at the Strangeways Research Laboratory on the effects of vitamin A on lysosomal stability have been summarized by Dingle (1963) and Fell (1965). In addition to the work of Fell and her associates quoted earlier, Dingle notes that studies on vitamin A and related compounds suggest that the initial effect of the vitamin is to penetrate the lysosomal membrane, making it unstable and, following this, enzymes are released. Evidence in favor of this suggestion comes from electron micrographic studies on various cytomembranes, following exposure to vitamin A, in cultured fibroblasts (Dingle et al. 1962), the epidermis of chick embryos (Fitton-Jackson and Fell 1963) and erythrocytes (Glauert et al. 1963) which demonstrate distortion of various membranous organelles; and from work done on lecithin/cholesterol monolayer models, which show increases in area at constant pressure following exposure to vitamin A (Bangham et al. 1964). From the viewpoint of the present chapter, the importance of the work on vitamin A is that it gives some insight into lysosomal stability, as distinct from the physiology of hypervitaminosis A. It may be mentioned that an alternative mechanism for the mode of action of vitamin A and the other fat-soluble vitamins D and E has been suggested by Brown et al. (1963), who proposed that the vitamins produce a change in rate of sulphation of sulphomuco-polysaccharides, and that this in turn alters the permeability of the cell membranes. This concept is not incompatible with those of Teorell (vide Frey-Wyssling 1935) on the regulation of permeability by porous, amphoteric ultrastructures. In addition, Blough and Ottewill (1966) have suggested that vitamin A interacts with proteins in the cell periphery which invaginate into the lipids causing membrane lysis.

So far, two main suggestions have been made for the mechanisms of the initial stages of lysosomal activation. The first is that various agents act directly on the lysosomal particle itself, and the second is that the agents act first on the cell periphery and this in turn fires off other activating processes. Evidence which at first sight favors the direct action of agents on lysosomes comes from such experiments as those of Weissmann and Dingle (1962) who found that ultraviolet radiation makes them unstable, in a manner which would account for the breakdown of irradiated, cultured foetal rat skin (Weissman and Fell 1962). In both cases hydrocortisone increases the stability of the irradiated material. Hydrocortisone exerts a similar protective effect on the release of enzymes from vitamin A-treated lysosomes (Weissmann and Thomas 1963), and Dingle et al. (1963) have shown that lysosomes isolated from the livers of hypervitaminotic A rats are unstable. On re-examination of experimental data of this type, which is based on the action of various agents on isolated lysosomes, it is clear that they do not prove that the same agents act in the same way when the particles are within cells. Evidence in favor of an indirect action of agents on lysosomes comes out of studies made on the response of cells to antisera. The well-known changes following treatment of cells with potent antibodies involve massive vacuolation, which suggests interference with cellular osmoregulation through structural changes in the cell periphery. These changes have been observed by many, including Niven (1929), Pulvertaft et al. (1959) and Abramoff et al. (1961), and are reviewed by Bitensky (1963b). Dumonde et al. (1961) showed that the rate of cytolysis following exposure of ascites tumor cells to antisera, could be controlled by alteration in serum and complement concentrations and/or temperature. Such exposure to antisera which made the lysosomes more fragile, followed increase in cellular volume and preceded breakdown of the whole cell. Bitensky and Gahan (1962) showed by acid phosphatase staining of antibody-treated tumor cells, that lysosomal enzymes could be released from tumor cells which were morphologically intact and apparently viable. It was further shown that if cells were treated with antibody alone, under conditions when the antibody is said not to get inside the cell (Bitensky 1963a) the lysosomes became increasingly fragile; however, if the exposure to antibody was brief, the fragility apparently returned to normal. In the absence of complement, Easton et al. (1962) were unable to demonstrate the entry of ferritin-tagged antibody into cells by electron microscopy. Bitensky (1963a) then, subscribes to the view that the initial event in at least antibody-induced lysosomal activation are changes in the (permeability) properties of the plasma membranes. Direct support of this view, comes from the experiments made by Weiss and Dingle (1964), who prepared antisera in rabbits against fractions rich in lysosomes obtained from rat livers. They showed that the rabbit sera reacted *in vitro* against the original antigenic lysosomal preparation, and that during this interaction, complement was fixed. When slices of rat liver were incubated with either the antiserum or control serum, and assayed for bound acid phosphatase, the antiserum treated liver showed a progressive loss of enzyme which was greater than that observed in the control. However, when partially purified lysosomal preparations were incubated for periods of up to 3 hours at 37 °C with and without antiserum, there was no appreciable release of cathepsins, acid phosphatase or aryl sulphatases whether antiserum was present or not. Weiss and Dingle (1964) also observed that when monolayers of rat dermal fibroblasts growing on glass were treated with the same batch of antiserum, within a few minutes their cytoplasmic processes retracted and the cells became intensely vacuolated. These appearances were associated with cell death as confirmed by prolonged culture of the cells. In parallel cultures which were fixed and stained for acid phosphatase at different times after exposure to either potent antiserum or serum from which anti-body had been adsorbed out on rat erythrocytes, the discrete brown granules associated with the lysosomal acid phosphatase disappeared within 30 sec of adding potent antiserum and the brown coloration diffused throughout the whole cell; after 7 min the brown color had completely disappeared from the great majority of the cells. This demonstrable loss of staining pro-perties was retarded but not prevented by 25 μg/ml of hydrocortisone, which under these conditions, protected the lysosomes while not preserving cell viability. In the presence of low concentrations of antiserum, foetal rat fibroblasts may lose all their staining reaction for acid phosphatase without loss of viability (Weiss 1965a). These results show clearly that, in the case of antiserum, its initial reaction is with the cell periphery, not with the lyso-somes, and that subsequent lysosomal activation is not due to antiserum entering the cell and reacting directly with these particles. It was also shown by Weiss (1965a) that the entry of neutral red and trypan blue into viable rat fibroblasts in both normal serum and antiserum, was retarded by the pres-ence of final concentrations of less than 10 μg/ml hydrocortisone. However, as hydrocortisone also retards the loss of phosphatase staining properties in lysosomes, within cells killed by exposure to antibodies, it is concluded that this steroid protects both the plasma membrane and the lysosomal membrane or complex. A common factor in lysosomal activation is ionic inbalance, and it is suggested that alteration of the semi-permeable properties of the plasma membrane by any agent will tend to activate the lysosomal complexes, by diluting out their normal microenvironment with the extracellular fluids. The two views on whether enzyme release is mediated by direct or indirect action of various agents with the lysosomes are not mutually exclusive, and there is no reason why both mechanisms should not operate, particularly with low molecular weight agents which can penetrate the plasma membrane.

It has been shown that in the case of cultured embryonic mouse bones (Fell and Weiss 1965) and embryonic chick rudiments (Fell and Weiss, unpublished data), dramatic loss of cartilaginous matrix and intense osteoclasis occur following exposure to antisera, and that these can be prevented by as little as 0.1 μg hydrocortisone per ml of medium. It has also been shown (Weiss 1965a) that sublethal amounts of antiserum facilitate the detachment of cultured rat fibroblasts from glass, which coincides with the disappearance of positive staining for acid phosphatase from the cells and is considered to be due to sublethal autolysis of parts of the cell periphery. Both the facilitation of detachment and the loss of staining properties are prevented by hydrocortisone. Thus, the interaction of cells with an environmental protein, in this case antibody, can bring about autolytic non-lethal modification of the cell periphery and adjacent intercellular matrix and, furthermore, this type of process can be under hormonal control.

From the limited amount of data quoted, it seems that there are two types of lysosomal enzyme release from cells. The first is a massive type consequent upon cell death, in which once the enzymes are released, more enzymatic modification of tissues will depend on replacement of the dead cells. The second type, which may well be of greater biological interest, is the non-lethal loss of enzymes, which, in the presence of a continuous stimulus, could resemble a 'chronic weeping' lesion at cellular level and which will depend on synthesis of new lysosomal complexes. This synthesis is expected to follow the pattern protein synthesis generally, and could thus provide a possible case of how continuous modification of the peripheral zone of cells can be brought under 'central' control.

To the cell biologist, one of the most perplexing things about the lysosomal acid hydrolases is the low environmental pH required for their optimal activity with a large number of substrates. It is not suggested that these enzymes have no activity at all around pH 7, but an intuitive respect for cellular efficiency prompts the question of whether these low optimal pH's (circa 3–5) bear any relationship to the control and/or spatial location of their activity, particularly with regard to the cell periphery. It seems distinctly possible that any understanding of lysosomal or other enzymatic activity near cytomembranes must involve a consideration of the conditions peculiar to hydrogen ion activity in these regions.

2.5.1 'Surface pH'

It has been known for some time that there is a relationship between bulk phase pH and the tension at fatty acid or oil/water interfaces (Reinders 1910; Jahrisch 1922; Hartridge and Peters 1922; Peters 1931; Danielli 1937). Although the curve relating interfacial tension to pH closely resembles the dissociation/pH curve of various fatty acids in shape, it was noted that whereas the main changes in interfacial tension occur between pH 6–9, the corresponding changes in dissociation occur between pH 4–7. The reasons for this 'shift' in pH-range was discussed by Danielli (1936) and attributed to a combination of differences in dielectric constant between the region around the interface and the bulk phase; interference in ionization due to close proximity of carboxyl groups and the existence of Donnan equilibrium between the surface and the bulk phases. These factors are expected to result in a lower pH in the immediate region of a surface than in the bulk phase.

A technique for studying the pH in interfacial regions in model systems is to observe the color changes in aqueous solutions of indicator dyes when they are shaken with benzene for example, which emulsifies, thereby creating a large surface area. In the benzene water system, Deutsch (1927, 1928) showed that sulphonated acidic dyes indicated a more acid pH than in the unshaken bulk phase, and that the reverse occurs in the case of basic dyes.

The concentration of the various ions in the region of the cell periphery has been calculated from considerations of the Gibbs–Donnan equilibrium by Danielli (1937) and from zeta potential by Hartley and Roe (1940). It has been concluded that in the immediate vicinity of the negatively charged groups in the cell periphery there will be an excess of mobile cations, including hydrogen ions, and a relative deficiency of mobile anions. It should also be noted that this region might well concentrate calcium ions from the bulk phase, since as Wilbrandt (1940) has pointed out, if the Gibbs–Donnan equilibrium for monovalent ions is given by:

$$\frac{[\text{Na}^+]_{\text{surface}}}{[\text{Na}^+]_{\text{bulk}}} = r$$

then,

$$\frac{[\text{Ca}^{++}]_{\text{surface}}}{[\text{Ca}^{++}]_{\text{bulk}}} = r^2.$$

The treatment of Hartley and Roe considers that the local concentration of hydrogen ions near a particle surface $[\text{H}^+]_\text{S}$ is related to the zeta potential (ζ) by:

$$[\text{H}^+]_\text{S} = [\text{H}^+]_\text{B} \cdot e^{-\varepsilon\zeta/kT}, \tag{1}$$

where $[\text{H}^+]_\text{B}$ is the concentration of hydrogen ions in the bulk phase, ε is the dielectric constant, k is Boltzmann's constant and T is $^\circ$ Kelvin. The dissociation constant at the surface (K_S) is given by:

$$K_\text{S} = K \cdot e^{-\varepsilon\zeta/kT} = K \cdot e^{-F\zeta/RT}, \tag{2}$$

where K is the bulk thermodynamic dissociation constant, F is the faraday, and R is the gas constant.

At 25 °C equation (2) may be rewritten as:

$$p\text{H}_{\text{surface}} = p\text{H}_{\text{bulk}} + \zeta/60 \tag{3}$$

In the case of metazoal cells, which carry a net negative charge, ζ is always negative and

$$p\text{H}_{\text{bulk}} - p\text{H}_{\text{surface}} = \Delta p\text{H}.$$

The Helmholtz–Smoluchowski equation enables ζ in equation (3) to be estimated in determinations of electrophoretic mobility, V:

$$\zeta = \frac{4\pi\eta V}{D}, \tag{4}$$

where D is the dielectric constant and η the viscosity at the hydrodynamic slip plane. Thus $p\text{H}_\text{S}$ may be estimated from measurements of electrophoretic mobility on the assumption that η and D are known quantities.

Although the use of the zeta potential (ζ) as distinct from surface potential (ψ) implies that the values estimated indicate the pH in the region of fixed

charges, but not actually in the plane of these charges, Danielli (1941) showed that use of zeta potential in the case of solutions of ovalbumin molecules
fits in with the results obtained by titration. As will shortly be discussed, when
enzyme reactions are considered in the peripheral regions of cells, these may
or may not be in the plane of charged groups, but use of zeta potential estimated from electrophoretic mobility at least permits an experimental
approach.

An important step in the experimental evaluation of 'surface' pH has been
made by McLaren and his colleagues using enzymes as 'molecular pH-meters'
and much of the relevant literature has been reviewed by McLaren and Babcock (1959) and McLaren (1963). Bascially their techniques have involved
studying the activity of enzymes on substrates which are either bound to
the surfaces of kaolin and other particles, or which are in the free state.
McLaren and Estermann (1956) observed the action of chymotrypsin on
denatured lysozyme which was either in solution or bound to kaolin particles, and noted that the bulk pH for optimal enzymatic activity was some
2 pH units higher in the case of the adsorbed substrate than with it in the
free state. That is to say, the enzyme/substrate reaction near to the kaolin
particles proceeds as though it were occurring in an environment having a
pH some 2 units lower than in the bulk phase. These observations fit very
well with the estimate of Michaels and Morelos (1945) that the concentration
of hydrogen ions around the surface of kaolin particles should be approximately 100 times higher than in the bulk phase. This type of experiment is
of course always open to the criticism that adsorption of either enzyme or
substrate can produce conformational or other changes, and certainly
adsorption produces a wide range of changes in different enzymes (Gieseking 1949; Zittle 1953). However, as elution of adsorbed enzymes is a purification method (Schwimmer and Pardee 1953) it follows that adsorption
does not necessarily produce massive irreversible inactivation. The geometry
of particle to which binding occurs is of importance, and Estermann et al.
(1959) have shown that there is less loss of activity when an enzyme is adsorbed only at a particle surface as in the case of kaolin, than internally as in
the expanding lattice of montmorillonite.

McLaren's (1957) results on the pH/activity curves of yeast invertase
attached to, and free from yeast cells, suggest that in the negatively-charged
peripheral zone of these cells, the invertase is functioning at a lower pH
than in the bulk phase. Weiss (1963a) compared the pH/activity relationships
of the cell-bound penicillinase of *Bacillus subtilis* (749C) in the logarithimic
phase of growth with free penicillinase obtained in the cell-free supernatant

of older cultures of the same organism. This particular organism was chosen for study since Kushner and Pollock (1961) had shown that the penicillinase is firmly bound at its periphery, and a simple iodometric method was available for penicillinase assay (Perret 1954). From measurements of bacterial cell electrophoretic mobility, use was made of Hartley and Roe's formula to calculate the pH in the peripheral zone of *B. subtilis* under the conditions of the experiment. The data showed that not only was the cell-bound penicillinase apparently reacting at a lower pH than the free enzyme, but it also appeared to be acting at a higher pH than calculated from the measurements of electrophoretic mobility. As a check on the calculations, the pH/activity relationships of the same sample of penicillinase and penicillin were studied, free in solution, and with either the penicillin or the penicillinase bound to kaolin particles. In this case a shift corresponding to a ΔpH of approximately 1 unit was observed, which fitted very well the shift calculated with Hartley and Roe's formula from measurements of the electrophoretic mobilities of kaolin particles under the conditions of the penicillin/penicillinase interactions. It was noted that kaolin-bound penicillinase is not necessarily a good model for penicillinase naturally bound at the surface of *B. subtilis* as the binding in the two situations might have been different, and that this in itself might have so modified the penicillinase to produce a change in pH/activity relationships. Indeed in *B. cereus* two distinct penicillinase moieties are recognized, that liberated and that bound to the cytoplasmic membrane. These bound and free enzymes are thought to differ only in their tertiary configuration, yet have different immunological and enzymatic properties and also have different pH/activity relationships. To complicate matters further, Garber and Citri (1962) have noted that the distinct properties of the cell-bound (γ) penicillinase are closely related to its binding to solid surfaces and the cell envelope. In spite of these difficulties in the way of precise interpretation, the point could reasonably be made that whereas the pH/activity curve for penicillinase in the presence of kaolin is calculable by use of Hartley and Roe's formula, the curve for the cell-bound enzyme is not.

An attempt was made to account for the inability to calculate the pH/activity curve for the bound enzyme. Apart from the changes in tertiary structure which have been discussed, there is the possibility that the enzyme/substrate interactions occur outside the hydrodynamic slip plane, at which measurements of electrophoretic mobility are made. McLaren (1960) has pointed out that this question of location of the enzyme with respect to the electrophoretic plane of shear of particles presents a major problem in the use of enzymes as molecular pH-meters. Another possibility may be advanced which is certainly not proven by the pencillinase experiments, but which is nonetheless of general interest. From the equations quoted earlier, it is seen that electrophoretic mobility is a parameter of charge density, not of charge distribution. That is to say, cellular electrophoretic mobility measurements will not enable a distinction to be drawn between uniformly distributed charged groups and for instance, charged groups arranged in zones. The argument was developed that if the ionogenic groups are arranged in zones where the charge density is high compared with interzonal regions, it would be expected that the activity/bulk phase pH curve of enzymes acting in the region of a heterogenously charged surface would vary considerably, depending on whether their active centre were located within a high charge density zone, where the hydrogen ion activity per unit surface area would be higher than in the interzonal region and, indeed, higher than that calculated on the assumption of homogeneous charge distributions, On the other hand, it would not be expected that all of the ionogenic groups would be in the high charge density zones; some might be in interzonal locations, and this combined with the preferential adsorption of anions over cations, at any surface, would lead to the interzones having a higher effective negative charge, and hence greater hydrogen ion activity than the environmental bulk phase.

While it is clearly not possible to make any quantitative statements about the pH in the peripheral zone of cells, it seems distinctly possible that appreciable differences exist between hydrogen ion concentration in this region and the bulk phase of the cellular environment. The region of 'low' pH might be expected to extend through the double layer to a depth of some 5 to 8Å from the plane of the bound charged groups, which is probably deep enough to accommodate the 'active centres' of a number of enzymes. It also seems possible that in the case of enzymes having a narrow optimal pH range, their activity might well be regulated by the spatial relationships of their active centres and the vulnerable parts of their substrates to the electrical double-layer, which in turn is affected by the charge in this region. Thus, charge fluctuations in the cell periphery could partially control enzyme activity. In addition to controlling the rate of enzyme reactions by means of ΔpH, the charge on substrates can also affect their degradation by enzymes, possibly by affecting enzymatic orientation as suggested by studies of the activity of lecithinase on charged monolayers (Bangham and Dawson 1958; Dawson and Bangham 1959).

When enzyme activity in the region of the cell periphery is considered in general terms, mucopolysaccharides of the cell proper or of adjacent connective tissue may well be of considerable importance, and the possible activity of hyaluronate in this context has been noted by L. Weiss (1962) in terms of Rogers' general discussion of its structure and function (1961). Thus, hyaluronate is well known to control diffusion through intercellular spaces as demonstrated by Day (1952) who showed that the rate of flow of fluids through a sheet of fascia was markedly increased after treating the connective tissue with hyaluronidase. In a similar way the diffusion of enzymes towards or away from a cell might be limited. By virtue of its negative charge (carboxyl) hyaluronate could act as an ion exchanger with an affinity for cations such as Na^+ and K^+ (Abood and Abul-Haj 1956; Kulonen 1953; Aldrich 1958). Rogers (1957) has postulated that hyaluronate could inhibit enzyme reactions, as suggested by experiments with a number of both synthetic and natural macroanions (Spensley and Rogers 1956). Rogers (1961) has further suggested that as this inhibitory function is expected to be a function of molecular size, hydrolysis of the molecule would reduce the inhibition and thus, in special circumstances, a hyaluronic acid-hyaluronidase system might act as a regulator for the activity of other enzymes. Inhibition of activity would only occur with those enzymes having an optimal pH of neutrality or more alkaline; in the case of lysosomal acid hydrolases, hyaluronate would tend to promote activity by virtue of the postulated ΔpH effect. Presumably an analogous argument might be advanced for the regulation of enzyme activity in the intercellular region by the synthesis or degradation of other macroionic constituents of connective tissue.

2.6 Physiological variations in cellular electrophoretic mobility

In a noteworthy attempt to relate the electrokinetic properties of liver cells to their growth-rate, Eisenberg et al. (1962) measured the electrophoretic mobilities of rat liver cells isolated by perfusion with citrate from normal livers, following partial hepatectomy and during postnatal growth. They observed that during regeneration and the neonatal period there was an increase in electrophoretic mobility, and that the increases observed during regeneration returned to normal values when the process was complete. These results are in general accord with those of Ben-Or et al. (1960), Heard et al. (1961) and Ruhenstroth-Bauer and Fuhrmann (1961) who observed that some cells derived from embryonic or regenerating tissues have a higher electrokinetic charge than those from their 'normal' or adult counterparts. However, Simon-Reuss et al. (1964) finally concluded from their own studies on a number of mammalian cells grown *in vitro* and ascites tumours that 'it was not possible to generalize in regard to the relationship of electrokinetic charge to type of cell, site of origin, rate of growth, or malignancy of the parent tissue'. These and other results however, refer to shifts occurring within whole cell populations, and give little indication of whether the mobilities of individual cells are changing during their life cycles. Another general criticism of much of the work to date is the well-known difficulty in finding, 'normal' counterparts to compare with malignant, embryonic or regenerating cells. Also, with any procedure involving the separation of cells from their parent tissues, a certain amount of cellular trauma is inevitable, and liver is a well-known example of a tissue where standard perfusion techniques, such as used in the quoted papers, result in damaged cells which have not to date shown evidence of unimpaired viability by their subsequent growth *in vitro*. After isolation of the various cells described, their mobilities have been measured in a variety of suspending fluids which range from at best, those which cannot support vital processes for long, to, at worst, solutions which are overtly cytotoxic (Pulvertaft and Weiss 1963). To date, the mobilities of cells have not been measured in their natural environment, the tissue fluids.

Attempts have been made by Weiss (1966) to circumvent many of the difficulties outlined above, by using cells maintained *in vitro* in spinner cultures (Moore and Ulrich 1965) from which samples may be removed without potentially traumatic separation procedures, and examined by electrophoresis and other techniques, while in their normal (culture medium) fluid environment. The metabolic rate of such cells was altered either by incubating them at different temperatures or by adding dinitrophenol to the cultures; their electrophoretic mobilities were measured in culture fluid, in similar conditions to those under which oxygen utilization was measured manometrically. In comparing mobilities measured at different temperatures, allowance was made for changes in the physical properties of the suspending fluid, particularly with respect to viscosity, dielectric constant and ionic concentration. The formulation is discussed under techniques, in chapter 5. It was shown that both the oxygen utilization and electrophoretic mobility of a permanent strain of cultured cells, increased over the temperature range of 2 °C to 37 °C, and then decreased as the temperature was increased from 37 °C to 60 °C (fig. 2.1).

It was also shown that cells killed by heating to 60 °C or by formalin

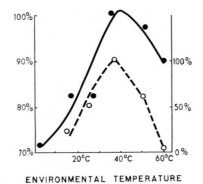

ENVIRONMENTAL TEMPERATURE

Fig. 2.1

treatment did not respond to increases in temperature by true increase in electrophoretic mobility, indicating that this particular electrokinetic change requires viable cells. After treatment with either neuraminidase or dinitrophenol, cells subjected to changes in temperature showed no change in electrokinetic properties. It was therefore considered possible that the changes in electrophoretic mobility at different temperatures are in some way dependent on the location of ionized carboxyl groups of sialic acid at the cell periphery, and that this was in some way related to the metabolic activity of the cell. The possible mechanisms whereby a cell can alter its electrophoretic mobility in relationship to its metabolic rate include: synthesis of new terminal sialic acid units; alteration of charge with increased ionic fluxes; and conformational changes in the peripheral region, which result in ionogenic sialic acids being reversibly brought up into the hydrodynamic slip plane as the cell moves in the electrophoresis chamber.

The explanation that mobility changes were tied to synthesis of new peripheral sialic acid was considered unlikely since this takes approximately six hours under the conditions of the experiments, rather than the observed periods of several minutes.

In discussing the thermodynamics of molecules penetrating lipid membranes Danielli (1952) has pointed out that all of the potential energy barriers encountered by diffusing molecules are among other factors, a function of absolute temperature, and Hempling's group (Aull and Hempling 1963) has demonstrated by experiment that in ascites tumour cells, sodium fluxes are temperature-dependent. The possibility was therefore considered that ionic fluxes were in some way responsible for the observed changes in electrophoretic mobility. In view of the dependence of electrokinetic change on the presence of sialic acid groups, fluxes would in some way depend on these. If, in fact, neuraminic acids are part of a charged site involved in the transport of cations, it would have been expected that at higher fluxes more sites would be occupied by cations, resulting in decreased electrophoretic mobility, rather than the observed higher mobility.

Another possibility to account for the sialic acid dependent change in electrophoretic mobility is that conformational changes take place within peripheral macromolecules which reveal or conceal sialic acid groups from the electrokinetic viewpoint. On the somewhat tenuous evidence that the changes parallel oxygen consumption and are inhibited by dinitrophenol, it could be cautiously suggested that the hypothetical conformational changes are linked to cellular metabolic activity. If the macromolecules are proteins, then the protein core should be flexible, Cheesman and Davies (1954) have noted that in an aqueous environment, globular protein molecules tend to be very rigid due to interactions between their hydrophobic side chains which are located mainly, but not exclusively, in the molecular 'interior'. However, in model systems, at an oil/water interface, penetration of the oil between the side chains may considerably reduce the cohesive energy and, under these conditions, the protein molecules become extremely flexible and unfold readily into conformations dictated by steric factors. Although as discussed in chapter 1, the precise arrangements of lipid relative to protein in the cell periphery are not known, proteins in this region may well be more flexible than in the bulk aqueous phase. As cellular electrophoretic mobility depends on charge density, not on total charge, simple folding of a surface, with consequent electrokinetic 'burial' of ionogenic groups, would not lead to a reduction of charge density if the charged groups were uniformly distributed, and if no non-charged filler materials were brought in to maintain surface area. If, however, as discussed, the charged groups have a mainly zonal distribution, then 'burial' of these zones could produce reduction in charge density, observable experimentally as decreased (negative) electrophoretic mobility. By virtue of the rigidity expected to be conferred on underlying attached macromolecules, by the electrostatic repulsion between the ionized carboxyl groups of terminal sialic acids (Weiss 1965b), these postulated high charge density zones might tend to be buried as units by movement of the encircling, less rigid peripheral material. The possibility of folding and unfolding of proteins at the cell periphery has been suggested by Goldacre and Lorch (1950), in connection with their experiments on amoebae, and is considered by them to be analogous to relaxation/contraction cycles in muscle, which require an energy source.

A similar temperature response in mobility was also reported in the case of human erythrocytes by Sachtleben (1963), where corrected mobilities of -0.79μ at $1\,°C$, and -1.27μ sec^{-1} volt^{-1} cm at $37\,°C$ were obtained in phosphate-buffered saline. However, this response of cells to different temperatures does not always lead to electrophoretic mobilities which differ from 'corrected' values. Merishi and Seaman (1966) have reported no difference between observed and expected results over the range 1 to $43\,°C$, in erythrocytes and a number of cultured cells detached from glass surfaces before electrophoresis. These differences cannot be dismissed as separation artefacts, since in my own laboratory a number of different cell types grown in suspension culture either showed a variable response to temperature or no effect at all.

Whatever the ultimate explanation, it appears that the electrokinetic properties of cells are capable of reversible change brought about by environmental conditions. The suggested possible metabolic link between these conditions and electrophoretic mobility serves to emphasize that observations of electrokinetic properties are best made when cells are not only viable, but are also in defined metabolic states. Until such conditions are met, comparisons of the electrokinetic properties of different, general classes of cells are not only premature, but possibly misleading.

In an attempt to study variations in the electrophoretic mobilities of cells in relation to their mitotic cycles, Mayhew and O'Grady (1965) and Mayhew (1966) have also studied populations of cells grown in suspension cultures. As only 2 to 3% of these cells are normally in mitosis at any one time, the effect of mitosis would be lost against the general background of cell population. In order to obtain more cells in mitosis at given times Mayhew and O'Grady used parasynchronous populations of cells, obtained either by the technique of double thymidine-blocking (Bootsma et al. 1964; Peterson and Anderson 1964) or by cold shock (Newton and Wildy 1959) in which up to 15% of the total population were in mitosis at the mitotic 'peak'. Using cells of similar type to those used by Weiss (1966) in experiments described above, Mayhew and O'Grady showed that these cells had their highest electrophoretic mobility during the mitotic peak phase when the population is in late interphase (G_2), mitosis and/or early interphase (G_1). After division the mobility falls sharply, and Mayhew (1966) concluded that the highest mobilities were really in G_2 and/or mitosis. Mayhew also showed that after treatment with neuraminidase, the mean mobilities of cells from parasynchronous populations are the same regardless of their temporal position within the mitotic cycle, suggesting that the increased electrophoretic mobilities at the mitotic peak phase may be due to higher concentration of the ionized carboxyl groups of sialic acid in the hydrodynamic slip plane. On the warrantable assumption that the dielectric constant, viscosity and Debye–Huckel parameter remain unaltered, and that changes in mobility reflect changes in charge density at the cell surface, Mayhew has considered the two possibilities that either the total volumes or total surface areas of daughter cells must change during division, and notes that the work of Prescott (1955) and Hiramoto (1958) would tend to rule out volume changes; however, if the total volume of two spherical daughter cells remains equal to the volume of their parent, this still represents a gain of approximately 28 % in surface area of the daughter cells (Wolpert 1960). Mayhew therefore tentatively advanced the hypothesis that the N-acetylneuraminic acid contributing to charge density is synthesized during late interphase and/or mitosis, and hence causes higher electrophoretic mobility during this period; however, the increase in surface area following cleavage, without accompanying synthesis, causes reduction in charge density and hence a reduction in mobility.

It may be useful to speculate that autolytic and synthetic activities involving enzyme activity in the peripheral zone of cells may be controlled to a variable extent by local pH; and that hydrogen ion activity in turn may be regulated by 'surface' charge which varies with different physiological states of the underlying cell. In this way local control of enzymatic processes could be integrated with cellular activity.

References

Abercrombie, M. (1962). Symp. Quant. Biol. **27**, 427

Abood, L. G., and Abul-Haj, S. K. (1956). J. Neurochem. **1**, 119

Abramoff, P., Saunders, J. W., and Gasseling, M. T. (1961). J. Natl. Cancer Inst. **26**, 585

Aldrich, B. I. (1958). Biochem. J. **70**, 236

Ambrose, E. J., James, A. M., and Lowick, J. H. B. (1956). Nature **177**, 576

Aoyama, Y. (1959). Japan. J. Exptl. Med. **20**, 535

Auerbach, R. (1961a). Develop. Biol. **3**, 336

Auerbach, R. (1961b). Proc. Natl. Acad. Sci. (Wash) **47**, 1175

Aull, F., and Hempling, H. G. (1963). Am. J. Physiol. **204**, 789

Avery, G., Chow, M., and Holtzer, H. (1956). J. Exptl. Zool. **132**, 409

Bail, O. (1925). Med. Klin. (Munich) **21**, 1271

Bangham, A. D., and Dawson, R. M. C. (1958). Nature **182**, 1292

Bangham, A. D., Dingle, J. T., and Lucy, J. A. (1964). Biochem. J. **90**, 133

Bautzmann, H., Holtfreter, J., Spemann, H., and Mangold, O. (1932). Naturwissenschaften **20**, 971

Beale, G. H. (1954). The genetics of paramecium aurelia. Cambridge University Press, London

Beale, G. H. (1957). Intern. Rev. Cytol. **6**, 1

Beale, G. H. (1958). Proc. Roy. Soc. B. **148**, 308

Beaufay, H., and De Duve, C. (1959). Biochem. J. **73**, 604

Bellairs, R. (1959). J. Embryol. Exptl. Morph. **7**, 94

Ben-Or, S., Eisenberg, S., and Doljanski, F. (1960). Nature **188**, 1200

Bertani, G. (1958). Advan. Virus Res. **5**, 151

Berthet, J., Berthet, L., Appelmans, F., and De Duve, C., (1951). Biochem. J. **50**, 182

Bitensky, L. (1963a) In, A. V. S. de Reuck and M. P. Cameron, eds., The lysosomes, Little, Brown and Co., Boston

Bitensky, L. (1963b). Brit. Med. Bull. **19**, 241

Bitensky, L., and Gahan, P. B. (1962). Biochem. J. **84**, 13

Bloom, W. (1937). Physiol. Rev. **17**, 589

Blough, H. A., and Ottewill, R. H. (1966). Exptl. Cell Res. **44**, 46

Bootsma, D., Budke, L., and Vos, O. (1964). Exptl. Cell Res. **33**, 301

Bordet, J. (1925). Ann. Inst. Pasteur **39**, 711

Brachet, J. (1960). The biochemistry of development. Pergamon Press, London

Brown, R. G., Button, G. M., and Smith, J. T. (1963). J. Theoret. Biol. **5**, 489–492

Browne, E. (1909). J. Exptl. Zool. **7**, 1

Buffet, R. F., and Furth, J. (1959). Cancer Res. **19**, 1063

Bungay, C., and Watkins, J. F. (1964). J. Exptl. Pathol. **45**, 48

Burkhalter, A., Jones, M., and Featherstone, R. M. (1957). Proc. Soc. Exptl. Biol. Med. **96**, 747

Cheesman, D. F., and Davies, J. T. (1954). Advan. Protein Chem. **9**, 439

Cook, G. M. W., Seaman, G. V. F., and Weiss, L. (1963). Cancer Res. **23**, 1813

Cooper, R. S. (1948). J. Exptl. Zool. **107**, 397

Daems, W. Th. (1962). Mouse liver lysosomes and storage. Luctor et Emergo, Leiden

Dalcq, A. (1941). L'œuf et son dynamisme organisateur. Michel, Paris

Danielli, J. F. (1936). J. Cellular Comp. Physiol. **7**, 393

Danielli, J. F. (1937). Proc. Roy. Soc. B. **122**, 155

Danielli, J. F. (1941). Biochem. J. **35**, 470

Danielli, J. F. (1952). Symp. Soc. Exptl. Biol. **6**, 1

Dawson, R. M. C., and Bangham, A. D. (1959). Biochem. J. **72**, 493

Day, T. D. (1952). J. Physiol. **117**, 1

De Duve, C. (1959). In, T. Hayashi, ed., Subcellular particles. Ronald Press, New York

De Duve, C. (1963). In, A. V. S. de Reuck, M. P. Cameron and J. Knight, eds., Lysosomes. Little, Brown and Co., Boston

De Duve, C. (1964). In, A. V. S. de Reuck, M. P. Cameron and J. Knight, eds., Cellular injury. Little, Brown and Co., Boston, p. 369

De Duve, C., and Beaufay, H. (1959). Biochem. J. **73**, 610

De Duve, C., Pressman, B. C., Gianetto, R., Wattiaux, R., and Appelmans, F. (1955). Biochem. J. **60**, 604

Deutsch, D. (1927). Sitzber. Akad. Wiss. Wien, **60**, 1036

Deutsch, D. (1928). Z. Phys. Chem. **136**, 353

Dianzani, M. U. (1951). Arch. Fisiol. **50**, 251

Dingle, J. T. (1961). Biochem. J. **79**, 509

Dingle, J. T. (1963). In, A. V. S. de Reuck, M. P. Cameron and J. Knight, eds., Lysosomes. Little, Brown and Co., Boston, p. 384

Dingle, J. T., Glauert, A. M., Lucy, J. A., and Daniel, M. (1962). Biochem. J. **84**, 76

Dingle, J. T., Moore, A., and Sharman, I. (1963). Brit. J. Nutr. **22**

Dodson, J. W. (1963). Exptl. Cell Res. **31**, 233

Dumonde, D. C., Walter, C. M., Bitensky, L., Cunningham, G. J., and Chayen, J. (1961). Nature **192**, 1302

Eakin, R. M. (1957). Anat. Rec. **129**, 532

Eakin, R. M., and Lehmann, F. E. (1957). Arch. Entur. Mech. Organ. **150**, 177

Easton, J. M., Goldberg, B., and Green, H. (1962). J. Exptl. Med. **115**, 275

Ebert, J. D. (1953). Proc. Natl. Acad. Sci. U.S. **39**, 333

Ebert, J. D. (1955). Growth Symposium **13**, 69

Eddy, D. E., Borman, G. S., Berkeley, W. H., and Young, R. D. (1961). Proc. Soc. Exptl. Biol. Med. **107**, 191

Eisenberg, S., Ben-Or, S., and Doljanski, F. (1962). Exptl. Cell Res. **26**, 451

Estermann, E. F., Conn, E. E., and McLaren, A. D. (1959). Arch. Biochem. Biophys. **85**, 103

Essner, E., and Novikoff, A. B. (1961). J. Biophys. Biochem. Cytal. **9**, 773

Fell, H. B. (1954). J. Embryol. Exptl. Morph. **2**, 348

Fell, H. B. (1965). In, E. N. Willmer, ed., Cells and tissues in culture. Vol 1. Academic Press, London–New York, p. 659

Fell, H. B., and Mellanby, E. (1952). J. Physiol. **116**, 320

Fell, H. B., Mellanby, E., and Pelc, S. R. (1956). J. Physiol. **134**, 179

Fell, H. B., and Thomas, L. (1960). J. Exptl. Med. **111**, 719

Fell, H. B., and Weiss, L. (1965). J. Exptl. Med. **121**, 551

Finkelstaedt, J. T. (1957). Proc. Soc. Exptl. Biol. Med. **95**, 302

Fitton-Jackson, S., and Fell, H. B. (1963). Develop. Biol. **7**, 394

Flickinger, R. A., and Nace, G. W. (1952). Exptl. Cell Res. **3**, 393

Frankland, D. M., and Wynn, C. H. (1962). Biochem. J. **84**, 20

Franks, L. M. (1963). Natl. Cancer Inst. Monogr. **11**, 83

Frey-Wyssling, A. (1953). Submicroscopic morphology of protoplasm. Elsevier, New York, p. 201

Garber, N., and Citri, N. (1962). Biochim. Biophys. Acta **62**, 385

Glauert, A. M., Daniel, M., Lucy, J. A., and Dingle, J. T. (1963). J. Cell Biol. **17**, 11

Gieseking, J. E. (1949). Advan. Agric. **1**, 159

Glick, M. C., Lash, J. W., and Madden, J. W. (1964). Biochim. Biophys. Acta **83**, 84

Goldacre, R. J., and Lorch, I. J. (1950). Nature **166**, 497

Golosow, N., and Grobstein, C. (1962). Develop. Biol. **4**, 242

Grobstein, C. (1954). Growth Symp. **13**, 233

Grobstein, C. (1956). Exptl. Cell Res. **10**, 424

Grobstein, C. (1957). Exptl. Cell Res. **13**, 575

Grobstein, C. (1959a). In, J. Brachet, and A. E. Mirsky, eds., The cell. Vol. I. Academic Press, New York and London, p. 437

Grobstein, C. (1959b). J. Exptl. Zool. **142**, 203

Grobstein, C. (1961a). Exptl. Cell Res. Suppl. **8**, 234

Grobstein, C. (1961b). Coll. Intern. du C. N. R. S. **101**, 169

Grobstein, C. (1963). In, M. Locke, ed., Cytodifferentiation and macromolecular synthesis. Academic Press, New York–London, p. 1

Grobstein, C., and Dalton, A. J. (1957). J. Exptl. Zool. **135**, 57

Gross, J., Lapiere, C. M., and Tanzer, M. L. (1963). Symp. Soc. Study Develop. Growth **21**, 175

Guidotti, G., and Foà, P. P. (1961). Am. J. Physiol. **201**, 869

Guidotti, G., Kanameishi, D., and Foà, P. P. (1961). Am. J. Physiol. **201**, 863

Haffen, K. (1961) In, La culture organotypique, Colloques Intern. C.N.R.S. **101**, 133

Harris, M. (1964). Cell culture and somatic variation. Hall, Rinehart and Winston, New York

Harris, H., and Watkins, J. F. (1965). Nature, **205**, 640

Harris, H., Watkins, J. F., Ford, C. E., and Schoefl, G. I., (1966). J. Cell. Sci. **1**, 1

Hartley, G. S., and Roe, J. W. (1940). Trans. Faraday Soc. **36**, 101

Hartridge, H., and Peters, R. A. (1922). Proc. Roy. Soc. A **101**, 348

Heard, D. H., Seaman, G. V. F., and Simon-Reuss, I. (1961). Nature **190**, 1009

Henle, G., Deinhardt, F., and Girardi, A. (1954). Proc. Soc. Exptl. Biol. Med. **87**, 386

Hibbs, R. G. (1956). Am. J. Anat. **99**, 17

Hiramoto, Y. (1958). J. Exptl. Biol. **35**, 407

Ho, Y. D., and Gorbunova, A. S. (1962). Acta Virol. **6**, 193

Hollande, A. (1942). Arch. Zool. Exp. Gen. **83**, 125

Holt, S. J. (1959). Exptl. Cell Res. Suppl. **7**, 1

Holt, S. J., and Hicks, R. M. (1961). J. Biophys. Biochem. Cytol. **11**, 47

Holtfreter, J. (1945). J. Exptl. Zool. **98**, 161

Holtfreter, J. (1947). J. Exptl. Zool. **106**, 197

Holtfreter, J. (1955). Exptl. Cell Res. Suppl. **3**, 188

Holtfreter, J., and Hamburger, V. (1955). In, B. H. Willier, P. A. Weiss and V. Hamburger, eds., Analysis of development. Saunders, Philadelphia–London, p. 230

Holtzer, H. (1959). In, C. Thornton, ed., Regeneration in vertebrates. University of Chicago Press, Chicago, p. 15

Holtzer, H. (1961). Growth Symp. **19**, 335

Holtzer, H., Abbott, J., and Cavanaugh, M. W. (1959). Exptl. Cell Res. **16**, 595

Hunt, H. (1961). Develop. Biol. **3**, 175

Jacob, F. (1960). Harvey Lectures **54**, 1

Jacob, F., and Monod, J. (1961). J. Mol. Biol. **3**, 318

Jacob, F., and Monod, J. (1963). In, M. Locke, ed., Cytodifferentiation and macromolucar synthesis. Academic Press, New York–London, p. 30

Jacob, F., and Wollman, E. L. (1959). In, G. Tuneval, ed., Recent progress in microbiology. Almqvist and Wiksell, Stockholm, p. 15

Jahrisch, S. (1922). Biochem. Z. **134**, 163

Jollos, V. (1921). Arch. Protisteuk. **43**, 1

Kato, Y., and Moog, F. (1958). Science **127**, 812

Klein, E. (1960). Exptl. Cell Res. **21**, 421

Klein, E. (1961). Exptl. Cell Res. **22**, 226

Klein, R. L. (1960). Am. J. Physiol. **199**, 613

Klein, R. L. (1961). Am. J. Physiol. **201**, 858

Klöne, W., Kulemann, H., Ward, E. N., and Salk, J. E. (1963). Exptl. Cell Res. **31**, 438

Koenig, H. (1962). Nature **195**, 782

Koenig, H., and Jibril, A. (1962). Biochim. Biophys. Acta 65, 543

Knox, W. E., Auerbach, V. H., and Lin, E. C. C. (1956). Physiol. Rev. **36**, 164

Kulonen, E. (1953). Acta Physiol. Scand. **27**, 82

Kushner, D. J., and Pollock, M. R. (1961). J. Gen. Microbiol. **26**, 255

Lacey, B. W. (1960). J. Hyg. Camb. **58**, 57

Lacey, B. W. (1961). Symp. Soc. Gen. Microbiol. **11**, 343

Langhans, Th. (1868). Virchow's Arch. Pathol. Anat. Physiol. Klin. Med. **42**, 382

Lasfargues, E. Y. (1957). Exptl. Cell Res. **13**, 553

Lash, J. W., Holtzer, H., and Whitehouse, M. W. (1960). Develop. Biol. **2**, 76

Lasnitzki, I. (1953). Brit. J. Cancer **7**, 238

Lejeune, N., Thinès-Sempoux, D., and Hers, H. G. (1963). Biochem. J. **86**, 16

Lewis, W. H. (1904). Am. J. Anat. **3**, 505

Loomis, W. F. (1961). In, H. Lennhoff and W. F. Loomis, eds., The biology of hydra. University Miami Press, Miami, Florida, p. 337

Loomis, W. F. (1964). J. Exptl. Zool. **156**, 289

Lucy, J. A., Dingle, J. T., and Fell, H. B. (1961). Biochem. J. **79**, 500

Lwoff, A. (1953). Bacteriol. Rev. **17**, 269

Lwoff, A., and Guttmann, A. (1950). Ann. Inst. Pasteur **78**, 711

Mangold, O. (1929). Arch. Entwicklungsmech. Organ. **117**, 586

Mangold, O. (1932). Naturwissenschaften **19**, 905

Margolin, P. (1956). Genetics **41**, 685

Markert, C. L. (1956). Cold Spring Harbor Symp. Quant. Biol. **21**, 339

Markert, C. L. (1960). Natl. Cancer Inst. Monograph **2**, 3

Markert, C. L. (1963). Symp. Soc. Study Develop. and Growth **21**, 65

Marston, R. Q. (1958). Proc. Soc. Exptl. Biol. Med. **98**, 853

Mayhew, E. (1966). J. Gen. Physiol. **49,** 717

Mayhew, E., and O'Grady, E. A. (1965) Nature **207**, 86

McLaren, A. D. (1957). Science **125**, 697

McLaren, A. D. (1960). Enzymologia **21**, 356

McLaren, A. D. (1963). In, H. D. Brown, ed., Cell interface reactions. Scholars Library, New York

McLaren, A. D., and Babcock, K. L. (1959). In, T. Hayaski, ed., Subcellular particles. Ronald Press Co., New York

McLaren, A. D., and Estermann, E. F. (1956). Arch Biochem. Biophys. **61**, 158

McLoughlin, C. B. (1963). Symp. Soc. Exptl. Biol. **17**, 359

Mehrishi, J. N., and Seaman, G. V. F. (1966). Biochim. Biophys. Acta **112**, 154

Michaels, A. S., and Morelos, O. (1945). Ind. Eng. Chem. **47**, 1801

Moog, F. (1947). J. Exptl. Zool. **105**, 209

Moore, C. E., and Ulrich, K. (1965). J. Surg. Res. **5**, 270

Needham, J. (1942). Biochemistry and morphogenesis. Cambridge University Press, London

Newton, A. A., and Wildy, P. (1959). Exptl. Cell Res. **16**, 624

Nieuwkoop, P. D. (1959). In, C. H. Waddington, ed., Biological organization cellular and subcellular. Pergamon Press, London, p. 212

Niven, J. S. F. (1929). J. Pathol. Bact. **32**, 527

Novikoff, A. B. (1959). Biol. Bull. **117**, 385

Novikoff, A. B. (1961). In, J. Brachet and A. E. Mirski, eds., The cell, vol. 2. Academic Press, New York–London, p. 423
Okada, Y. (1962). Exptl. Cell Res. **26**, 98
Okada, Y., and Murayama (1965). Bikers J. **8**, 7
Okada, Y., Suzuki, T., and Hosaka, Y. (1957). Med. J. Osaka Univ. **7**, 709
Okada, Y., and Tadokoro, J. (1962). Exptl. Cell Res. **26**, 108
Paigen, K. (1961). Exptl. Cell Res. **25**, 286
Paigen, K., and Griffiths, S. K. (1959). J. Biol. Chem. **234**, 299
Pasternak, G. (1965). J. Nat. Cancer Inst. **34**, 71
Perlmann, P. (1953). Exptl. Cell Res. **5**, 394
Perret, C. J. (1954). Nature **174**, 1012
Peters, R. A. (1931). Proc. Roy. Soc. A **133**, 140
Petersen, D. F., and Anderson, E. C. (1964). Nature **203**, 642
Pollock, M. R. (1959). In, P. D. Boyer, H. Lardy and K. Myrback, eds., The enzymes, vol. 1., 2nd ed., Academic Press, New York, p. 619
Prescott, D. M. (1955) Exptl. Cell Res. **9**, 328
Pulvertaft, R. J. V., Doniach, D., Roitt, I. M., and Vaughan-Hudson, R. (1959). Lancet **11**, 214
Pulvertaft, R. J. V., and Weiss, L. (1963). J. Pathol. Bact. **85**, 473
Ranzi, S. (1963). Develop. Biol. **7**, 285
Reinders (1910). Cited by Peters, R. A. (1931). Proc. Roy. Soc. A **133,** 140
Reuck, A. V. S. de and Cameron, M. P., eds., (1963). Lysosomes. Little, Brown and Co., Boston
Rogers, H. J. (1957). Ann. N. Y. Acad. Sci. **65**, 132
Rogers, H. J. (1961). Biochem. Soc. Symp. **20**, 51
Roizman, B. (1961). Virology **13**, 387
Roizman, B. (1962). Symp. Quant. Biol. **27**, 237
Ross, R. W., and Orlans, E. (1958). J. Pathol. Bact. **76**, 393
Rous, P. A. (1910). J. Exptl. Med. **12**, 696
Ruhenstroth-Bauer, G., and Fuhrmann, G. F. (1961). Z. Naturforsch. **166**, 252
Sachtleben, V. P. (1963). Z. Naturforsch. **188**, 233
Saxén, L., and Toivonen, S. (1962). Primary embryonic induction. Academic Press, London
Schardinger, F. (1899). Sitzber. Akad. Wiss. Wien. Malt. Naturw. **108**, 713
Schaudinn, F. (1896). Sitzber. Deut. Akad. Wiss. Berlin **2**, 31
Schwimmer, S., and Pardee, A. B. (1953). Advan. Enzymol. **14**, 375
Sengel, P. (1958). Ann. Sci. Nat. Zool. Biol. Animale **20**, 431
Simon-Reuss, I., Cook, G. M. W., Seaman, G. V. F., and Heard, D. H. (1964). Cancer Res. **24**, 2038
Sippel, T. O. (1955). J. Exptl. Zool. **128**, 165
Sobel, H. (1958). J. Embryol. Exptl. Morph. **6**, 518
Spemann, H. (1938). Embryonic development and induction. Yale University Press, New Haven, Connecticut
Spensley, P. C., and Rogers, H. J. (1956). Nature **173**, 1190
Spiegelman, S. (1948). Symp. Soc. Exptl. Biol. **2**, 286
Stent, G. S. (1963). Molecular biology of bacterial viruses. W. H. Freeman and Company, San Francisco–London
Stent, G. S., and Fuerst, C. R. (1956) Virology **2**, 737

Stoker, M. G. P. (1958). Nature **182**, 1525

Stoker, M. G. P., and Newton, A. (1959). Virology **7**, 438

Szabó, G. (1962). In, E. O. Butcher and R. F. Sognaes, eds., Fundamentals of keratinization, American Association Advances in Science, Washington

Thomas, L., McCluskey, R. T., Potter, J. L., and Weissmann, G. (1960). J. Exptl. Med. **111**, 705

Toivonen, S. (1954). J. Embryol. Exptl. Morphol. **2**, 239

Trinkhaus, J. P. (1956). Am. Naturalist **90**, 273

Uetake, H., Luria, S. E., and Burrous, J. W. (1958). Virology **5**, 68

Uetake, H., Nakagawa, T., and Akiba, T. (1955). J. Bacteriol. **69**, 571

Vainio, T., Saxén, L., and Toivonen, S. (1963a). Acta Pathol. Microbiol. Scand. **58**, 205

Vainio, T., Saxén, L., and Toivonen, S. (1963b). J. Natl. Cancer Inst. **31**, 1533

Vainio, T., Saxén, L., Toivonen, S., and Rapola, J. (1962). Exptl. Cell Res. **27**, 527

Waddington, C. H. (1932). Phil. Trans. Roy. Soc. **221**, 179

Waddington, C. H. (1948). Symp. Soc. Exptl. Biol. **2**, 145

Weiss, L. (1960). Intern. Rev. Cytol. **9**, 187

Weiss, L. (1962a). Exptl. Cell Res. **30**, 509

Weiss, L. (1962b). J. Theoret. Biol. **2**, 236

Weiss, L. (1963). J. Gen. Microbiol. **32**, 331

Weiss, L. (1965a). Exptl. Cell Res. 37, 540

Weiss, L. (1965b). J. Cell Biol. **26**, 735

Weiss, L. (1966). J. Natl. Cancer Inst. **36**, 837

Weiss, L., and Dingle, J. T. (1964). Ann. Rheumat. Dis. **23**, 57

Weiss, P. (1933). Am. Naturalist **67**, 322

Weiss, P. (1939). Principles of development. Holt, New York

Weiss, P. (1947). Yale J. Biol. Med. **19**, 235

Weiss, P. (1949). Exptl. Cell Res. Suppl. **1**, 475

Weiss, P. (1950). Quart. Rev. Biol. **25**, 177

Weiss, P. (1953). J. Embryol. Exptl. Morphol. **1**, 181

Weiss, P. (1958). Intern. Rev. Cytol. **7**, 391

Weiss, P. (1959a). In, J. N. Oncley, ed., Biophysical science; a study programme, J. Wiley and Sons, Inc., New York, p. 11

Weiss, P. (1959b). In, C. H. Waddington, ed., Biological organization in cellular and subcellular. Pergamon Press, London, p. 231

Weiss, P. (1960). Proc. Natl. Acad. Sci. U.S. **46**, 993

Weiss, P. (1963). J. Theoret. Biol. **5**, 389

Weiss, P., and Jackson, S. F. (1961). Develop. Biol. **3**, 532

Weissmann, G. (1965). New England J. Med. **273**, 1084, 1143

Weissmann, G., and Dingle, J. T. (1962). Exptl. Cell Res. **25**, 207

Weissmann, G., and Fell, H. B. (1962). J. Exptl. Med. **116**, 365

Weissmann, G., and Thomas, L. (1963). J. Clin. Invest. **42**, 661

Wessels, N. K. (1962). Develop. Biol. **4**, 87

Wilbrandt, W. (1940). Arch. Ges. Physiol. **243**, 519

Wildy, P., Stoker, M. G. P., and Ross, R. W. (1959). J. Gen. Microbiol. **20**, 105

Willmer, E. N. (1956). J. Exptl. Biol. **33**, 583

Willmer, E. N. (1958). J. Embryol Exptl. Morphol. **6**, 187

Willmer, E. N. (1961a). Exptl. Cell Res. Suppl. **8**, 32

Willmer, E. N. (1961b). Biol. Rev. **36**, 368
Willmer, E. N. (1965). In, E. N. Willmer, ed., Cells and tissues in culture, Vol 1. Academic
    Press, London–New York, p. 143
Wolpert, L. (1960). Intern. Rev. Cytol. **10**, 163
Yamada, T. (1950). Biol. Bull. **98**, 98
Yamada, T. (1962). J. Cell. Comp. Physiol. **60** Suppl. **1**, 49
Zittle, C. A. (1953). Advan. Enzymol. **14**, 319

CHAPTER 3

Cell contact phenomena

Cell contacts are thought to be of importance in a wide range of phenomena, which involve active, crawling movements of cells on which directional conditions are imposed. This chapter will therefore be initially concerned with cell movement and its direction. As many current ideas on cell contacts have been derived from *in vitro* studies on cells separated from their parent tissues, these comparatively simple systems will be described and discussed in fairly gross terms before considering the more complex and less well studied *in vivo* systems.

3.1 Amoeboid movement

Amoeboid movement is a type of active locomotion during which a cell crawls over a substratum by means of pseudopodial attachment and detachment.

On account of their size, it is not surprising that much work on the nature of amoeboid movement has been done on actual amoebae. It must not be assumed that there is only one basic mechanism of amoeboid movement which is used both by amoebae and metazoal cells, since as Bovee (1964) has pointed at, even among amoebae there is wide variation in both fundamental mechanisms and the particular ways in which the mechanisms are used. Wolpert et al. (1964) note that among the difficulties in the way of analysis of movement is that to date no definite structures may be directly associated with it, as in the case of muscle fibres or cilia. In addition, it is not known whether the motive force is attributable to changes in the membrane and/or underlying cytoplasm.

Many of the earlier theories of amoeboid movement were reviewed by Fauré-Fremiet (1929), Lewis (1931), Holtfreter (1946) and De Bruyn (1947); the more recent ones regard locomotion as the result of contraction of a

117

plasmagel tube enclosing a plasma-sol, as set out by Pantin (1923), Mast (1926), Landau (1959) and others. By analogy with the ATP-dependent contraction of muscle proteins, Goldacre and Lorch (1950) implicated a similar contractile protein in amoeboid movement. Support for this hypothesis came from the work of Loewy (1952) who isolated an actinomyosin-like protein from slime-molds, Hoffmann-Berling (1960) who isolated a similar contractile protein by glycerol extraction from fibroblasts and others including Ts'o et al. (1956) and Simard-Dusquesne and Couillard (1962), who isolated an actomyosin-like ATP-ase from *A. proteus*. However, many have commented that the isolation of contractile proteins from a cell does not necessarily implicate them in locomotor mechanisms.

Marsland (1956) reviewed data which show that many cell movements are stopped when organisms are subjected to high hydrostatic pressure, which is associated with gel$\rightleftharpoons$sol transformations. Landau (1959), on the basis of his own extensive work on the effect of high pressures on cells, also concluded that sol$\rightleftharpoons$gel transformations are an essential part of cell movement which are directly related to endoplasm$\rightleftharpoons$ectoplasm transitions. However, Wolpert (1965) has expressed doubt on whether the sol$\rightleftharpoons$gel transformations brought about by artificially generated high hydrostatic pressures are strictly analogous to the naturally occurring endoplasm$\rightleftharpoons$ecto- plasm transitions. Allen (1961b) has emphasized that in the case of *Chaos chaos* at least, the endoplasm cannot be regarded as an ideal Newtonian sol, since it behaves as a thixotropic system. I do not regard these points of Wolpert and Allen as major qualitative objections, since it is to be expect- ed that although any fluid within the cell will be rheologically anomalous, this in itself would only complicate the mathematical analysis of sol$\rightleftharpoons$gel transformations, thereby making exact extrapolation from the high pressure experiments impossible; these objections are not in themselves valid argu- ments against such transformations.

Over the last few years much argument has centered on whether amoeboid movement as seen in amoebae results from a propulsive mechanism located at the rear of the cell, as suggested by Pantin, Mast, Goldacre and Lorch and others, or whether the cell is pulled along by a mechanism located at its front, as inherent in Allen's (1961a, b) 'fountain zone' theory.

Goldacre (1961, 1964) has summarized his views and evidence to support the theory that locomotive energy results from cytoplasmic sol$\rightleftharpoons$gel trans- formations, in which contraction produces solation. Initiation of contraction in the gel is brought about by contact with the surface membrane, and ATP plays some part in this. A consequence of this theory appears to be that membrane would be resorbed at the tail end of the amoeba and reformed at its front end, so that the whole membrane would be reformed *de novo* as the cell moves through its own length. A variation of this theory is that of Bell (1961) who suggests that the formation of new surface itself provides the motive force. Attempts have been made by Wolpert and his colleagues (Wolpert and O'Neill 1962; Wolpert et al. 1964) to test the proposition that new membrane formation on a massive scale is necessary for movement, by staining part of the membranes of single amoeba proteus with fluorescent-labelled antibody made against their surface membranes. It should be noted that the antibodies prepared by these workers may well have been the response to antigens in the 'surface coat' which was described by Pappas (1959), Mercer (1959) and O'Neill (1963). This coat is a fibrillar layer some 0.2μ thick, when viewed in the electron microscope, is muco-proteinaceous in nature, and lies externally to the trilaminar 'unit membrane'. Wolpert et al. studied the movements of partially labelled viable moving amoebae for some hours in order to observe how quickly it was replaced with new unlabelled surface. They concluded that there was no evidence for rapid turnover of the amoebic surface or for formation of new surface in the region of the advancing pseudopods (see also Jahn 1964) as required by Goldacre, but noted that as the antibody probably attaches to the 'surface coat', as distinct from the plasma membrane, they could not exclude the extremely unlikely possibility that the 'surface coat' is flowing freely over the plasma membrane. These authors also note that there is a slow turnover of membrane, corresponding to a replacement of some 0.2% per minute of the total surface area, which matches the time required by the surface to recover from pinocytosis (Chapman-Andresen 1963), and which is much slower than that required by Goldacre's hypothesis. However, Nachmias' (1966) studies with Alcian Blue coated *Chaos chaos* lead her to propose a complete surface turnover in 35 minutes. Wolpert and his colleagues have also isolated a cytoplasmic fraction in bulk which is 'motile' and capable of gelation, syneresis and streaming; which contains oriented fibres visible in electron micrographs, and which responds to ATP. They tend to favour this fraction as the source of propulsive energy as distinct from the surface membranes, but acknowledge that the behaviour of this isolated fraction cannot be used to distinguish the claims of any of the current theories of contraction in relation to amoeboid movement.

The tail contraction theories generally require contraction of the tail ectoplasm which solates to form endoplasm which is squeezed to the front of the organism where it gels to reform ectoplasm. In contrast to these theories, Allen (1961a, b) has advanced a frontal contraction theory of amoeboid movement which proposes that at the front of each pseudopod the endoplasm becomes everted to form a 'fountain-zone' which shortens and stiffens to become the advancing edge of the tubular ectoplasm. This ectoplasmic contraction pulls forward more axial endoplasm, thereby providing the locomotive force. One strong piece of supporting evidence in favour of Allen's theory is that in, for example, the amoebae *Chaos carolensis* and *A. proteus*, streaming movements have been observed after the membrane and ectoplasmic tube (including the tail) have been removed. Full discussions of protoplasmic streaming are given by Kamiya (1959, 1964). In a very lucid discussion of this very confused subject, Griffin (1964) concludes that whereas the available evidence on the movements of *C. carolinensis* and *A. proteus* is compatible with Allen's theory; as Allen (1961a) himself has pointed out, the data on *Pelomyxa palustris* are not. In the case of the latter organism it appears that contraction in the tail region or ectoplasmic tube provides the motive force.

There seems to be general agreement that movement requires local areas of attachment between the plasmalemma and both the substratum over which the cell moves and the underlying plasmagel; and further, as also proposed by Mast (1934), that plasmosol is converted into plasmagel at the advancing end of the organism and plasmagel into plasmasol at its rear end. The fact that Allen and Goldacre are in disagreement over the interpretation of the same experimental data for amoebae of the same type would suggest that more unequivocal experimental evidence is required to localize the source of locomotive force within the amoebae. It would also appear that there is even less evidence to support theories of amoeboid movement invoking electrophoresis (Bingley and Thompson 1962) or indeed a type of jet propulsion (Kavanau 1963), and these will consequently not be discussed.

The tacit assumption that isolated cells from metazoa have locomotory mechanisms similar to those of amoebae, probably derive from the fact that, owing to their comparatively small size, very little experimental data were available on metazoan cells until fairly recently.

Holtfreter (1946) noted that wavy movements are seen along the borders of fibroblasts *in vitro*, and suggested that in these cells movements of their peripheries are directly involved in translatory movements. Algard's (1953) evidence strongly suggests that movement of amphibian propigment cells is also due to traction exerted at their pseudopodial tips. Since that time, many observations of different types of moving cells by phase-contrast cinemicrography has demonstrated the occurrence of wavy peripheral

movements at their advancing edges. For any type of crawling movement
to occur, part of the cell must be adherent to the substratum over which it
moves. It is therefore of interest that the undulating part of the periphery
of spreading, stretching and moving cells has been demonstrated to be the
most difficult part to detach from glass surfaces by microdissection in the
case of fibroblasts from chick embryos (Chambers and Fell 1931), amphibia
(Algard) and fish (Goodrich 1920). It has also been shown by immunofluorescent techniques that when rat fibroblasts retract previously advancing
processes, pieces of them may be left behind on the underlying substratum
(Weiss and Lachmann 1964).

Ambrose (1961) has described *in vitro* studies of embryonic chick heart
fibroblasts with interference and surface contact microscopy. He notes that
for this type of observation, interference microscopy is preferable to phase-
contrast, because of the absence of halo. The undulatory movements at the
leading edge of the fibroblasts, which give rise to the 'ruffled membrane',
could be due to either wave-like movements extending the whole length of
the cell or to local cytoplasmic expansion. Ambrose observed that interference measurements of three cells show that the ruffled areas have optical
paths some four to five times the value of the adjacent areas. Obviously more
data are required before drawing conclusions. On the assumption that simple
folding of the membrane into a wave-form would not be observed as an
optical path difference by interferometry, whereas a local increase in cell
thickness would. Ambrose favors the latter. Observations of moving fibroblasts with the surface contact microscope (see chapter 5) show them to be
in true contact with their substrata over only a comparatively small percentage of the total areas of the cell in apparent contact. These points of true
contact are not fixed, but flicker over the periphery of the cell where it is
opposed to its substratum. The ruffles seen with the interference microscope
and the points of contact observed with the surface contact microscope
apparently correspond in position; also use of a stroboscope as described by
Sleigh (1960) to study periodicity of cilia, fails to 'stop' the flickering contact
movements, although it slows them down considerably, suggesting concom-
mittant periodicity and randomness. Ambrose is of the opinion that locomotion in this type of cell takes place by means of demonstrable intermittent
contacts with solid substrata. He also put forward the entirely speculative
suggestion that the undulatory movements associated with these contacts
could be produced by 'contractile fibrils lying just within the cytoplasm and
parallel to the cell surface'. It is of very considerable interest in connection
with the source of energy for amoeboid movement, that structures lying

subjacent to the plasma membrane having a tubular or fibrillar nature and contractile properties, have been described in such assorted cells as slime molds (Wohlfarth-Botterman 1962, 1964), protozoa (Rouiller et al. 1956; Randall 1956, 1957; Steinert and Novikoff 1960; Schulz and MacClure 1961) hydra (Slautterback 1963), pigmented epithelial cells from frog retina (Porter and Yamada 1960), chick kidney and liver cells (Taylor and Robbins 1963) Walker 'carcinoma' (Mercer 1962) and human conjunctival and HeLa cells (Taylor 1966). Many other examples are cited by Kavanau (1965). Wolfarth-Bottermann (1964) has proposed that the 'plasma-filaments' or tubular structures observed by him, and which possess ATP-ase activity, are composed of the contractile protein myxomyosin. This protein was first described in *Physarum plasmodia* by Loewy (1952) and shown to be ATP-sensitive by Ts'o et al. (1956; 1957a, b). In view of its obvious, possible importance, by analogy, to animal cells, it should be noted that its properties vary depending on the method of extraction, and Nakajima (1964) describes a contractile plasmodial myosin B which is chemically distinct from myosin obtained from similar organisms, but which has similar enzymatic properties to myosin B from vertebrate smooth muscle.

Much work on the mechanochemical aspects of movement in fibroblasts has been carried out by Hoffman-Berling and has recently been reviewed by him (Hoffman-Berling 1964). Contractile proteins have been extracted from fresh and glycerinated fibroblasts and have been compared to actomyosin isolated from muscle. It has been shown that such reactions with ATP as dephosphorylation, solubility and viscosity changes are exhibited by both fibroblast contractile protein and actomyosin (Hoffmann-Berling 1956). In addition, whole fibroblasts which have been depleted of endogenous ATP by glycerination, will, under given conditions, contract, on adding ATP. Hoffman-Berling (1964) makes it clear that the evidence for fibroblast contractile proteins having actin-like and myosin-like components is indirect, and comes from viscosity measurements. In fact, a two-component contractile protein system has so far only been demonstrated in extracts from human platelets (Bettex-Galland and Lüscher 1961). This is somewhat confusing, as platelets are not usually considered as actively motile cells. Hoffman-Berling (1964) has also observed that inhibition of contraction in fibroblasts may be brought about by so-called 'relaxing grana' derived from disintegrated muscle cells, and that, conversely, inhibition or contraction of muscle cells may be brought about by products derived from fibroblasts. The 'relaxing grana' appear to act by causing the withdrawal of calcium ions and releasing a low molecular weight 'relaxing substance'. Local contractions in glycerinated cells leading to the movements of cytokinesis may be induced by adding both ATP and grana, but not with either separately. The work quoted shows that fibroblasts contain a contractile proteinaceous system, which is ATP-dependent, which will respond in a similar way to the same rather ill-defined 'relaxing grana' as muscle and, rather importantly, that localization of contraction is possible. The work, as presented, does not yet justify Hoffman-Berling's (1964) statement that fibroblasts, amoebae and thrombocytes 'make use of the same general mechanochemical principles involved in muscle contraction for the purpose of generating movement'.

3.2 The direction of cell movement

3.2.1 Chemotaxis

Cell movements in morphogenesis, inflammatory and other processes do not appear to be random, but under the control of some sort of directing mechanisms. In order that the scope of these mechanisms can be appreciated, it is proposed to follow patterns in a number of different living systems, but it should be made clear, at the onset, that it appears most unlikely that all of the mechanisms that are to be described apply to all cells, or indeed to all of the cells within any one organism.

A basic and elegant pattern of directed aggregation is seen in one of the Mycetozoa, the Acrasiales or 'cellular slime molds'. Bonner (1959) agrees with the suggestion first made by De Bary in 1887 that these organisms are probably descended from the free-living soil amoebae. At the close of their vegetative stage, single myxamoebae, which in the case of artificially rounded-up *Dictyostelium discoideum*, have diameters ranging from 5 to 16 micra (Bonner and Frascella 1953), cease feeding, become elongated, and in any single area show uniform orientation. The myxamoebae then crawl centripetally to form a pseudoplasmodial aggregate, in which their peripheries are in intimate contact without loss of individual trilaminar membranes, which tend to be separated by some 200Å in osmium-fixed specimens, as clearly shown in Mercer and Shaffer's (1960) electron micrographs. Earlier electron micrography was done on slime molds by Mühlethaler (1956) and Gazelius and Ranby (1957). The aggregate passes through the stage of a motile slug, and develops into a multicellular, stalked, fruiting body, containing differentiated tissues. Spores are cast off from this, which germinate to give rise to fresh myxamoebae. Reviews of the life cycles of the Acrasiales have been given by Olive (1902), Raper (1951), M. Sussman (1956) and Bonner (1952, 1959). The biological significance of aggregation in this organism has been discussed by Bonner (1958), who considers that it may serve as substitute for sexuality, since, although it lacks the advantage of chromosomal recombination, the nuclei of many of the cells forming the pseudoplasmodial organism are gathered into the fruiting body to be redistributed to form new combinations in the uninucleate spores, which may well be a homeostatic mechanism. Bonner also postulates that if single myxamoebae in close proximity to each other developed 'mutual deficiencies', then there would be a selective pressure in favour of aggregation. If these suggestions are correct, then there is no good reason why the directing mechanisms in the cellular slime molds should have much in common with directing mechanisms in animal cells, where there is probably different significance in cell contact reactions. However, as pointed out earlier (L. Weiss 1960), it is of interest in a comparative sense to consider some of the problems raised in observations on aggregation in the Acrasiales.

It was suggested that chemotaxis was involved in the aggregation of myxamoebae by Olive (1902), Potts (1902), Arndt (1937) and others, but direct evidence in support of this suggestion was provided by Runyon (1942), who showed that when myxamoebae began aggregating on one side of a cellophane membrane, cells placed on the other side oriented and moved in the same streams and aggregated at the same centre. Bonner (1947) showed that if a slow stream of saline was passed over myxamoebae which were beginning to aggregate, then cells downstream would move towards the centre of aggregation, whereas cells upstream would not. Shaffer (1953) showed that material extracted from aggregates would attract fresh dispersed myxamoebae, but that this attractant, termed 'acrasin' by Bonner (1947), was unstable. However, the instability is presumably due to enzymatic degradation (Shaffer 1956). The chemical nature of 'acrasin' is as yet undetermined, however its partial fractionation into three components has been described by Sussman's group. It is of interest that apparently steroids in the urine of pregnant women elicit a chemotactic response in these organisms in view of Willmer's (1961) suggestion that steroids may induce changes in cell polarization, by their activity on the plasma membrane. Although chemotaxis undoubtedly plays a part in directing aggregative movements in the cellular slime molds, as Shaffer (1958) has pointed out, the problem is not simply one of a single large 'acrasin' gradient.

The release of chemotactic stimuli may be initiated by some degree of malnutrition (Potts 1902; von Schuckmann 1924; Arndt 1937; Raper 1940a).

The initiation of aggregation is also dependent on an optimal concentration of myxamoebae, since aggregation can be delayed by dilution, and on the other hand, in crowded cultures, the myxamoebae will aggregate even if fresh food (bacteria) is added (Raper 1940b; Bonner 1947).

Possibly one of the best established cases of chemotaxis is the movement of bracken spermatozoids to the archegonium, as described by Pfeffer in 1884. Brokaw (1958) confirmed Pfeffer's observation that the spermatozoids are attracted by sodium malate and, in addition by malic, maleic and citraconic acids, but not by the related fumaric, mesaconic, dihydroxymaleic and malonic acids. Brokaw proposed that malate ions are reversibly adsorbed onto sensory elements of the sperm, on the evidence that such cells migrate to the anode in an electric field. This is an interesting proposition.

The unequivocal demonstration of chemotaxis in animal cells has proved considerably more difficult than in either bracken spermatozoids or the cellular slime molds. Early attempts to demonstrate chemotaxis involved placing test substances within capillary tubes which were then placed in tissues *in vivo*, or in leucocyte preparations *in vitro*. The results obtained by this technique alone are unreliable, since, as pointed out by Pfoehl (1898), both cells and inert particles tend to be drawn into the tubes by convection currents and/or capillarity. Another technique introduced by Kiaer (1925) was to cultivate explants of tissues *in vitro*, and to observe whether the cells migrated out asymmetrically towards test substances. Harris (1961) advises caution in the interpretation of data obtained by this technique due to effects other than purely chemotactic ones, on the explants. Reviews of chemotaxis in leucocytes are given by McCutcheon (1946) and Harris (1954).

Harris (1954, 1961) has described an elegant technique for testing chemotaxis in leucocytes, which involves placing them in medium between a slide and coverslip and introducing test substances into the capillary space between them; the cells are observed with dark ground illumination, and their movements recorded as traces on continously exposed film. Harris has shown that neutrophil polymorphonuclear leucocytes are attracted by clumps of *Staphylococcus albus*, and monocytes by *Mycobacterium tuberculosis*. These cells and eosinophil polymorphonuclear leucocytes are also attracted by other organisms, but no pure chemotactic substance was isolated by him. No chemotaxis was exhibited by granulocytes to dead tissue fragments, or by tissue autolysed, or degraded by pepsin or trypsin (Harris 1953). He also noted that a chemotactic response was not observed in lymphocytes.

Another technique for the study of quantitative aspects of chemotaxis has been described by Boyden (1962). Small plastic chambers are divided into two by an interposed millipore filter. Cell suspensions are placed in one half and test substances into the other. After incubation the millipore filter is removed, fixed and cleared, when the cells on each side can be enumerated. The number of cells which have migrated through the filter is taken as an index of the chemotactic properties of the test substance. By use of this ingenious technique, Boyden has studied the chemotactic effect of mixtures of antibody and antigen on polymorphonuclear leucocytes, and has shown that antibody/antigen complexes incubated at 37 °C in fresh serum are chemotactic and appear to act through the agency of substance(s), which is stable on heating to 56 °C. This chemotactic substance is not produced when antibody/antigen complexes are incubated in serum previously heated at 56 °C, for 30 min. Boyden therefore suggests the following scheme for production of this type of chemotactic substance:

$$\text{Antibody} + \text{antigen} \longrightarrow \text{Antibody/antigen complex}$$
$$\text{(stable at 56 °C)} \qquad\qquad [\text{Ab/Ag}]$$

$$\text{Inactive serum enzyme } [\text{Ab/Ag}] \text{ Active enzyme}$$
$$\text{(labile at 56 °C)} \qquad \longrightarrow$$

$$\text{Precursor chemotactic substance} \xrightarrow[\text{enzyme}]{\text{active}} \text{chemotactic substance}$$
$$\text{(stable at 56 °C)}$$

Hurley and Spector (1961) incubated a variety of tissues with normal rat or rabbit serum for one to two hours at 38 °C, and noted that when injected intradermally in rats, these preparations caused an immediate and massive leucocytic emigration from local blood vessels. They found that granulocytes were more efficient in 'activating' serum than any organ tested. Hurley (1963) later demonstrated by Boyden's (1962) technique that the passage of leucocytes across a membrane *in vitro*, matched the leucocytic emigration observed by Hurley and Spector (1961) *in vivo*, and that the chemotactic effect of tissue homogenates for leucocytes is in some way dependent on the interaction of normal serum components with cell debris. This fits in with Boyden's (1964) suggestion that the reaction due to cell injury is similar to that due to antibody/antigen interactions, because cellular damage may result in the local formation of antibody/antigen complexes.

Attempts were made in the past to explain the migration of cells out of cultured tissue explants in terms of negative chemotaxis, with substances diffusing out from the centre of the tissue (Ephrussi 1933; Fischer 1946a). However, it was shown by Jacoby (1936) that standing a culture vertically, which would drain any chemotaxin downwards, did not affect the symmetry of outgrowth. In addition, culture of two adjacent explants should result in overlap of diffusion gradients, producing two zones of higher chemotaxin concentration than in the circular zones immediately inside them, which in turn should be reflected in the numbers of migratory cells found within the zones. This has not been observed (Harrison 1914; Abercrombie and Heaysman 1954).

It would appear that negative chemotaxis has been demonstrated by Twitty and Niu (1948, 1954) in cultured melanoblasts from the undifferentiated neural-crest of *Triturus*. It was observed that when pairs of melanoblasts were confined within capillary tubes filled with coelomic fluid, they tend to move away from each other before their peripheries could make physical contact. Having moved an apparently critical distance apart, cells go into a state of random movement, both towards and away from their companions.

P. Weiss and Scott (1963) have examined other tactic stimuli with regard to polarization of cell movement. They noted Whitaker's (1940) observation that the eggs of Fucus can be polarized by external gradients of electric potential, pH or light and examined the behaviour of human conjunctival cells, and those from freshly dissociated embryo chick liver and heart in pH gradients. The gradients were applied across whole coverslip cultures in bicarbonate buffered medium, by exposing one end of the coverslip to a CO_2 gas phase and the other to air. On a smaller scale, opposite ends of single cells were exposed to streams of media at different pH through micropipettes. Alkalization produced local contraction and acidification local gelation; both effects 'paralyse' one side of the cell, leaving the other free for locomotory movement. The effect observed by Twitty and Niu, described earlier, could thus be explained by a mutual paralysis of parts of the cells facing each other in the capillary by CO_2 accumulation and acidification of the local environment.

An often quoted experiment was that of Roux (1894) who attributed the reaggregation of cells separated mechanically from amphibian embryos to some sort of chemical tropism, which played an important function in morphogenesis. However, later work by Voightlander (1932), Kuhl (1937a and b) and Lucey and Curtis (1959), in which the movements of individual reaggregating cells were observed, showed these movements to be random, which mitigates against chemotaxis. In a review of chemotaxis and chemotropism, Rosen (1962) concludes that apart from the case of leucocytes, positive chemotaxis appears to be a very doubtful quantity in metazoan cells and work done since then has not altered its status.

3.2.2 Contact guidance

Harrison (1910) noted that a characteristic property of many embryonic cells is their capacity for amoeboid movement and that the direction of this movement could be along oriented fibrils, such as would occur in and around tissues cultured by him in clotted lymph (Harrison 1912, 1914). Harrison (1914) used the term 'thigmotaxis' to cover this concept of cellular orientation by solid surfaces. Matsumoto (1918) cultured frog corneal epithelium in hanging-drop preparations and noted that cells moved actively on both glass and celloidin, and grew along the fibres of spiders' webs, silk, glass-wool, and asbestos. In retrospect, the experiments of Harrison and Matsumoto tell us that given a choice between moving over a solid surface or through fluid, a cell incapable of (swimming) locomotion through fluid but capable of (crawling) locomotion over a solid, will move over the solid. As pointed out by Graciun (1927), contact with a solid surface is not the cause of cell migration, but is rather a stipulation for migration. These observations were nonetheless of very considerable importance, in that they focussed attention on the guidance of cell movements by contact.

A more sophisticated approach to the problem of substrate guided cell movements is due to Loeb and Fleisher (1917), who pointed out that in the case where the substrate is a mesh of fibrils, then large fibrils would take precedence over smaller, in orienting cells; furthermore, the fibrils themselves will be oriented by tension. P. Weiss (1929, 1934, 1941) has repeatedly stressed the importance of substrate orientation on cellular orientation, and has used the term 'contact guidance' to cover this group of phenomena. P. Weiss (1958, 1961a) has summarized his views on contact guidance to produce changes in cell shape, which are followed by changes in direction of movement, initially to a competition between two opposing forces, on the one hand, surface tension, rheological properties and contractile networks which tend to favour a cell having minimal surface area with spherical shape, and on the other hand, expansive forces at the cell margin including adhesion to substratum and inertial flow which make for spreading of the cell. P. Weiss (1959) in review, specifically considers that contact of a cell periphery with fibre produces a localized 'herniation' of the cell at this site of contact. As protoplasmic outflow is more favoured by the larger diameter protrusions, it might be expected that if cells were grown on different fibrous substrata, containing fibres of different diameter, then the cells on the larger diameter fibres should have more major protrusions than cells grown on those of smaller diameter. This postulate was in fact tested by P. Weiss and Garber (1952) and Garber (1953) when they cultured cells in plasma clots in which the mean diameter of the fibrin fibres could be increased either by reduction in pH or by increased plasma concentrations. They observed that the ratio of cells having few processes over multipolar cells, increased as a linear function of either plasma concentration or acidity. Other examples of contact guidance or orientation have been demonstrated *in vitro* with fibroblasts cultured on either glass coverslips in which fine grooves have been turned, or on the inside of fish scales (Weiss and Taylor 1956). In both cases the cells line up along the scratches or fibres. More recently Rosenberg (1963) has demonstrated the extreme sensitivity of contact guidance by showing that fibroblasts growing on behenic acid films *in vitro* will apparently detect troughs in them of only 60°Å.

Another illustration of contact guidance *in vitro* comes from the studies of organ explants cultured near to each other in the same plasma clot (P. Weiss 1952). It is observed that the highest densities of migrating cells are to be found in the imaginary lines connecting the two or three explants. This has been interpreted by P. Weiss to be due to shrinkage of the explants within their fibrin mesh, which imposes stress orientation on the fibres in a radial direction, along which the migratory cells can move. Thus P. Weiss (1959) associates a purely scalar change (explant size) with vectorial effects when translated through a fibrous continuum.

This whole question of the mechanics of the translation of orientational information through contact with a substratum is at the moment as vague as it is important. P. Weiss (1945) suggested that cells excrete a colloidal, macromolecular exudate, or 'ground-mat' which spreads along fibres and/or other channels, and that this exudate in some way guides cells (see also Fischer, 1946b). The presence of 'exudates' has been demonstrated by Rosenberg (1960) using ellipsometric methods for the detection of very thin films, although their part in cell orientation has not been demonstrated. These exudates may correspond to the ECM (extracellular matrix) described by Moscona (1960) in connection with the segregation phenomena seen in cultured embryonic cells, which will be discussed in detail later. On the other hand, as the 'exudates' were demonstrated by Rosenberg after the cells had been detached from their solid substratum by a fluid stream, it could also be argued that the material was ruptured off the cells during the detachment process (L. Weiss 1961a; see chapter 4) and is therefore not an exudate at all, but is better regarded as a part of the cell periphery.

In his review of mechanisms of morphogenetic movements, Trinkaus (1965) considers that there is as yet no indisputable evidence for contact guidance in the intact organism, but that a number of observations are most readily accounted for on the assumption that it is a functional entity. This includes the movement of groups of precardiac mesodermal cells on oriented endoderm (De Haan 1963a) the movement of neural crest cells along the neural tube (Weston 1963), the migration of pigment cells and axons along blood vessels and the movements of the Wolffian duct (De Haan 1964).

It appears to the present author that the case for contact guidance is established, in that cells which move by amoeboid locomotion require to crawl along 'solid' substrata. Other things being equal, it is to be expected that if cellular orientation occurs along fibres or grooves, then up to a width approaching cellular dimensions, the wider those fibres or grooves, the more likely are cells to orient along them. Contact guidance would not be expected to operate when cells crawl over unoriented smooth surfaces such as glass coverslips, and a wealth of experimental data shows cellular movements to be random under these conditions. Attempts to discriminate whether cells can detect molecular orientation at a lower level than fibres and grooves visible under the light microscope, or the 'steps' observed by ellipsometry, are intrinsically difficult because of the problem of obtaining surfaces of different molecular orientation or constitution, but of similar surface 'finish'. Johnsson and Hegyeli (1965) have found an agent in extracts of human urine which sensitizes certain cultured cells to orient along sub-microscopic 'directional clues' on coverslips. They report that of the nine cell lines so far examined, four malignant lines responded to the extract whereas five normal lines did not. Quite apart from the difficulties and dangers of using the terms 'malignant' and 'normal' in connection with cell lines, this is a fascinating observation, and it will be of great interest if the active fraction can be chemically identified.

The limitation of contact guidance is summed up by P. Weiss (1961a) as follows: 'Contact guidance, as a critical limiting condition for all cells bound to interfacial support, delineates the limited tracks still open to a given cell at a given point in a given environment; in the extreme, on a strictly oriented medium, this leaves the individual cell, now a bipolar one, with only a single track. Yet, even on a single track, there are still two alternative directions left in which to advance, and evidently contact guidance remains ambiguous as to which one will be taken.' One mechanism of giving directional information to a moving cell is chemotaxis, which has already been discussed. Another mechanism of imposing direction – through cell contacts – will now be considered.

3.2.3 Contact inhibition

In a stimulating review of cell locomotion, Abercrombie (1965) emphasizes the distinction between oriented and unoriented responses, and considers that these must be considered along the general lines put forward for whole animals by Patlak (1953) and Fraenkel and Gunn (1961) in which speed, change of speed, direction and change of direction are considered in terms of randomness and frequency with regard to each other.

The way in which cells change direction is variable, and depends on how permanently the ruffled locomotory membrane is located with respect to the rest of the cell. Thus, lymphocytes turn by turning the cell as a whole (Lewis and Webster 1921; De Bruyn 1945; Pulvertaft and L. Weiss 1956–58); fibroblasts may turn either by asymmetric activity of their leading ruffled membranes or by suppression of the leading membrane and development of a new one elsewhere in the cell (Abercrombie). In contrast to these, macrophages in culture are never permanently polarized, but are characterized by the appearance of transient pseudopodia all round their peripheries (De Bruyn).

As previously stated, the centrifugal movement of cells from an explant cultured in clotted plasma could be explained in terms of contact guidance along radially oriented fibrin fibres. The fact that cells also show the same centrifugal migration away from tissue explants cultured directly on glass made it necessary to invoke radially oriented macromolecules in P. Weiss's 'ground mat'. Another explanation of this centrifugal movement may also be offered. In 1921, Loeb noted the radial movement of cultures of *Limulus amoebocytes* and interpreted this to mean that contact of one cell with another leads to 'a resting condition at the place of contact', whereas the interaction of environment with the rest of the cell periphery leads to the production of new pseudopods, which determine the direction of their movement. Loeb went on to say that as migrating cells were more likely to meet other cells if they moved inwards, and that this contact would result in their putting pseudopods in an outwards direction, then the general direction of movement of cells migrating from an explant would be centrifugal. Loeb did not put this suggestion of his to experimental test, and it remained totally neglected until unknowingly revived as the result of precise experiments

carried out by Abercrombie and Heaysman (1953, 1954). Much of this work
has been summarized and reviewed by Abercrombie (1957, 1961 and 1965)
to indicate that when a cell moving over a non-cellular substratum makes
contact with another cell, it will stop moving in the same direction and,
if free space is available, will move in another direction, away from contact.
The phenomenon was termed 'contact inhibition' by Abercrombie and,
in a statistical way, accounts for the migration of cells away from explants,
from regions where the probability of cellular collision is high to regions
where it is lower. The microscopic features of reactions occurring between
individual fibroblasts moving over glass substrata was described by Abercrombie and Ambrose (1958). When the ruffled membrane at the advancing
edge of fibroblast meets the periphery of another fibroblast, the ruffling locomotory movements cease as do other membrane movements such as pinocytosis. The fibroblasts form a short-lived but apparently firm adhesion,
since they spring apart when they subsequently separate by movement away
from each other following the development of a new ruffled membrane.

Although contact inhibition occurs between different species fibroblasts,
and epithelial cells in sheets (Harrison 1910; Howes 1943; Lash 1955), it
does not occur between all types of cells, and it is of very considerable interest
that contact inhibition is not demonstrable between fibroblasts and sarcoma
cells (Abercrombie et al. 1957) and fibroblasts and chick leucocytes (Oldfield
1963). The relationship of contact inhibition to malignant processes will be
discussed in chapter 8.

It must be constantly borne in mind that the contact reactions of cells
in culture may be considerably modified by environmental conditions which
affect the state of the cells involved. Thus, Trevan and Roberts (1960) have
described how movement of the peripheries of cultured ascites cells ceases
on exhaustion of the medium, and is restored on its replenishment. L. Weiss
(1964) has shown that activity may be restored to fibroblasts cultured over-
night in protein free media, within minutes, following the addition of
serum. Loeb (1912) showed that proliferative cells start moving away from
explants more quickly than resting ones, and Simms and Stillman (1937)
showed that pretreatment of explants with trypsin would produce the same
effect. Curtis (1961a) and Abercrombie and Gitlin (1965) have shown that
the higher the density of the population, the less contact inhibition observed.

Groups of two to four fibroblasts at the peripheries of explants of chick
embryo heart cultured on cover slips, were isolated by scraping their migrating
neighbours away from the glass with a fine knife and then recorded on film
for a further 8 hours of culture (Abercrombie and Gitlin 1965). According

to the hypothesis of contact inhibition each group located in the cleared zone around the central explant should itself form a minature explant from which its constituent cells should migrate radially. On the other hand, if chemotaxis from the central original explant were involved, than the cells constituting the little groups should migrate radially from the central large explant, not radially from the centre of their own small group. In only one group of three cells did isolation lead to separation of the constituent cells. In all the others, the cells retained contact for most of the time. Interpretation of the experimental data was made difficult because the numbers of cells within each small group increased by mitotic division. In addition, it was considered by Abercrombie and Gitlin that movement of cells across the areas of glass from which their fellows had been scraped was hindered by the presence of residual material ruptured off the removed cells, as suggested by L. Weiss (1961a) and L. Weiss and Lachmann (1964). It was concluded that there was little evidence for chemotaxis in the migration of fibroblasts from an explant. However, the postulated interference of the expected movements of cells from the small groups by debris from the peripheries of removed cells, suggests to the present author that contact inhibition may well be induced by this peripheral material, as distinct from a whole cell.

In my opinion, the simple statistical concept of contact inhibition fulfills the directional requirements of contact guidance, which have been referred to earlier, and possibly make it unnecessary to postulate the existence of a cell-orienting 'ground mat'.

3.3 Cellular aggregation and segregation phenomena among dissociated cells

Mixtures of many different types of isolated living cells show a remarkable capacity to aggregate and segregate. Some of these phenomena will be described and discussed against the background on cell locomotion and its direction, described earlier in this chapter.

3.4.1 Slime molds

The beautiful development patterns seen in the slime molds make these organisms ideal material with which to study correlation of changes in the cell periphery during morphogenetic movements. Olive (1902) mixed vegetative cells of the slime molds *D. mucoroides* and *D. purpureum* and observed that they aggregated to form their own characteristic fruiting bodies within the same culture, and that no coalescence of the different strains was apparent. Raper and Thom (1941) showed that whereas mixtures of vegetative amoebae of *D. discoideum* and *P. violaceum* also formed separate aggregates, mixtures of *D. discoideum* and *D. mucoroides* formed mixed aggregates in which separate and distinct fruiting bodies appeared. Bonner and Adams (1958) extended these experiments to include mixtures of different species as well as strains and showed that different species sometimes fused, whereas different strains within the same species may not. They also described a further degree of mixing in which a single sorus could develop, containing discrete prespores belonging to different strains. When the spores are shed, the resulting amoebae segregate out again. The genetic basis of aggregation and segregation in these organisms has been studied by Sussman and his associates, particularly with regard to the mutants produced by ultra-violet irradiation (M. Sussman 1956) which have specific aggregation patterns, or lack of them, and which culminate in abnormal fruiting bodies. If various mutants, which show a deficient developmental pattern when grown separately, are mixed, some sort of synergy occurs and their development proceeds further than on separate growth. This synergism is not demonstrable if the two mutants are grown on separate sides of a thin agar membrane (Sussman and Lee 1955) and it is therefore concluded that the substances involved are passed from one group of cells to another by direct contact. It is a pity that the more sophisticated techniques used in studying transmembrane embryonic induction in animal tissues (Saxén and Toivonen 1962) have not been applied to this interesting observation.

The association of peripheral changes in slime mold amoebae with genetically related aggregative behaviour has been investigated by Gregg (1956) and Gregg and Trygstad (1958) using antigenic markers. The technique stems from the work of von Schuckmann (1925) who demonstrated that rabbits would make species specific antisera against injected sorocarps of *D. mucoroides*. Gregg (1956) showed that rabbit anti-*D. discoideum* and anti-*D. purpureum* sera caused agglutination of only homologous amoebae from 24 to 26 hour cultures, agglutination of some heterologous amoebae from 30 to 36 hour cultures, and agglutination of all heterologous amoebae from 43 to 48 hour cultures, showing that new antigens are revealed at the cell peripheries, with the passage of time. Morphogenetic interactions of the types already described between cells in mixed cultures do not occur until the appearance of similar surface antigens. Gregg also suggested that the new antigens which appear are in some way involved in cell adhesion. On the evidence presented, this viewpoint is unacceptable, since it cannot be assumed that antigen/antibody reactions are a good model for normal cell adhesion in the absence of antibody, and furthermore, there is no evidence that such adhesions in fact occur between cellular antigenic sites. In a later paper, Gregg and Trygstad (1958) describe similar experiments involving antiserum induced aggregation of wild type and variant strains of *D. discoideum* obtained by ultraviolet irradiation (Sussman and Sussman 1953). They suggested that the failure of aggregateless variants to adhere and undergo normal development is associated with the alteration or elimination of peripheral antigens, but that this interpretation of the results of agglutination experiments 'does not preclude the existence of metabolic or other abnormalities which could also contribute to developmental failure'. A more detailed review of overall development processes in the cellular slime molds is given by Gregg (1964).

3.3.2 Sponges

Wilson (1907, 1910, 1932) observed that if marine sponges were forced through bolting silk, individual viable cells were separated from them. When placed in a dish of sea-water, some of the cells moved over the bottom of the dish and adhered to their fellows to form small groups. These threw out pseudopodia which made contact with neighbouring groups, leading to the formation of progressively larger masses of cells. Wilson remarked that 'in the tendency to fuse with the production of a plasmodium, the dissociated cells of sponges resemble the amoebocytes of the mycetozoa'. Other early work on reaggregation phenomena in sponges is described by Huxley (1911), but does not add essentially to Wilson's general observations which are also applicable to certain hydroids (Wilson 1911). These experiments do not permit the detailed observation of the part played by different cells from the same sponge, in the reaggregation process, because when dissociated, individual cells look very much alike. It was therefore impossible to determine whether sponges reconstituted from previously separated cells are the results of cell movements following some sort of definite pattern, or whether they are, in fact, due to differentiation in randomly arranged cells (see Ganguly 1960). Pappenfuss (1934) working with Hydra, and Beadle and Booth (1938) with Cordylophora, have shown that reconstitution requires the presence of both endodermal and ectoderm cells.

    The reaggregation of separated sponge cells was investigated by Galtsoff (1923, 1925, 1926, 1929) who made the first attempts to study the process in a quantitative way. He confirmed (Galtsoff 1925) and extended the critical observation of Wilson (1910) that cells from different species, when mixed, would not form common aggregates (see also De Laubenfels 1927). Spiegel (1955) points out that although in the case of red *Microciona prolifera* and yellow *Cliona celata*, interspecies mixtures are not observed, a few cells of one species could not be distinguished in aggregates consisting mainly of the other species. Recently Sindelar (1965 – cinefilm) has filmed reaggregating sponge cells and has shown that they do not crawl together as believed for sixty years, but in fact put out filopodia which, having made contact with other cells, contract and bring the cells together by traction. Galtsoff also concluded that calcium ions were necessary for reaggregation, on the evidence that sponge cells kept in calcium-free media remained as single cell suspensions; and De Laubenfels (1932) reported that isolated cells of *Iotrochota bitorulata* will also not form aggregates outside a narrow range of calcium concentrations. In contrast to these reports, Agrell (1951) observed that cells isolated from *Halichondria panicea* did reaggregate in the presence of citrate or oxalate. The position was somewhat clarified by Spiegel (1954a), who noted little or no reaggregation of microciona or Cliona when the isolated cells were maintained in stationary cultures, in calcium-free media in the presence of EDTA. If, however, flasks containing such suspensions were swirled, large aggregates were formed. Spiegel therefore concluded, essentially, that calcium ions are in some way necessary for cell movement, which is a vital preliminary to cell contact, but that calcium ions are unnecessary for cell contact under his experimental conditions. In this connection, Pantin's (1926) observation that marine limax amoebae are unable to move in calcium-free media is of some relevance.

Loeb (1922) advanced the hypothesis, in somewhat vague terms, that antigenic change in cells might affect various contact phenomena. More recently, and in much more definite terms, Tyler (1940, 1947, 1955) and P. Weiss (1941, 1947) have advanced the hypothesis that cell adhesion and separation may invoke the mechanisms of antibody/antigen interactions, thereby accounting for the specificity manifest, by the apparent ability of cells to recognize self and nonself. They further suggested that the various movements seen in organizing cell systems might result from antigenic changes in the cell periphery, which cause differences in cell adhesion. Behind the Tyler/Weiss hypothesis is the implication that cell-to-cell adhesion involves the type of chemical and steric 'specificities' well-known to immunologists.

A notable attempt to elucidate the role of surface antigens in the reaggregation of dispersed cells from Microciona and Cliona has been made by Spiegel (1954, 1955). It was found that reaggregation was reversibly inhibited in homologous antisera, previously prepared in rabbits, whereas in normal rabbit serum, dispersed cells reaggregated as previously described. In the presence of antisera prepared against mixtures of both species, mixed aggregates of sponges were seen, whereas in the presence of normal rabbit serum mixed aggregates were not observed. Although the failure of cells to reaggregate in the presence of homologous antisera would appear to mitigate against the Tyler/Weiss hypothesis, Spiegel points out that three conditions may prevent aggregation, namely:

(1) *Antibody excess*. The antibody may block antigenic sites at the cell periphery, and if these sites are in fact involved in cell adhesion, it will therefore prevent its occurrence. Experiments with much lower concentrations of antisera to avoid this type of blockade are not reported.

(2) *Univalency of antibodies*. If the rabbit antibodies are univalent, they would not be expected to promote cell-to-cell adhesion, since they would merely block antigenic sites as above. However, as mixed aggregates of cells form in the presence of antisera prepared against mixtures of both species, it appears that divalent antisponge sera do exist.

(3) *Folding of the cell periphery*. If the sponge cell periphery is considered as a flexible, folded structure, then a multivalent antibody could become attached to adjacent antigenic sties in the same cell, thereby blocking them and preventing reaggregation.

Although Spiegel concluded that his experiments are compatible with the Tyler/Weiss hypothesis, they certainly do not confirm it. P. Weiss (1958) has remarked that these and similar experiments made with the cellular slime molds '... can only prove, at best, that surface molecules which are involved in cell adhesion also have antigenic properties, but not that these very same properties are instrumental in the normal coupling of cells'. In addition to this, the present author cannot discriminate on this type of experimental evidence, whether cell-to-cell adhesion is prevented by antibody/antigen reactions blocking the antigenic sites involved in adhesion, or whether on the other hand, the adsorbed antibody merely shields 'adhesive sites' which are adjacent to the antigens, leaving the possibility that antigens are uninvolved in normal adhesion.

A rather different approach to the question of the specificity in sponge cell adhesion is that of MacLennan (1963) who in contrast to Spiegel, found that dissociated sponge cells of six species reaggregated in the presence of homologous rabbit antisera. These antisera were specifically neutralized by water-soluble glycopeptides extracted from homologous whole sponges. When fowl erythrocytes were coated with the extracts, they could be agglutinated by antisera prepared either against homologous glycopeptides or whole sponge cells. This and other evidence suggested that the glycopeptides are present in the peripheries of sponge cells. Examination of glycopeptides from seventeen species of sponges showed them to contain the same sugars in different quantities, but to be serologically distinct. MacLennan points out that Gross et al. (1956) analyses of sponge collagen show it to contain many, if not all, of the sugars identified by him in the glycopeptide extracts. He therefore suggests that by participating in extracellular polymerization processes, the glycopeptides can provide a mechanism for species-specific reaggregation, in which he postulates that cells adhere through the agency of peripheral mucinous polymers, the formation of which is competitively inhibited by glycopeptide monomers of other species. Obviously, biosynthetic studies need to be made on collagen formation in the presence of heterologous glycoproteins before this ingenious suggestion which has very wide implications, can be seriously considered. However, supportive evidence in favour of this hypothesis comes from the work of Humphreys (1963) and Moscona (1963) on the reaggregation of dissociated cells of *Microciona prolifera* and *Haliclona occulata*. When the sponges were dissociated mechanically by forcing them through cloth, they reaggregated in flasks in a gyratory shaker (Moscona 1961) to form species specific aggregates at 24 °C and more slowly at 5 °C. However, cells obtained by dissociating sponges in calcium- and magnesium-free sea-water reaggregated in the presence of calcium ions at 24 °C (more slowly than those separated mechanically), but scarcely at all when shaken at 5 °C. This thermal sensitivity suggests, although it does not prove, a synthetic process. Cells dissociated chemically were centrifuged slowly at 0 °C; the supernate was then centrifuged at 11,000 r.p.m. to remove particulate matter. This final supernate, on the addition of calcium ions, not only caused the reaggregation of chemically dissociated cells at 5 °C, but also exhibited specificity. Thus, the final supernate from Microciona would not cause reaggregation of Haliclona cells, and that obtained from Haliclona similarly would not act on Microciona cells. When the supernate from Microciona was added to a suspension of cells from both species at 5 °C, only the Microciona reaggregated. When both supernates were added to a mixture of both species cells, the cells from each species formed separate and distinctly coloured aggregates. The fact that the aggregative activity of the supernates was destroyed by periodate pointed to the possible role of carbohydrates in this capacity. The chemical nature of the supernate was partially determined later (Margoliash et al. 1965) and was found to consist predominantly of glycoprotein. The carbohydrate appeared to be firmly bound to the protein on the evidence that the two could not be separated on a Sephadex column, and when some 80% of the protein was removed by proteolytic enzymes, the carbohydrate moiety remained bound to the residual peptide. These authors sound a note of caution in regarding the glycoprotein as the biologically active substance, even though the purity and homogeneity of the preparation has been demonstrated by ultracentrifugation and electron microscopy.

Humphreys (1965) has shown that in the case of *Microciona prolifera*, the aggregation factor appears to be uniform particles containing protein and polysaccharide and which probably corresponds in the case of spherical particles to 100 to 200 Å diameter. Humphreys is prepared to speculate that these extramembranous structures are responsible for the 100 to 200 Å gap seen in electron micrographs between the trilaminar structures of adherent cells throughout the animal kingdom. Needless to say, evidence in favour of this speculation is sparse, and whether Humphrey's 100 *s* fraction exists in the form of 100–200 Å particles at the sponge cell periphery or whether this is a preparative artefact, is entirely uncertain.

3.3.3 Amphibia

Holtfreter (1943) showed that amphibian embryos could be disaggregated into free cells by raising the pH of their media. He later showed (Holtfreter 1944a) that dissociated prospective pronephric cells from amphibian embryos in the gastrula stage would reaggregate in culture to form pronephric systems. Over the years, Holtfreter has made many valuable contributions to this field, and they are summed up in a paper by Townes and Holtfreter (1955) on the directed movements in isolated, embryonic, amphibian systems. When neurulae were placed in media at pH 9.8, cellular disaggregation occurred through the ruptured surface coat after about 5 min. When the medium was restored to normal pH 8.0, the cells reaggregated to form a compact mass. Microscopic examination of the aggregations revealed that the cellular adhesion which had occurred was entirely random; any cell adhered to any other cell with which it came into contact. Roux (1896) had maintained that there was some sort of attraction between like cells, but Kuhl (1937a) could not demonstrate this by means of time-lapse cinemicrography, but the techniques used left much to be desired. Holtfreter (1943, 1944b) maintained that the initial contacts between reaggregating cells were random, and the work of Townes and Holtfreter (1955) substantiated this viewpoint, which later received direct support from the time-lapse films of Lucey and Curtis (1959).

When cultures of random aggregates of reassociated cells of different type were left under optimal conditions, after a short time the cells began to reorient themselves within the aggregate, to form well-defined groups of isotypic cells. On an argument developed previously, Holtfreter (1939a, b) had postulated that this type of phenomenon is not caused by isotypic cells seeking each other out, but that negative or positive affinity is manifest only by cells in contact. Thus previously adherent cells may develop negative affinity and separate; the process being repeated until all the cells of like affinity become attached to each other. The concept of 'positive affinity' in this context, presages the concept of 'contact inhibition', which could thus be used to 'explain' the sorting out of cells within a mixed aggregate.

The experiments of Townes and Holtfreter (1955) on the recombination of dissociated mesodermal and epidermal cells from *Amblystoma tigrinum* reveal that eventually the mesodermal cells come to lie together at the center of the aggregate, surrounded by the epidermal element. It might be tentatively suggested that the peripheries of these cells may be involved in these reshuffling movements in terms of developing affinities, on the basis of Clayton's (1953) work showing differences in the antigenic composition of the peripheries of epidermal and mesodermal cells from embryos of *Triton alpestris*, which also exhibit similar sorting-out phenomena.

In line with his previously quoted experiments on sponges, Spiegel (1954b) attempted to determine the role of peripheral antigens in the reaggregation of amphibian cells. Spiegel observed that if dissociated ectoderm and endoderm from *Rana pipiens* embryos were incubated in the presence of antisera made in rabbits against cell extracts, reaggregation is prevented. This antiserum had no effect on the reaggregation and subsequent segregation of dissociated cells from the embryos of *Triton alpestris*. Spiegel interprets his results in favour of the Tyler/Weiss hypothesis discussed previously, and considers that the failure of cells to aggregate in the presence of antibody is due to surface folding or deep location of the antigenic sites within the peripheral zone of the cells involved. If, as argued, the deep-seated nature of the antigenic sites prevents antibodies attached to them from reaching to the receptors on another cell, it is difficult to see how such antigens can participate in normal cell-to-cell binding. The same general criticisms of the interpretations of Spiegel's work on sponge cells apply here, and I do not consider the experiments argue one way or the other in favour of normal cell-binding mechanisms having an immunological basis.

3.3.4 Avian and mammalian material

These will be considered together because technically similar approaches have been made to the problem.

The basic problem confronting those studying contact phenomena at cellular level, in reaggregation experiments with avian and mammalian embryonic material, was concerned with the isolation of viable cells from tissues. Ringer and Sainsbury (1894) showed that small amounts of calcium salts would prevent the disintegration of the fresh-water *Olgiochaete tubiflex* by distilled water. Later, Herbst (1900) demonstrated that blastomeres of *Echinus microtuberculatus* could be dispersed in calcium-free sea-water. They continued to divide while they remained viable, but in the continued absence of calcium the cells remained separate from each other, and further embryonic development was prevented. Zweifach (1940) demonstrated that the cells of capillary endothelium could be loosened by calcium depletion, and Moscona (1952) observed that pretreatment with calcium and magnesium-free solutions enhanced the dissociating effect of trypsin. This latter effect may well have been due to the absence of calcium ions, inhibiting the autodigestion of trypsin (Green and Neurath 1953). EDTA in calcium and magnesium-free solutions was used by Zwilling (1954) to dissociate chick blastoderms and by Brochart (1954) on rabbit blastomeres.

The further applications of removal of divalent cations to tissue dissociation have been reviewed by Rinaldini (1958), L. Weiss (1960) and Moscona et al. (1965). It should be noted that in the case of tissues from higher vertebrates, complete dissociation cannot be accomplished without a varying, but usually large amount of trauma, simply by treating tissue with calcium and magnesium-free solutions with or without the addition of EDTA or citrate.

The most effective methods of dissociating the type of embryonic tissues at present under discussion involve the use of enzymes. Rous and Jones (1916) appear to be the first to describe the liberation of cells from plasma-clots, by incubation with trypsin, and Willmer (1945) described the culture of chick embryo heart cells, dissociated with trypsin. Further, more extensive studies on the liberation of cells from embryonic organs by trypsin were described by Moscona (1952) and Moscona and Moscona (1952). A most detailed study of the effects of trypsin (and other proteolytic enzymes) on tissue disaggregation was made by Rinaldini (1958, 1959), whose review (1958) should be consulted. In the ensuing discussion of the results of various reaggregation experiments, little will be said of the techniques of tissue dissociation used by the various authors, and the reader should consult the original papers.

Starting with isolated embryonic cells, a number of different techniques have been used for culturing them, to study reaggregation. Among the earliest were those described by Ebeling and Fischer (1922) and Drew (1923), in which fibroblasts and epithelial cells which had migrated out of plasma-clot cultures of tissue fragments would, when confronted, form tubular structures surrounded by stroma. The more recently used techniques involve starting with cell suspensions, and have been very adequately reviewed by Moscona (1965). In their early experiments Moscona and Moscona (1952) and Moscona (1957) allowed isolated cells suspended in culture media to sediment to the floor of a stationary dish where they began to aggregate. Similar techniques were used by Abraham (1959) in demonstrating the ability of trypsin-isolated cells from the chick embryo testis to reform into histologically recognizable tubules. Time-lapse films of this situation (Stefanelli and Zacchei 1958) suggested that, as in the case of amphibian cells, aggregates result from random collisions and that fresh cells join the aggregates, which may also merge with other aggregates. However, better proof for the formation of aggregates initially by random, and then by some sort of selective process, comes from Trinkaus' (1961) experiments in which reaggregation of various embryonic chick cells was followed precisely by isotopically labelling them with tritiated thymidine or ^{35}S. As the interaction of the cells is complicated by their interaction with the bottom of the culture vessel, this technique does not permit much quantitative analysis. A technique is described by Grover (1961, 1962) in which dissociated cells are cultured in hanging drops, thus avoiding the cell/glass interaction and also permitting the use of very small quantities of cells in an accurately determined gas-phase. Another approach used by Trinkaus and Groves (1955), P. Weiss and James (1955) and Trinkaus and Lentz (1964) is to centrifuge a suspension of cells to produce a loose pellet, which may then be cultured in a plasma-clot, or subsequently transplanted to the chorioallantoic membrane of other chick embryos (P. Weiss and Taylor 1960). Although Moscona (1965) is critical of this technique on account of the cellular trauma and possible stratification produced by the centrifugation, the results do not warrant these criticisms. A more elegant technique, which permits analysis of both the initial contact reactions between the cells and their subsequent sorting-out, is due to Moscona (1961), in which the dispersed cells are cultured in conical flasks on a gyratory shaker. The cells tend to be thrown together in the fluid vortex and are well equilibrated with the gaseous phase in the rest of the culture vessel. This method does not depend for aggregation on the variable, technique-dependent migratory capacities of the cells, and may be standardized to give very reproducible results. Obviously, it could not be used to give information on the part played by active cell movements in determining the initial contacts between cells. The resulting cell aggregates are a resultant of the flow into the vortex which brings the cells together, and the shearing forces that tend to separate the cells. The slower speeds tend to produce larger aggregates, and higher speeds, where the shearing forces are higher, produce smaller aggregates, or even keep the cells separate, one from another. A useful detailed examination of the kinetics of cell aggregation in Moscona's technique is given by Steinberg and Roth (1964), and will be discussed later.

Regardless of technique, a number of important observations have been made on the reaggregation of dispersed cells. Moscona (1952, 1956) examined the behaviour of mixtures of embryonic chick mesonephric and limb-bud cells of the same and different ages, and observed that cellular aggregates developed to histologically resemble the tissues from which they came. In order to exhibit their histogenetic potentialities, cells had to be present in mixed cultures in more than minimal proportions and similar results have been demonstrated on other tissues by other workers. Trinkaus and Groves (1955) showed that mixed dissociated cells of the chick mesonephros and wing-bud would segregate and form characteristic cellular arrangements of peripheral keratinizing epidermis surrounding a layer of mesonephric tubules, which in turn surrounded cartilage. They also noted that on histological parameters, tissue cells from diverse sources did not influence each other's pattern of differentiation. Moscona (1957) showed that trypsin-dispersed embryonic mouse organs will also exhibit histotypic reaggregation of chondrogenic, nephrogenic and hepatogenic cells. When cell suspensions from 12-day mouse and 4-day chick embryos were cultured together, he observed that cells of the same embryonic organs came together to form chimeric aggregates. Cells of the different animals could be recognized by utilizing their different staining properties as shown by Wolff and Weniger (1954). When heterotypic combinations of chick and mouse cells were cultured, aggregates were formed in which the two constituent cell types formed separate groups. These cellular groups subsequently developed in accordance with the original histogenetic properties of their constituent cells. Moscona thus demonstrated that in this type of experiment, organ-type identity took precedence over genetic origin. More detailed reviews of certain aspects of this work are given by Moscona (1960, 1962a, 1965) and Trinkaus (1961, 1965).

To date, the remarkable ability of isolated cells to reform histotypic aggregates has been confined to cells from embryos. Even in the embryonic chick, there is wide variation in the abilities of cells of different ages to aggregate in a reproducible manner. In a well-documented study, Grover (1962) showed that reaggregation is well-marked among the lung cells of 7 to 12-day chick embryos, with complex reorganization being optimal from 11 to 12 days, after which there is a decline. Grover also showed that cultures of epithelial cells obtained by tryptic digestion of 12-day lung, fail to form typical histological features, unless cultured with mesenchymal cells obtained by further incubating the trypsinized organs with collagenase. The failure of the two types of cell to organize, unless they are in intimate contact, was thought to rule out an inductive interaction.

Within an aggregate of cells, the problem is one of how cells segregate. Contact inhibition could account in a statistical way for cell segregation, since presumably when cells come into contact with others of a similar type, their movements through the random aggregate would be progessively restricted in direction. Following on the concept of contact guidance, Moscona and Moscona (1952) suggested that the strands of transparent, slimy substance, apparently exuded by cells, and along which cells in culture move, may correspond to P. Weiss "ground mat' and orient-moving cells. It is of interest that in amphibians at least, Bell (1960) has isolated an intercellular 'membrane-like matrix' from the ectoderm of *Rana pipiens* embryos and larvae, by the use of ultrasonic techniques. Although this matrix is initially structureless, by Stage 18 fibrils appeared which had a diameter of about 0.06μ in electron micrographs. Bell suggested that the matrix might not only act as a suitable substrate for cellular movements, but in accordance with Meier's (1958) suggestion, it might also stimulate quiescent cells to move. In addition, Moscona (1960, 1961) has also suggested that in some way, this extracellular matrix or ECM plays a part in binding cells together. While there is little doubt from the work of Moscona and others that ECM *can* orient cells, and bind them together, a controversial point is whether or not this is a normal mechanism.

The mucinous ECM is seen particularly when cells are treated with trypsin, which is an essential part of the dissociation technique. In the case of murine Sarcoma 37 ascites tumour cells, which were used as models for technical reasons, L. Weiss (1958) showed by microscopical interferometry that standard trypsin treatment caused the cells to lose a considerable amount of dry mass, without detectable change in cell viability, as assessed by animal inoculation, dye exclusion tests and phase contrast microscopy. This was considered at the time to be analagous to Moscona's ECM. Later, Steinberg (1963a) showed that ECM obtained from embryonic chick cells is a highly hydrated deoxyribonucleoprotein gel, apparently formed by the action of trypsin on the chromosomal protein of ruptured cells. Although Steinberg's experiments quite clearly indicate the intracellular origin of much of the material obtained by treating cells with trypsin, they do not necessarily indicate the origin of all of it. The gaps of low electron density seen between adherent cells and the diminution in electrophoretic mobility due to the loss of peripheral mucopolysaccharides when *some* cells are treated with trypsin, strongly suggest that the concept of an extracellular matrix suggested by Rhumbler (1898), Jennings (1904), Gray (1926), Vogt (1929), Lehmann (1932), Chambers (1938), Holtfreter (1943), Moscona and others is with modification, valid, even though most of the ECM described, following trypsinization by Moscona, has an immediate intracellular origin.

Moscona (1961) observed that the reaggregation of embryonic cells *in vitro* was inhibited at temperatures lower than about 15 °C, and interpreted this to indicate that synthesis of materials necessary for cell adhesion and aggregation was inhibited at low temperatures. Steinberg (1962a) and L. Weiss (1964) showed that adhesions between cells and cells and glass respectively, were prevented by low temperatures, but suggested that as distinct from its effects on biosynthesis of peripheral materials, low temperature might inhibit cells from putting out low radius of curvature probes which could help them overcome potential energy repulsion barrier to contact (vide chapter 4). Steinberg (1962) in an elegant series of experiments, showed that if cells were cultured at 30 °C when they could presumably synthesize ECM, but were prevented from aggregating by increasing the speed of the gyratory shaker, they still would not adhere at temperatures of 6.5 °C, after the mechanical restraint to contact had been removed. In apparent contrast to Steinberg's observations, Moscona (1962a) has demonstrated that dissociated cells which were preincubated for 1 hour at 38 °C, and then incubated at 25 °C, continued to adhere and form 'sizeable aggregates' compared with the 'minute clusters' formed by cells incubated continuously at 25 °C. It appears to the present author that although the presence or absence of synthesized peripheral material does not affect the mutual adhesion of cells at 6.5 °C, it is perhaps more pertinent to ask whether or not it affects the adhesion of cells at more physiological temperatures. L. Weiss and Kapes (1966) showed that the adhesion to glass of a permanent line of cells developed from a human osteogenic sarcoma, was retarded following incubation with Difco 1:250 trypsin, when compared with controls; and their detachment from glass was facilitated for more than 4 hours after such treatment. They suggested on their data that the cells behaved as though material had been removed from their peripheries, which affected their adhesion to, and detachment from glass and, in addition, the restoration of these properties to the cells followed a definite time course, which may have been related to synthesis of peripheral material. Weiss and Kapes concluded that although their experiments were made with only one cell line, in the extremely artificial cell/glass system, they lent support to the concept that the basic mechanisms of cell adhesion and separation, on which cellular segregation depends, are modified by the process of post-trypsin regeneration.

Steinberg and Roth (1964) treated dispersed embryonic chick neural retina cells with 'prothidium bromide' (2-amino-6-methylpyrimidyl-4-amino)-9-*p*-aminophenyl-phenanthridine 10, 1'-dimethobromide) and confirmed an earlier observation of L. Weiss (1963) that such treatment enhanced cell adhesion as manifest by the appearance of larger aggregates than normal. This effect was abolished if the cells were incubated with deoxyribonuclease after prothidium treatment, suggesting that the enhanced cell aggregation was brought about by release of deoxyribonucleoprotein from the cells, which gelled to produce intermeshed strands, which acted as foci of aggregation. In any population of cells undergoing developmental or other physiological or pathological processes, some die. It is therefore conceivable to me that released material from dead cells need not invariably be dismissed as an experimental artifact, but may have a physiological role in cell adhesion. On the other hand, there seems little evidence to substantiate the suggestion that ECM normally plays a part in directing cell movements *in vivo*.

3.4 Gross mechanisms of cellular segregation

The phenomena described present common problems, some of which were succintly formulated by Holtfreter as the development of positive and negative affinities between cells, after they had made contact. By superimposing directionality on moving cells, probably by contact inhibition and possibly by contact guidance, an 'explanation' can be given at a fairly gross level for the selectivity which is seen in cellular segregation and other contact phenomena. This group of problems may be summed up in terms of cell contact and eventual cell 'trapping'. However, not only must cell segregation be considered, but also the location of groups of like cells in relation to other groups. This problem is exemplified by the earlier observation of Moscona and Moscona (1952), that when mixtures of isolated embryonic chick cells from limb precartilage and premuscle were cultured, the chondrogenic mass was eventually invariably surrounded by myogenic cells. Other examples of the spatial location of segregated cellular groups have been collected by Steinberg (1964).

Curtis (1961a, 1962) has made the suggestion that the system of aggregation of dissociated cells is in a sense misleading as a model. Curtis made the very reasonable assumption that the peripheries of cells studied by reaggregation techniques are modified by the dissociation process. It is well-known that the electrokinetic properties of cells may be altered by a variety of enzymes. L. Weiss and Kapes (1966) showed that a number of dissociating agents altered the ability of cells to stick to, and be detached from glass. L. Weiss (1965, 1966, 1967) and L. Weiss and Clement (1966) have shown that enzyme treatment and chelation can alter the mechanical properties of tumour cells. Curtis proposed that such alterations would make cells abnormally motile and adhesive until they recovered from the treatment. Here again the various experiments carried out by my colleagues and I on cells reacting with glass surfaces would support the feasibility of this part of Curtis' proposition. Curtis then goes on to say that different cells may have different time sequences for regeneration. Although this has not been proved directly, this also seems reasonable. As a result of their random movements, cells reach the surface of aggregates. Curtis suggests that the cells which recover first are trapped at the surface of a combination of reduced motility and increased adhesiveness. He proposes therefore that the sorting-out processes observed are due to a 'temporal specificity', rather than the fixed properties usually assumed to exist. As a further complication, Curtis (1961a) points out that the surface of a cell at the free edge of an aggregate is subjected to less shear than the surface of a moving cell within the aggregate, and that shear might affect cell adhesion (Curtis 1960) by altering charge density and thus the balance of intercellular attractive and repulsive forces. This last suggestion has not been substantiated by the work of Nordling and Mayhew (1966).

The data offered by Curtis (1961a) in support of his timing hypothesis were obtained from reaggregation experiments made with cells dissociated from *Xenopus laevis* embryos (Nieuwkoop stage 12; midgastrulae). In essence, by the use of accurately staged embryos, dissociated cells were allowed to reaggregate for various periods of time before adding freshly dissociated of other types to them. When endodermal cells were allowed to reaggregate for 4 hours before ectodermal and mesodermal cells were added inter-

nally or externally, the ectoderm associated with the endoderm, a phenomenon not normally observed. The longer the time which the endoderm
had been reaggregating before the ectoderm and mesoderm were added,
the deeper down within the aggregate were the ectoderm and endoderm.
Curtis (1962) provided additional evidence in favour of his hypothesis, with
his experiments on dissociated sponges. When the dissociated cells from two
different species are mixed and cultured, they segregate. If the more slowly
segregating cells were allowed some hours start, before mixing them with
freshly dissociated 'fast' cells, a chimeric aggregate is formed. Also, if the
cells from species with similar reaggregation rates are mixed, segregation
does not occur. The demonstration of temporal specificity in dissociated
cells has not been confirmed by Grover (1962) in his experiments with
embryo chick lungs. This author noted the continued 'normal' sorting-out
interactions between epithelial cells, maintained in pure culture for periods
up to 19 hours, and added mesenchymal cells. Evidence which is against
Curtis' timing hypothesis as a general mechanism includes that of Wolff
(1954), Townes and Holtfreter (1955), Bresch (1955), and Steinberg (1962b),
in which fragments of organs, obtained without chemical dissociation, fused
in culture and underwent cellular reshuffling, leading to the same basic
segregated pattern as seen in mixed cultures of dissociated cells.

Although stressing the concept of temporal specificity, Curtis does not
wholly reject the more conventional concepts of 'areal' specificities, and
remarks that timing mechanisms could be modifying these. The available
evidence suggests that while there is a good case for the concept of temporal
specificity in the reaggregation of chemically dissociated cells from sponges
and Xenopus: there is not for embryonic chick material. Temporal specificity
also does not appear to be a valid explanation for the segregation seen in
fused organ fragments. I think that the concept is of value in stressing time-
dependent changes in cellular interrelationships and the cell periphery.

Another approach to cellular interactions based on adhesive selectivity
has been developed by Steinberg (1962b,c,d; 1963b; 1964), based on
considerations of free surface energy. This will be discussed in the next
chapter.

3.5 *Cell contact phenomena in embryogenesis*

On turning to whole embryos, as distinct from reaggregating, dissociated
cell systems, the study of cell contact phenomena becomes increasingly

difficult technically. In this section an attempt will be made to select a few examples which illustrate some of the problems and approaches to solving them, without reviewing the whole of the vast literature. More detailed reviews of the literature have been made by Gustafson and Wolpert (1963), Bonner (1963), De Haan and Ebert (1964), Trinkaus (1965) and others.

3.5.1 Morphogenesis in the sea urchin

During the first 10 hours after fertilization, the sea urchin egg undergoes some 10 divisions to form a hollow, spherical blastula, containing about 1,000 cells arranged in a layer, one cell thick. A few hours later, cells from the vegetal pole of the organism push into the blastula; these primary mesenchymal cells take up a defined position on the wall of blastocoele in the form of a ring with two branches extending towards the opposite animal pole of the egg. The next developmental stage is gastrulation in which the primitive gut, the archenteron, is formed. Cells from a zone lying between the vegetal and animal poles invaginate into the blastocoele in the form of a tube which eventually fuses with the ectoderm of the animal pole; a hole develops in the region of contact between the two fused ectodermal elements to form the primitive mouth (Horstadius 1939; Dan 1960). Gustafson and Wolpert (1963 – for review) attempted to use the developmental patterns seen in the early embryo of the sea urchin as a model for some general principles of cellular patterns. The sea urchin is ideal, technically, for this type of study because after hatching, larvae can be observed continuously with the time-lapse microscope while trapped in the web of a nylon net, on which calcium carbonate crystals have been grown (Gustafson and Kinnander 1956).

As a result of their studies on morphogenesis in the sea urchin, Gustafson and Wolpert have postulated cellular mechanisms involving cell adhesion to account for movements involving cell sheets (Wolpert and Gustafson 1961; Gustafson and Wolpert 1962) and filopodial exploration to account for directed movements of cells (Gustafson and Wolpert 1961). Gustafson and Wolpert have considered the many mechanisms advanced in the past to account for changes in the form of cell sheets, as seen in gastrulation. These include shape changes due to cell surface changes (Rhumbler 1902); differential swellings (Bütschli 1915) or contractions of the cell sheets (Gillette 1944; Lewis 1947); uneven growth with layers leading to infolding or outgrowths (His 1894); uneven patterns of attraction between constituent cells due to fibrils (Waddington 1940) and the development of fluid pressures. In contrast to these theories which are not satisfactory (Moore 1930; Picken 1960) in explaining all of the various observations, Gustafson and Wolpert attempt to account for the changes in terms of adhesive changes between the surfaces of adjacent cells in a sheet, and their bounding basement membrane. The cells are assumed to be bounded by a flexible, elastic membrane 'whose resistance to bending may be neglected', and the cells are assumed to tend towards a spherical shape unless otherwise deformed. The basis for the first assumption is Wolpert's (1960a, b) work on the sea urchin egg, which in my view is not necessarily a good general model even for other embryonic sea urchin cells. Nonetheless, it is postulated that increase in adhesion causes a cell to flatten on its substrate; this type of deformation on contact with progressive increase in contact area is well-known among engineers and has been discussed by L. Weiss (1960) in a manner suggested in Schmitt's (1941) zipper hypothesis, in which calcium ions, for example, can desolvate the space between two cells, thereby promoting progressive contact. Thus, in the case of a tube, if its constituent cells increased their mutual adhesiveness along adjacent edges, this would lead to a decrease in external and internal tubal diameters, and vice versa. On the other hand, if the cells increased their adhesiveness to a surrounding basement membrane, and decreased their areas of contact for each other, a larger diameter tube would be expected, and its constituent cells would be flattened. Thus, by imposing localized changes in adhesiveness, almost any change in form may be accounted for. This model has the merit of simplicity, but until the adhesivenes is measured, it cannot be considered proven. In addition it offers no mechanisms for the changes in adhesivity, and the ultrastructural studies of Balinsky (1959) make it clear that at this level, three distinct types of cell junction can be recognized and have a complex relationship to gastrulation.

During development, as stated, mesenchymal cells migrate into the blastocoele and attach to well defined, constant sites on the ectoderm. The problem of how randomly arranged mesenchymal cells come to form an organized system is another example of directed movement, which can be followed continuously by Gustafson and Kinnander's (1956) technique at cellular level. It has been observed that as the mesenchymal cells invade the blastocoele, they put out pseudopods which may be 30μ in length. Pseudopods making contact with the wall of the blastocoele shorten, and thus apparently pull the rest of the cell after them. Those pseudopods not making contact with the wall are withdrawn after a time back into the mesenchymal cells. This process which leads to the centrifugal movement of cells away from the vegetal plate and their migration towards the animal pole is what might be expected from considerations of contact inhibition. Cells forming the mesenchymal ring concentrate in two regions, and from these regions two 'branches' project towards the animal pole. The pseudopods of the constituent cells of the branches become entwined to form a type of cable from which pseudopods project, from time to time. The organization of the mesenchymal cells appears to be due to some sort of selective fixation of exploring pseudopods, as distinct from a mechanism of contact guidance within the blastocoele cavity. However, the blastocoele does contain mucopolysaccharide (Monné and Hårde 1951; Immers 1961) and fibrous material (Wolpert and Mercer 1963), so that contact guidance might conceivably play a role in directing pseudopods over the surface of the ectoderm *after* they have made contact with it. These movements are thus presented as the result of adhesion of mesenchymal cells to ectoderm in such a way as to suggest selective fixation.

3.5.2 *Epiboly in the teleost gastrula*

Epiboly is the expansion of one cell layer over another, and has been studied extensively in the teleost egg, where such movements are well-marked and play an important part in gastrulation. Von Baer (1835) first described epibolic movements in the teleost gastrula, and the phenomenon is of historic interest in that it was taken by His (1874) to provide support for his theory that morphogenetic movements are caused by differential growth. This is not in fact the case, since experiments have shown that large increases in the area of the spreading blastoderm are not accompanied by corresponding increase in mass (cited by Trinkaus 1951a). Until fairly recently, the generally accepted hypothesis for epiboly in teleosts, due to Lewis (1949), regarded the movements as being due to passive stretching of the blastoderm over the yolk, by the tension of the surface gel layer. Following the work of Devillers (1951a,b) and Trinkaus (1951a,b), it became clear that expansion is not due only to tension in the yolk gel layer, but in some way resides in the blastoderm itself and in the periblast over which it spreads. The literature on this topic has been well reviewed by Devillers (1960, 1961) and by Trinkaus (1963, 1965); and Trinkaus supports the idea that epiboly is to be explained in terms of the development of differing adhesiveness between the blastodermal cells themselves, and between them and the periblast cells. When the margins of the spreading blastoderm are separated from the periblast, the blastoderm retracts. It has been suggested that the marginal cells are the prime movers in epiboly, and that their adhesiveness to the periblast is in some way due to their marginal position, since if the central cells are made marginal by removing the existing marginal cells, then they also become adhesive. *In vitro* experiments on cells isolated from the blastoderm at different stages of development showed that the cells isolated during the later stages, when epiboly is beginning, spread more extensively on glass than earlier cells (Trinkaus 1963). Although these *in vitro* experiments only provide data on cell/glass adhesions and not blastoderm/periblast adhesions, they are suggestive of time-dependent changes at the peripheries of the blastodermal cells. On the other hand, the properties of the periblast may also be changing with time, and the role of tension in the intact *in vivo* system cannot be entirely excluded. Epiboly has not yet been analyzed at a deeper level. Thus, it is not known whether the spreading of cells radially from the blastoderm in a manner reminiscent of cultures on plasma-clot is to be explained in terms of contact inhibition, or contact guidance or yet the type of filopodial traction seen in the developing sea urchin. Are these different properties to be explained in terms of new chemical species appearing in the peripheries of the involved cells, or are the apparent changes in peripheral properties to be related to other cellular activities, such as differing metabolic rates?

3.5.3 Gastrulation in the chick embryo

Although the area opaca of the developing chick embryo undergoes epiboly, blastoderms do not expand when cultured on plasma-clots or agar gels (Waddington 1932, Spratt 1946). New (1959) observed that when blastoderm is cultured on the inner surface of a vitelline membrane, which is its normal substratum, it adheres to it and expands. This emphasized that descriptions of cell adhesiveness are useless unless they include a description of both the cell and the substratum to which it adheres (L. Weiss 1961a), and that cell adhesion or interaction plays a part in epibolic movements. The possibility of some specific interaction between the blastoderm and vitelline membrane causing epiboly is made unlikely by Spratt's (1963) observation that the blastoderm will expand if cultured on a substratum of cellulose-type filter. As in teleosts, only the edges of the blastodermal sheet adhere markedly to the substratum; however in contrast to the teleosts, the more centrally located cells are not adherent to the membrane even if surgically relocated at the edges of the blastodermal sheet. The marginal cells are very phagocytic (Bellairs and New 1962) when compared with the central cells, which would indicate a difference in surface activity; however, in itself this observation cannot be taken to indicate more than positional activity, since observations of clusters of a number of different types of mammalian and avian cells *in vitro* also indicates more activity at the free edges, as expected (L. Weiss, unpublished observations). New regards the tension developed at the edge of the blastoderm as a requirement for its spread, since if it were not, the rates of expansion and movement of the expanding edges might get out of phase, leading to overlapping of its own edges by an expanding blastodermal sheet; an occurence which has not been observed. Expansion is not due to a *vis a tergo* from more rapidly dividing cells, as emphasized by Spratt (1963), since peripheral pieces of blastoderm continue to expand even when isolated from central pieces (Schlesinger 1958) and Bellairs (1954) has found that epiboly occurs even when mitotis is inhibited with folic acid antagonists. Although radial movements of its constituent cells which would account for blastodermal expansion could conceivably be explained in terms of contact inhibition, the fact that tension in the substratum is required is suggestive of contact guidance.

3.5.4 *Movements of precardiac mesoderm in the chick embryo*

De Haan (1963a-c) has studied the movements of precardiac mesoderm leading to the formation of the heart, with time-lapse cinemicrography. At stages 4 and 5 of embryonic development, small clusters of mesodermal cells migrate on an endodermal substratum, to form an outer, medial crescentic cardiogenic plate, which later forms the heart. Within the plate, the mesodermal cells apparently differentiate into pacemaker cells and the like. De Haan has suggested that the initial phases of organization of the cardiogenic plate result from random movements during a period when some sort of selection adhesion is developing. After stage 6, the mesodermal clusters move in an oriented way up the cardiac crescent and then to the site of the developing mid-line heart. At this time, according to De Haan (1963b), the endoderm shows signs of orientation, visible on silver staining, in regions underlying the precardiac material. He speculates that the mesodermal cells may be guided by contact with the lines of the junctions between endodermal cells, which, in this region at this time, tend to a spindle-shape. As previously discussed, such substratum-orientation would leave the migrating cells with a choice of two directions along any one track.

De Haan (1964) has proposed that direction is provided to the migrating cells by a selective adhesion mechanism operated through exploratory filopodia, as in the developing sea urchin (vide supra). In support of this hypothesis, but by no means proving it, are observations of the presence of filopodia in both 2-day and 4-day heart cells (Rumery et al. 1961; De Haan 1964). In this connection, it may be mentioned in passing, that the orientation of nerve fibres may also be guided by this method of filopodial 'selective adhesion' and traction as evidence from the appearance of projections of 10 to 20 μ, and longer, from the tip of axons in culture (Nakai and Kawasaki 1959; Stefanelli 1960). More evidence is reviewed by De Haan and Ebert (1964) and suggests the feasibility of this exploration and selective fixation approach, both *in vitro* and in regeneration studies *in vivo*. Great care must be taken in attributing specific functions to filopodial projections from cells *in vitro*, as I have observed on many occasions that such projections are promoted by unfavorable culture conditions in a number of different cells, particularly sarcomata.

3.5.5 Migration of neural crest cells in the chick embryo

Soon after the temporary appearance of the neural crest in the chick embryo, cells begin to migrate out from it, to differentiate in different sites, into various tissues. Although a great deal of work has been done on the problems of cell migration from this region, as reviewed by Hörstadius (1939), the general problem of recognizing migratory cells in a large population of other cell types prevented clear cut answers on the possible existence and fate of small groups of neural crest cells in other tissues, particularly before they differentiate. A recent attempt to describe the pattern of migration and the fate of undifferentiated cells has been made by Weston (1963), using cells labelled with tritiated thymidine, which Trinkaus and Gross (1961) have shown to be a stable, non-toxic marker in this type of experiment. Weston has also thoroughly reviewed the literature in this field, and only some salient, illustrative points will be remarked on here. Cells migrate out of the neural crest in two streams, one going ventrally in the mesenchyme between the neural tube and the myotome, the other going dorsally and laterally into the superficial ectoderm. Grafting experiments have shown that the initial orientation of the migrants depend on the dorso-ventral orientation of the neural tube, and their subsequent direction through the somitic mesenchyme is independent of the cellular environment in the context of contact guidance. The initial direction of migration has been attributed to a negative chemotaxis by Twitty and Niu (1948, 1954), although their experiments with isolated cells in capillary tubes may be misleading, quantitatively, in that metabolic products probably cannot diffuse away as readily as *in vivo*. Weston is of the opinion that the migration may be explained in terms of contact inhibition; however, the evidence does not really permit a choice of mechanisms.

Other examples of cell contact phenomena in morphogenetic processes could be quoted. The processes of wound repair (P. Weiss 1961b) and regeneration in lower animals (Tardent 1963; Wolff 1961) provide other examples of apparently well-regulated cell interactions, as do the very specific sperm/egg interactions seen in fertilization (Austin and Bishop 1957; Rothschild 1958; Austin 1961; Colwin and Colwin 1964). The problems of fertilization point to the fact that at least after this type of contact between cells the peripheral zone of the fertilized ovum undergoes a rapid change, as evidenced by the block to polyspermy. The possibility of changes analogous to fertilization occurring in other cells as a result of contact or penetration by lymphocytes, as in emperipolesis (Humble et al. 1956), has been largely ignored.

3.6 Conclusions

The various contact phenomena illustrate and confirm the suggestion made by P. Weiss (1947) that, regardless of terminology, there are only three ways in which cells get from one point to another, with 'specificity' in any system: (1) guidance, involving ordered movement; (2) selective fixation, in which randomly moving cells are trapped at selected sites; (3) selective disposal, in which both cell movements and trapping are random, but cells are selectively destroyed at certain sites. These concepts will be discussed again in the 'special' case of cancer, in later chapters.

References

Abercrombie, M. (1957). Proc. Zool. Soc. Bengal. Mookerjee Mem. Vol. **129**

Abercrombie, M. (1961). Exptl. Cell Res. Suppl. **8**, 188

Abercrombie, M. (1964). Arch. Biol. (Liège) **75**, 351

Abercrombie, M. (1965). In, E. N. Willmer, ed., Cells and tissues in culture. Academic Press, London and New York, Vol. 1, p. 177

Abercrombie, M. and Ambrose, E. J. (1958). Exptl. Cell Res. **15**, 332

Abercrombie, M. and Gitlin, G. (1965). Proc. Roy. Soc. B **162**, 289

Abercrombie, M. and Heaysman, J. E. M. (1953). Exptl. Cell Res. **5**, 111

Abercrombie, M. and Heaysman, J. E. M. (1954). Exptl. Cell Res. **6**, 293

Abercrombie, M. Heaysman, J. E. M. and Karthauser, H. M. (1957). Exptl. Cell Res. **13**, 276

Abraham, M. M. (1959). Compt. Rend. Acad. Sci. **249**, 2627

Agrell, I. (1951). Arch. Zool. **2**, 519

Algard, T. F. (1953). J. Exptl. Zool. **123**, 499

Allen, R. D. (1961a). Exptl. Cell Res. Suppl. **8**, 17

Allen, R. D. (1961b). In, J. Brachet, and A. E. Mirsky, eds., The cell. Academic Press, New York, Vol. 2, p. 135

Ambrose, E. J. (1961). Exptl. Cell Res. Suppl. **8**, 54

Arndt, A. (1937). Arch. Mikroskop. Anat. Entwicklungsmech. **136**, 681

Austin, C. R. (1961). Mammalian egg. Blackwell: Oxford

Austin, C. R. and Bishop, M. W. H. (1957). Biol. Rev. **32**, 296

Baer, K. E. von (1835). Untersuchungen über die Entwicklungsgeschichte der Fische, nebst einem Anhange über die Schwimmblase. Leipzig

Balinsky, B. I. (1959). Exptl. Cell Res. **16**, 429

Beadle, L. C. and Booth, F. A. (1938). J. Exptl. Biol. **15**, 303

Bell, E. (1960). Exptl. Cell Res. **20**, 378

Bell, L. G. E. (1961). J. Theoret. Biol. **1**, 104

Bellairs, R. (1954). In, Wostenholme and M. P. Cameron, eds., Chemistry and biology of pteridines. Ciba Foundation Symposium, London, p. 356

Bellairs, R. and New, D. A. T. (1962). Exptl. Cell Res. **26**, 275

Bettex-Galland, M. and Lüscher, E. F. (1961). Biochim. Biophys. Acta **49**, 536

Bingley, M. S. and Thompson, C. M. (1962). J. Theoret. Biol. **2**, 16

Bonner, J. T. (1947). J. Exptl. Zool. **106**, 1

Bonner, J. T. (1952). Am. Nat. **86**, 79

Bonner, J. T. (1958). The evolution of development. Cambridge University Press, London

Bonner, J. T. (1959). The cellular slime molds. Princeton University Press, Princeton, New Jersey

Bonner, J. T. (1963). Morphogenesis. Atheneum, New York

Bonner, J. T. and Adams, M. S. (1958). J. Embryol. Exptl. Morphol. **6**, 346

Bonner, J. T. and Frascella, E. B. (1953). Biol. Bull. **104**, 297

Bovee, E. C. (1964). In, R. D. Allen and N. Kamiya, eds., Primitive motile systems in cell biology. Academic Press, New York and London, p. 189

Boyden, S. (1962). J. Exptl. Med. **115**, 453

Boyden, S. V. (1964). Nature **201**, 200

Bresch, D. (1955). Bull. Biol. Fr. Belg. **89**, 179

Brochart, M. (1954). Nature **173**, 160

Brokaw, C. J. (1958). J. Exptl. Biol. **35**, 197

Bütschli, O. (1915). Sitzber. Akad. Wiss. (Heidelberg) **6 B**, 1

Chambers, R. (1938). J. Cell. Comp. Physiol. **12**, 149

Chambers, R. and Fell, H. B. (1931). Proc. Roy. Soc. B **109**, 380

Chapman-Andresen, C. (1963). Proc. 1st Intern. Congr. Protozool

Clayton, R. M. (1953). J. Embryol. Exptl. Morphol. **1**, 25

Colwin, A. L., and Colwin, L. H. (1964). In, M. Locke, ed., Cellular membranes in development. Academic Press, New York, p. 233

Curtis, A. S. G. (1960). Ann. Naturalist **94**, 37

Curtis, A. S. G. (1961a). Exptl. Cell Res. Suppl. **8**, 107

Curtis, A. S. G. (1961b). J. Natl. Cancer Inst. **26**, 253

Curtis, A. S. G. (1962). Nature **196**, 245

Dan, K. (1960). Intern. Rev. Cytol. **9**, 321

De Bruyn, P. P. H. (1945). Anat. Rec. **93**, 295

De Bruyn, P. P. H. (1947). Quant. Rev. Biol **22**, 1

De Haan, R. L. (1963a). Exptl. Cell Res. **29**, 544

De Haan, R. L. (1963b). Acta Embryol. Morphol. Exptl. **6**, 26

De Haan, R. L. (1963c). J. Embryol. Exptl. Morphol. **11**, 65

De Haan, R. L. (1964). J. Exptl. Zool. **157**, 127

De Haan, R. L. and Ebert, J. D. (1964). Ann. Rev. Physiol. **26**, 15

Devillers, C. (1951a). Arch. Anat. Microscop. Morphol. Exptl. **40**, 298

Devillers, C. (1951b). Compt. Rend. Acad. Sci. **232**, 1599

Devillers, C. (1960). Advan. Morphogenesis **1**, 379

Devillers, C. (1961). Exptl. Cell Res. Suppl. **8**, 221

Drew, H. (1923). Brit. J. Exptl. Pathol. **4**, 46

Ebeling, A. H. and Fischer, A. (1922). J. Exptl. Med. **36**, 285

Ephrussi, B. (1933). Arch. Anat. Micr. **29**, 95

Fauré-Fremiet, E. (1929). Protoplasma **6**, 521

Fenn, W. O. (1922). J. Gen. Physiol. **4**, 373

Fischer, A. (1946a). In, The biology of tissue cells. Cambridge University Press

Fischer, A. (1946b). In, The biology of tissue cells. Cambridge University Press, p. 169

Fraenkel, G. S., and Gunn, D. L. (1961). The orientation of animals. Dover Publications, New York

Galtsoff, P. S. (1923). Biol. Bull. **45**, 153

Galtsoff, P. S. (1925). J. Exptl. Zool. **42**, 183

Galtsoff, P. S. (1926). J. Gen. Physiol. **10**, 239

Galtsoff, P. S. (1929). Biol. Bull. **57**, 250

Ganguly, B. (1960). Roux' Arch. Entwicklungsmech. Organ. **152**, 22

Garber, B. (1953). Exptl. Cell Res. **5**, 132

Gazelius, K. and Rånby, B. G. (1957). Exptl. Cell Res. **12**, 265

Gillette, R. (1944). J. Exptl. Zool. **96**, 201

Goldacre, R. J. (1961). Exptl. Cell Res. Suppl. **8**, 1

Goldacre, R. J. (1964). In, R. D. Allen and N. Kamiya, eds., Primitive motile systems in cell biology. Academic Press, New York and London, p. 237

Goldacre, R. J. and Lorch, I. J. (1950). Nature **166**, 497

Goodrich, H. B. (1920). Biol. Bull. **46**, 252

Graciun, E. C. (1927). Compt. Rend. Ass. Anat. **22**, 46

Gray, J. (1926). Brit. J. Exptl. Biol. **3**, 167

Green, M. and Neurath, H. (1953). J. Biol. Chem. **204**, 379

Gregg, J. H. (1956). J. Gen. Physiol. **39**, 813

Gregg, J. H. (1964). Physiol. Rev. **44**, 631

Gregg, J. H. and Trygstad, C. W. (1958). Exptl. Cell Res. **15**, 358

Griffin, J. L. (1964). In, R. D. Allen and N. Kamiya, eds., Primitive motile systems in cell biology. Academic Press, New York and London, p. 303

Gross, J., Sokal, Z., and Rougvie, M. (1956). J. Histochem. Cytochem. **4**, 227

Grover, J. W. (1961). Develop. Biol. **3**, 555

Grover, J. W. (1962). Exptl. Cell Res. **26**, 344

Gustafson, T. and Kinnander, H. (1956). Exptl. Cell Res. **11**, 36

Gustafson, T. and Wolpert, L. (1961). Exptl. Cell Res. **24**, 64

Gustafson, T. and Wolpert, L. (1962). Exptl. Cell Res. **27**, 260

Gustafson, T. and Wolpert, L. (1963). Intern. Rev. Cytol. **15**, 139

Harris, H. (1953). J. Path. Bact. **66**, 135

Harris, H. (1954). Physiol. Rev. **54**, 529

Harris, H. (1961). Exptl. Cell Res. Suppl. **8**, 199

Harrison, R. G. (1910). J. Exptl. Zool. **9**, 787

Harrison, R. G. (1912). Anat. Rec. **6**, 181

Harrison, R. G. (1914). J. Exptl. Zool. **17**, 521

Herbst, C. (1900). Roux' Arch. Entwicklungsmech. Organ. **9**, 424

His, W. (1874). Unsere Körperform und das physiologische Problem ihrer Entstehung. Leipzig

His, W. (1894). Arch Anat. Physiol. Anat. abt. **1**

Hoffman-Berling, H. (1956). Biochim. Biophys. Acta **19**, 453

Hoffman-Berling, H. (1960). In, M. Florkin and H. S. Mason, eds., Comparative biochemistry. Academic Press, New York, Vol. II, p. 341

Hoffman-Berling, H. (1964). In, R. D. Allen and N. Kamiya, eds., Primitive motile systems in cell biology. Academic Press, New York and London, p. 365

Holtfreter, J. (1939a). Roux' Arch. Entwicklungsmech. Organ. **139**, 110

Holtfreter, J. (1939b). Roux' Arch. Entwicklungsmech. Organ. **139**, 227

Holtfreter, J. (1943). J. Exptl. Zool. **93**, 251

Holtfreter, J. (1944a). Rev. Can. Biol. **3**, 220

Holtfreter, J. (1944b). J. Exptl. Zool. **95**, 171

Holtfreter, J. (1946). J. Morphol. **79**, 27

Hörstadius, S. (1939). Biol. Rev. **14**, 132

Howes, E. L. (1943). Surg. Gynecol. Obstet. **76**, 738

Humble, J. C., Jayne, W. H. W. and Pulvertaft, R. J. V. (1956). Brit. J. Heamatol. **2**, 283

Humphreys, T. (1963). Develop. Biol. **8**, 27

Humphreys, T. (1965). Exptl. Cell Res. **40**, 539

Hurley, J. V. (1963). Nature **198**, 1212

Hurley, J. V. and Spector, W. C. (1961). J. Pathol. Bact. **82**, 403, 421

Huxley, J. S. (1911). Phil. Trans. Roy. Soc. **B 202**, 165

Immers, J. (1961). Exptl. Cell Res. **24**, 356

Jahn, T. L. (1964). In, Primitive motile systems in cell biology. R. D. Allen and N. Kamiya, eds., Academic Press, New York and London, p. 279

Jacoby, F. (1936). J. Exptl. Biol. **13**, 393

Jennings, H. S. (1904). Publ. Carnegie Inst. **16**, 129

Johnsson, R. and Hegyeli, A. (1965). Proc. Natl. Acad. Sci. U.S. **54**, 1375

Kamiya, N. (1959). Protoplasmatologia **8**, 1

Kamiya, N. (1964). In, Primitive motile systems in cell biology. R. D. Allen and N. Kamiya, eds., Academic Press, New York and London, p. 257

Kavanau, J. L. (1963). Develop. Biol. **7**, 22

Kavanau, J. L. (1965). In, Structure and function in biological membranes. Holden-Day Inc., San Francisco, Vol. 2, p. 511 et seq.

Kiaer, S. (1925). Arch. Exptl. Zellforsch. **1**, 289

Kuhl, W. (1937a). Roux' Arch. Entwicklungsmech. Organ. **136**, 593

Kuhl, W. (1937b). Arch. Entwicklungsmech. Organ. **139**, 393

Landau, J. V. (1959). Ann. N. Y. Acad. Sci. **78**, 487

Lash, J. W. (1955). J. Exptl. Zool. **128**, 13

Laubenfels, M. W. de (1927). Carnegie Inst. Wash. **26**, 219

Laubenfels, M. W. de (1932). Carnegie Inst. Wash. **28**, 38

Lehmann, F. E. (1932). Arch. Entwicklungsmech. Organ. **125**, 566

Lewis, H. W. (1931). Johns Hopkins Hosp. Bull. **49**, 29

Lewis, W. H. (1947). Anat. Rec. **97**, 139

Lewis, W. H. (1949). Lecture Ser. Roscoe B. Jackson Mem. Lab. p. 59

Lewis, W. H. and Webster L. T. (1921). J. Exptl. Med. **33**, 261

Loeb, L. (1912). Anat. Rec. **6**, 109

Loeb, L. (1921). Am. J. Physiol. **56**, 140

Loeb, J. (1922). Science **55**, 22

Loeb, L. and Fleisher, M. S. (1917). J. Med. Res. **37**, 75

Loewy, A. G. (1952). J. Cell Comp. Physiol. **40**, 127

Lucey, E. C. A. and Curtis, A. S. G. (1959). Med. Biol. Illust. **9**, 86

MacLennan, A. P. (1963). Biochem. J. **89**, 99P

Margiolash, E., Schenck, J. R., Hargie, M. P., Burokas, S., Richter, W. R., Barlow, G. H. and Moscona, A. A. (1965). Biochem. Biophys. Res. Commun. **20**, 383

Marsland, D. (1956). Intern. Rev. Cytol. **5**, 199

Mast, S. O. (1926). J. Morphol. **41**, 347

Mast, S. O. (1934). Physiol. Zool. **7**, 470

Matsumoto, S. (1918). J. Exptl. Zool. **26**, 545

McCutcheon, M. (1946). Physiol. Rev. **26**, 319

Meier, R. (1958). In, Chemistry and biology of mucopolysaccharides. Little, Brown and Co. Boston

Mercer, E. H. (1959). Proc. Roy. Soc. B **150**, 216

Mercer, E. H. (1962). Brit. Med. Bull. **18**, 187

Mercer, E. H. and Shaffer, B. M. (1960). J. Biophys. Biochem. Cytol. **7**, 353

Monné, L. and Hårde, S. (1951). Arkiv. Zool. **1**, 463

Moore, A. R. (1930). Protoplasma **9**, 25

Moscona, A. (1952). Exptl. Cell Res. **3**, 535

Moscona, A. (1956). Proc. Soc. Exptl. Biol. Med. **92**, 410

Moscona, A. (1957). Proc. Natl. Acad. Sci. U.S. **43**, 184

Moscona, A. (1960). In, Developing cell systems and their control, 18th Growth Symposium, Ronald Press, New York, p. 45.

Moscona, A. (1961). Exptl. Cell Res. **22**, 455

Moscona, A. (1962a). Intern. Rev. Exptl. Path. **1**, 371

Moscona, A. (1962b). J. Cell. Comp. Physiol. Suppl. Vol. **60**, 65

Moscona, A. (1963). Proc. Natl. Acad. Sci. U. S. **49**, 742

Moscona, A. (1965). In, E. N. Willmer, ed., Cells and tissues in culture. Academic Press, London and New York, Vol. **1**, p. 489

Moscona, A. and Moscona, H. (1952). J. Anat. **86**, 287

Moscona, A., Trowell, O. A. and Willmer, E. N. (1965). In, E. N. Willmer, ed., Cells and tissues in culture. Academic Press, London and New York, Vol. 1, p. 19

Mudd, S., McCutcheon, M. and Lucké, B. (1934). **14**, 210

Mühlethaler, K. (1956). Am. J. Botan. **43**, 673

Nachmias, V. T. (1966). Exptl. Cell Res. **43**, 583

Nakai, J. and Kawasaki, Y. (1959). Z. Zellforsch. **51**, 108

Nakajima, H. (1964). In, R. D. Allen and N. Kamiya, eds., Primitive motile systems in cell biology. Academic Press, New York and London, p. 111

New, D. A. T. (1959). J. Embryol. Morphol. **7**, 146

Nordling, S. and Mayhew, E. (1966). Exptl. Cell Res. **43**, 77

Oldfield, F. E. (1963). Exptl. Cell Res. **30**, 125

Olive, E. W. (1902). Proc. Boston Soc. Nat. Hist. **30**, 451

O'Neill, C. H. (1963). Cited by Wolpert, Thompson and O'Neill. (1964)

Pantin, C. F. A. (1923). J. Marine Biol. Assoc. (U.K.) **13**, 24

Pantin, C. F. A. (1926). Brit. J. Exptl. Biol. **3**, 275

Pappas, G. D. (1959). Ann. N. Y. Acad. Sci. **78**, 448

Pappenfuss, E. J. (1934). Biol. Bull. **67**, 223

Patlak, C. S. (1953). Bull. Math. Biophys. **15**, 311, 431

Pethica, B. A. (1961). Exptl. Cell Res. Suppl. **8**, 123

Pfeffer, W. (1884). Unter. Botan. Inst. Tübingen **1**, 304

Pfoehl, H. (1898). Zentr. Bakteriol. **24**, 343

Picken, L. E. R. (1960). The organization of cells and other organisms. Oxford University Press, London and New York

Ponder, E. (1927). Protoplasma, 611

Porter, K. R., and Yamada, E. (1960). J. Cell. Biol. **8**, 181

Potts, G. (1902). Flora (Jena), **91**, 291

Pulvertaft, R. J. V. and Weiss, L. (1956–1958). Time-lapse cine studies on human material

Randall, J. T. (1956). Nature **178**, 9

Randall, J. T. (1957). Symp. Soc. Exptl. Biol. **10**, 185

Raper, K. B. (1940a). Am. J. Botan. **27**, 436

Raper, K. B. (1940b). J. E. Mitchell Sci. Soc. **56**, 241

Raper, K. B. (1951). Quart. Rev. Biol., **26**, 169

Raper, K. B. and Thom, B. (1941). J. Washington Acad. Sci. **22**, 93

Rhumbler, L. (1898). Roux' Arch. Entwicklungsmech. Organ. **7**, 103

Rhumbler, L. (1902). Roux' Arch. Entwicklungsmech. Organ. **14**

Rinaldini, J. M. L. (1958). Intern. Rev. Cytol. **7**, 587

Rinaldini, L. M. (1959). Exptl. Cell Res. **16**, 477

Ringer, S. and Sainsbury, H. (1894). J. Physiol. **16**, 1

Rosen, W. G. (1962). Quart. Rev. Biol. **37**, 242

Rosenberg, M. D. (1960). Biophys. J. **1**, 137

Rosenberg, M. D. (1963). Science **139**, 411

Rothen, A. (1951). Ann. N. Y. Acad. Sci. **53**, 1054

Rothen, A. (1960). Amer. Chem. Soc. **70**, 2732

Rothschild, Lord (1958). Biol. Rev. **33**, 372

Rouiller, C., Fauré-Fremiet, E. and Gauchery, M. (1956). J. Protozool. **3**, 194

Rous, P. and Jones, F. S. (1916). J. Exptl. Med. **23**, 546

Roux, W. (1894). Arch. Entwicklungsmech. Organ. **1**, 43

Roux, W. (1896). Arch. Entwicklungsmech. Organ. **3**, 381

Rumery, R. E., Blandau, R. J. and Hagey, P. W. (1961). Anat. Rec. **141**, 253

Runyon, E. H. (1942). Collecting net (Woods Hole) **17**, 88

Saxén, L. and Toivonen, S. (1962). Primary embryonic induction. Academic Press, London
Schlesinger, A. G. (1958). J. Exptl. Zool. **138**, 223
Schmitt, F. O. (1941). Growth Suppl. **5**, 1
Schuckmann, W. von (1924). Cited by Bonner, J. T. (1959)
Schuckmann, W. von (1925). Arch. Protistenk. **51**, 495
Schulz, H. and MacClure, E. (1961). Z. Zellforsch. Mikroskop. Anat. **55**, 389
Shaffer, B. M. (1953). Nature **171**, 975
Shaffer, B. M. (1956). J. Exptl. Biol. **33**, 645
Shaffer, B. M. (1958). Quart. J. Microbiol. Sci. **99**, 103
Simard-Duquesne, N. and Couillard, P. (1962). Exptl. Cell Res. **28**, 85, 92
Simms, H. S. and Stillman, N. P. (1937). J. Gen. Physiol. **20**, 603
Slautterback, D. B. (1963). J. Cell Biol. **5**, 441
Sleigh, M. A. (1960). J. Exptl. Biol. **37**, 1
Spiegel, M. (1954a). Biol. Bull. **107**, 130
Spiegel, M. (1954b). Biol. Bull. **107**, 149
Spiegel, M. (1955). Ann. N. Y. Acad. Sci. **60**, 1056
Spratt, N. T. (1946). J. Exptl. Zool. **103**, 259
Spratt, N. T. (1963). Develop. Biol. **7**, 51
Stefanelli, A. (1960). Acta Embryol. Morphol. Exptl. **3**, 159
Stefanelli, A. and Zacchei, A. M. (1958). Acta Embryol. Morphol. Exptl. **2**, 1
Steinberg, M. S. (1962a). Exptl. Cell Res. **28**, 1
Steinberg, M. S. (1962b). Proc. Natl. Acad. Sci. U.S. **48**, 1769
Steinberg, M. S. (1962c). Proc. Natl. Acad. Sci. U. S. **48**, 1577
Steinberg, M. S. (1962d). Science **137**, 762
Steinberg, M. S. (1963a). Exptl. Cell Res. **30**, 257
Steinberg, M. S. (1963b). Science **141**, 401
Steinberg, M. S. (1964). In, M. Locke, ed., Cellular membranes in development. Academic Press, New York, p. 321
Steinberg, M. S. and Roth, S. A. (1964). J. Exptl. Zool. **157**, 327
Steinert, M. and Novikoff, A. B. (1960). J. Cell Biol. **8**, 583
Sussman, M. (1956). Ann. Rev. Microbiol. **10**, 21
Sussman, M. and Lee, F. (1955). Proc. Natl. Acad. Sci. U.S. **41**, 70
Sussman, R. R. and Sussman, M. (1953). Ann. N. Y. Acad. Sci. **56**, 949
Tardent, P. (1963). Biol. Rev. **38**, 293
Taylor, A. C. (1966). J. Cell Biol. **28**, 155
Taylor, A. C. and Robbins, E. (1963). Develop. Biol. **7**, 660
Townes, P. L. and Holtfreter, J. (1955). J. Exptl. Zool. **128**, 53
Trevan, D. J. and Roberts, D. C. (1960). Brit. J. Cancer **14**, 724
Trinkaus, J. P. (1951a). J. Exptl. Zool. **118**, 269
Trinkaus, J. P. (1951b). Anat. Rec. **111**, 550, 551
Trinkaus, J. P. (1961). Colloque Internt. C.N.R.S. (Paris) **101**, 209
Trinkaus, J. P. (1963). Develop. Biol. **7**, 513
Trinkaus, J. P. (1965). In, R. L. De Haan and H. Ursprung, eds., Organogenesis. Holt, Rinehart and Winston, New York, p. 55
Trinkaus, J. P. and Gross, M. (1961). Exptl. Cell Res. **24**, 52
Trinkaus, J. P. and Groves, P. W. (1955). Proc. Natl. Acad. Sci. U.S. **41**, 787
Trinkaus, J. P. and Lentz, J. P. (1964). Develop. Biol. **9**, 115

Ts'o, P. O. P., Bonner, J., Eggman, L., and Vinograd, J. (1956). J. Gen. Physiol. **39**, 325

Ts'o, P. O. P., Eggman, L. and Vinograd, J. (1957a). Arch. Biochem. Biophys. **66**, 64

Ts'o, P. O. P., Eggman, L. and Vinograd, J. (1957b). Biochim. Biophys. Acta **25**, 532

Twitty, V. C. and Niu, M. C. (1948). J. Exptl. Zool. **108**, 405

Twitty, V. C. and Niu, M. C. (1954). J. Exptl. Zool. **125**, 541

Tyler, A. (1940). Proc. Natl. Acad. Sci. U. S. **26**, 249

Tyler, A. (1947). Growth **10** (Suppl.), 7

Tyler, A. (1955). In, B. H. Willier, P. A. Weiss and V. Hamburger, eds., Analysis of development. W. B. Saunders, Philadelphia, p. 556

Vogt, W. (1929). Arch. Entwicklungsmech. Organ. **120**, 384

Voightlander, G. (1932). Arch. Entwicklungsmech. Organ. **127**, 151

Waddington, C. H. (1932). Phil. Trans. Roy. Soc. B **221**, 179

Waddington, C. H. (1940). Organizers and genes. Cambridge University Press, London

Weiss, L. (1958). Exptl. Cell Res. **14**, 80

Weiss, L. (1960). Internat. Rev. Cytol. **9**, 187

Weiss, L. (1961a). Exptl. Cell Res. Suppl. **8**, 141

Weiss, L. (1961b). Exptl. Cell Res. **25**, 504

Weiss, L. (1962). J. Theoret. Biol. **2**, 236

Weiss, L. (1963). Exptl. Cell Res. **31**, 61

Weiss, L. (1964). Exptl. Cell Res. **33**, 277

Weiss, L. (1965). J. Cell Biol. **26**, 735

Weiss, L. (1966). J. Cell Biol. **30**, 39

Weiss, L. (1967). J. Cell Biol. **33**, 341

Weiss, L. and Clement, K. (1966). Ann. Med. Exp. Biol. Fenn. **44**, 155

Weiss, L. and Kapes, D. L. (1966). Exptl. Cell Res. **41**, 601

Weiss, L. and Lachmann, P. J. (1964). Exptl. Cell Res. **36**, 86

Weiss, P. (1929). Roux' Arch. Entwicklungsmech. Organ. **116**, 438

Weiss, P. (1934). J. Exptl. Zool. **68**, 393

Weiss, P. (1941). Growth Suppl. **5**, 163

Weiss, P. (1945). J. Exptl. Zool. **100**, 353

Weiss, P. (1947). Yale J. Biol. and Med. **19**, 235

Weiss, P. (1952). Science **115**, 293

Weiss, P. (1958). Intern. Rev. Cytol. **7**, 39

Weiss, P. (1959). In, J. L. Oncley, ed., Biophysical science–a study programme. J. Wiley and Sons Inc., New York, p. 11

Weiss, P. (1961a). Exptl. Cell Res. Suppl. **8**, 260

Weiss, P. (1961b). Harvey Lectures, Ser. **55**, 13

Weiss, P. and Garber, B. (1952). Proc. Nat. Acad. Sci. (U.S.) **38**, 264

Weiss, P. and James, R. (1955). J. Exptl. Zool. **129**, 607

Weiss, P. and Scott, B. I. H. (1963). Proc. Nat. Acad. Sci. **50**, 330

Weiss, P. and Taylor, A. C. (1956). Anat. Rec. **124**, 381

Weiss, P. and Taylor, A. C. (1960). Proc. Natl. Acad. Sci. U. S. **46**, 1177

Weston, J. A. (1963). Develop. Biol. **6**, 279

Whitaker, D. M. (1940). Growth Suppl. **8**, 260

Willmer, E. N. (1945). In, W. Le Cross Clark, ed., Essays on growth and form. Oxford University Press, New York

Willmer, E. N. (1961). Biol. Rev. **36**, 368

Wilson, H. V. (1907). J. Exptl. Zool. **5**, 245

Wilson, H. V. (1910). Bull. Bureau Fish., **30**, 1

Wilson, H. V. (1911). J. Exptl. Zool. **11**, 281

Wilson, H. V. (1932). Am. Naturalist **66**, 159

Wohlfarth-Bottermann, K. E. (1962). Protoplasma **54**, 514

Wohlfarth-Bottermann, K. E. (1964). In, R. D. Allen, and N. Kamiya, eds., Primitive motile systems in cell biology. Academic Press, New York and London, p. 79

Wolff, E. (1954). Bull. Soc. Zool. Fr. **79**, 357

Wolff, E. (1961). Exptl. Cell Res. Suppl. **8**, 246

Wolff, E. and Weniger, J. P. (1954). J. Embryol. Exptl. Morphol. **2**, 161

Wolpert, L. (1960a). Proc. Roy. Phys. Soc. (Edinburgh) **28**, 107

Wolpert, L. (1960b). Intern. Rev. Cytol. **10**, 163

Wolpert, L. (1965). Symp. Soc. Gen. Microbiol. **15**, 270

Wolpert, L. and Gustafson, T. (1961). Exptl. Cell Res. **25**, 374

Wolpert, L. and Mercer, E. H. (1963). Exptl. Cell Res. **30**, 280

Wolpert, L. and O'Neill, C. H. (1962). Nature **196**, 1261

Wolpert, L., Thompson, C. M. and O'Neill, C. H. (1964). In, R. D. Allen and N. Kamiya, eds., Primitive motile systems in cell biology, p. 143

Zweifach, B. (1940). Cold Spring Harb. Symp. Quant. Biol. **8**, 216

Zwilling, E. (1954). Science **120**, 219

CHAPTER 4

Physical aspects of contact phenomena

Many of the phenomena described in the preceeding chapter fall into a simple pattern: cells approach each other, appear to make contact and then can be seen either to remain in apparent contact, or separate from each other. It would appear that many of the difficulties hindering physical analysis of these phenomena are semantic, and revolve around the confusion of the terms 'contact', 'adhesion' and 'separation'. In the present chapter these three terms will be considered separately.

4.1 Cell contact

All animal cells so far examined carry a net negative charge at their electrokinetic surfaces. Contact between them may initially be considered as contact between two charged particles with electrical double-layers, according to the theory of lyophobic colloids developed by Verwey and Overbeek (1948), as reviewed in their important monograph, and by Derjaguin and Landau (1941), and known as the DLVO-theory.

Flocculation of particles is governed by the balance of their free energies of repulsion V_R, and attraction V_A. At the flocculation point, the particles are still separated by a layer of fluid which, when removed, allows true contact and adhesion (coalescence) to occur. Factors tending to reduce V_R or to increase V_A will facilitate flocculation. Conversely reduction in V_A or increase in V_R will make flocculation less likely. Initially these will be considered individually, not with a view to deriving the various formulae mathematically, but in an attempt to show the logic behind the equations, and to discuss the individual factors constituting them.

4.1.1 The energy of repulsion, V_R

The energy of repulsion between two charged particles is due to the inter-action of their associated electrical double-layers.

If a situation is considered in which cells are suspended in an electrolyte solution, it will be appreciated that as the system as a whole is electrically neutral, the dispersion medium must provide an equal number of ions of opposite charge. If these ions are adsorbed at a phase boundary, counter ions of opposite charge will, on the one hand, be attracted by electrostatic interactions and, on the other hand, tend to be dispersed from the boundary by their Brownian movements.

Account can be taken of the thermal motion of ions within the diffuse part of the double-layer, if it is assumed that their average concentration at any point can be calculated from the average electrical potential μ, at the same point, by the use of Boltzmann's constant, k:

$$n_- = n \cdot \exp(V_- e\psi/kT)$$
$$n_+ = n \cdot \exp(-\bar{V}_+ e\psi/kT),$$

where n is the number of ions per cm^3 (where $n = n_- + n_+$), $\psi = 0$, T is the absolute temperature, e is the electronic charge, V_+ and V_- are valencies of cations and anions respectively (for ions of the same valency $V_+ = V_- = V$) (Verwey and Overbeek 1948). The net result is the formation of an electri-cally neutral ionic double-layer, which may extend over a distance of up to hundreds of Ångstrom units from the bound charged groups of the particle. In simple systems the 'inner' part of the double-layer can be visualized as being located at the interface between the particle and its en-vironment, or near to the charged groups at the cell periphery, while the 'outer' part of the double-layer is much more diffuse and extends out into the environment.

Modern concepts of the double-layer are due to Gouy (1910, 1917), Chap-man (1913), Debye and Hückel (1923, 1924), who regarded the counter ions as dimensionless carriers of a diffuse space charge. An excellent short review of the topic is given by Overbeek and Lijklema (1959), who point out that the Gouy–Chapman treatment has been modified by Stern (1924), Grahame (1947) and others, who have considered ions of finite size and hydration. The effective 'thickness', or units of the double-layer, are given by the Debye–Hückel parameter $1/\kappa$, which has the dimension of length, and in the case of surface potentials of less than 25 mV, which is the case in the biological situation, is that distance from a charged interface (x) at which the potential ψ_x is $1/e$ of the surface potential, ψ_0. That is:

$$\psi_x = \psi_0 \exp(-\kappa x). \tag{1}$$

$1/\kappa$ is given by

$$1/\kappa = \left(\frac{DkT}{8\pi e^2 V^2}\right)^{1/2}, \tag{2}$$

where D is the effective dielectric constant (Verwey and Overbeek).

In addition to ionic associations with charged groups, the adsorption of ions by noncharged surfaces is usually attributed to polarization of the 'surface' material by the ions, by an ion-induced dipole interaction; the induced dipoles then attract the ions (Alexander and Johnson 1950). Whether or not the ions are bound to the surface depends on the comparative magnitudes of the energies of attraction and the thermal energies (kT) of the ions. Among the factors influencing the magnitude of the attractive energies are ionic size, charge, hydration, polarizability and the polarizability of the surface. It will be appreciated that hydration of an ion reduces the force between it and the dipole it induces, because of the high dielectric constant for water. Anions are often less hydrated than cations; for example, the atomic radii of Na^+ and Cl^- determined in crystals are about $1.0\,Å$ and $1.8\,Å$ respectively, whereas their corresponding hydrated radii are $2.5\,Å$ and $1.95\,Å$. In addition to hydration, anions tend to be more polarizable than cations because they carry more electrons per nuclear charge. Consequently it has until recently been expected that any surface in a biological environment will tend to acquire a negative charge due to the preferential adsorption of anions. However, Seaman and Cook (1965) have studied the electrophoretic mobilities of aldehyde-fixed erythrocytes which were treated with either diazomethane or methanolic HC1; this treatment, described earlier by Gittens and James (1963), enables ionized carboxyl groups to be converted to non-ionogenic $-COOMe$ groups. In the case of the human erythrocyte, the bound ionogenic groups responsible for electrophoretic mobility, by virtue of their reflexion at the hydrodynamic slip plane, are the carboxyl groups of N-acetylneuraminic acid and the carboxyl groups of glumatic acid. Following treatment with diazomethane or methanolic HCl, Seaman and Cook (1965) noted that erythrocytes were isoelectric in saline over the range pH 6 to 8.

These findings, which are similar to those of Gittens and James (1963) who observed the isoelectric behaviour of diazomethane-treated *A. aerogenes*, suggest as pointed out by Seaman and Cook, that unless the ionized carboxyl groups themselves affect ion adsorption from the environment, there is no evidence of preferential adsorption of either anions or cations in the peripheral zone of erythrocytes or of *A. aerogenes*. In terms of the sensitivity of the electrophoretic method, these observations probably indicate that preferential adsorption of anions cannot account for more than 5% of negative charge, as reflected in electrophoretic mobility.

In the case of spherical particles where $\kappa a \gg 1$ and their radii are much larger than the distance separating them, as is the case for cells, the repulsion between them may be calculated according to the method of Derjaguin (1934, 1940), as discussed by Verwey and Overbeek.

The interactions may be considered along the dimensions shown in fig. 4.1, where two spherical particles of radius a, are separated by distance R between their centres O_1 and O_2. The distance between their peripheries, H_0, is given by

$$H_0 = R - 2a .$$

The energy of repulsion between the spheres is considered in terms of an infinite number of concentric rings of radius h and width dh, separated by distance H, and is given in the case of individual rings by

$$2\pi h \cdot 2 (f_H - f_\infty) \, dh , \qquad (3)$$

where $2f_H$ is the free energy per cm² of two rings, one of which is shown in fig. 4.1 in end-on view.

The total energy of repulsion V_R, may be found by integrating equation (3) over the whole surface of the spheres,

$$V_R = \int_0^\infty 2\pi h \cdot 2 (f_H - f_\infty) \, dh . \qquad (4)$$

The upper limit ∞ is used because the distance of separation H, is small in relation to the radius of curvature a, and contributions far from the axis $O_1 O_2$ are unimportant. As

$$\frac{H - H_0}{2} = a - (a^2 - h^2)^{\frac{1}{2}} ,$$

$$2h \cdot dh = a \cdot dH (1 - h^2/a^2)^{\frac{1}{2}} \cong a \cdot dH \qquad \text{(where } a \gg h)$$

$$\therefore V_R = 2\pi a \int_{H_0}^\infty (f_H - f_\infty) \, dH . \qquad (5)$$

In the case of the small surface potentials, ψ_0 met within cells, Verwey

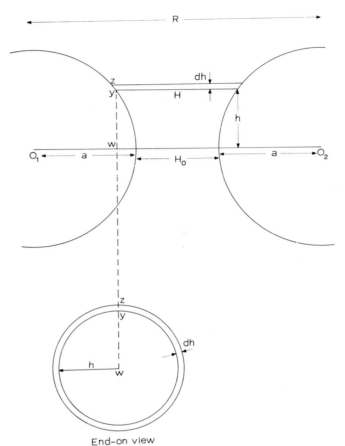

Fig. 4.1.   The interaction between two spherical particles with centres O_1 and O_2. An end-on view of one particle shows a ring (turned through 90°) centred at w, of thickness dh (located at points y and z) and diameter h, on which calculations are based (modified from Verwey and Overbeek 1948).

and Overbeek make the substitution

$$2(f_H - f_\infty) = \frac{Dk\psi_0^2}{4\pi}, \quad \left(1 - \tanh \frac{\kappa H}{2}\right)$$

in equation (5), leading to

$$V_R = \frac{Da\psi_0^2}{2} \int_{H_0}^{\infty} \left(1 - \tanh \frac{\kappa H}{2}\right) \cdot d\left(\frac{\kappa H}{2}\right),$$

$$= \tfrac{1}{2}Da\psi_0^2 \log e \left(1 + \exp\left(-\kappa H_0\right)\right). \tag{6}$$

This last form of the equation for the potential energy of repulsion between two charged spherical particles, is the one commonly used in treating this aspect of contact between cells.

4.1.2 *The energy of attraction,* V_A

When cell contact is treated in terms of straightforward colloid theory, the most important attractive interactions between the cell peripheries are thought to be due to Van der Waals' interactions. An equilibrium is reached when these attractive forces are balanced by forces resulting from the inter-penetration of the electronic shells of the individual atoms.

(1) The interaction between two molecules or atoms having permanent dipole movements were described by Keesom (1921). Brownian motion at low temperatures, permits the electrostatic dipole interactions to orient the molecules in energetically advantageous positions relative to one another. The interaction energy is $-2\mu_A\mu_B/R^3 D$, where μ_A and μ_B are the dipole moments of molecules or atoms A and B, separated by distance R in medium of dielectric constant D. At high temperatures, the more marked Brownian motion may negate the orientation effects almost completely, and under these conditions where k is Boltzmann's constant, the interaction energy is given by $-2/3 \, (\mu_A^2 \mu_B^2 / R^6 Dk T)$.

(2) The interaction between a polarizable molecule, in the field of another molecule having a permanent dipole moment, will also give rise to attractive forces, as described by Debye (1920, 1921). Where α is the polarizability of the molecule, the interaction energy is given by $-2\alpha\mu^2/R^6 D$. This term is not temperature dependent.

(3) The most important of the Van der Waals interactions from the quantitative viewpoint are those dependent on charge fluctuation, as described by London (1930, 1942), Wang (1927) and Eisenchitz and London (1930a, b). The charge fluctuations which cause rapidly changing fields due to change in dipole moment, polarize other molecules, leading to attractive interactions. The fluctuations themselves are due partly to Brownian motion shifting the position of electrons with respect to different quantum levels or, as postulated by Kirkwood and Shumaker (1952), due to shift of protons around basic sites. Also, since the quantum mechanical uncertainty principle involving zero point energy of electrons, implies inherent charge fluctuation in the ground state, as described by London and by Kronig and Kramers (1928) the London–Van der Waals dispersion forces may thus occur between molecules having no permanent dipole moments.

Many of the theoretical treatments of cell contact, including those of Pethica (1961), Curtis (1960, 1962), L. Weiss (1962) and L. Weiss and Woodbridge (1967), have used the London-Hamaker (Hamaker 1937) approximation, which in the case of close-range interactions between two spherical particles, expressed in terms of potential energies of attraction, V_A, between two spheres has been given by

$$V_A = -\frac{A}{6} \cdot \frac{2a^2}{R^2 - 4a^2} + \frac{2a^2}{R^2} + \log e \frac{R^2 - 4a^2}{R^2}, \tag{7}$$

where a is their radius, A is the effective Van der Waals constant, and R the distance between their centres. When $R - 2a = H$, and H is small, then

$$V_A = -\frac{Aa}{12H}, \tag{8}$$

where A is the effective Van der Waals constant, a is the radius of curvature of approaching cell processes, H is the distance separating them and $a \gg H$.

Hamaker's treatment of the interaction between macroscopic particles containing q atoms per cm^3 gives

$$W = \int_{V_1} dV_1 \int_{V_2} dV_2 \frac{q^2 A}{R^6}, \tag{9}$$

where dV_1, V_1, dV_2 and V_2 are volume elements and total volumes of the two particles respectively, R is the distance between them, and A is the London–Van der Waals constant (Hamaker 1937).

The interactions, in terms of dispersion energy W, are approximated by second-order perturbation treatment of dipole–dipole interactions between molecules A and B, and this is given by:

$$W = -\frac{3}{2} \frac{I_A I_B}{I_A + I_B} \cdot \frac{\alpha_A \alpha_B}{R_{AB}^6} \tag{10}$$

where I, α and R are the ionisation potentials, isotropic polarizabilities and distance separating A and B (Hamaker 1937).

In structures consisting of a number of molecules where the vibrations are not independent, as briefly discussed by Longuet–Higgins (1965), there are difficulties in simply summating two-body London interactions, as in equation (7). Although in the case of the interacting particles A and B, the force of attraction between them is derived from their potential energy V, and distance apart R, viz. dV/dR_{AB}, this simple relationship cannot be extended to many-body systems because the intermolecular potential energy will depend on the individual internal molecular coordinates, as well as their coordinates relative to one another.

In the case of three molecules A, B and C, interacting, in addition to the summated bimolecular interactions, a new three-body term, E_3 must be

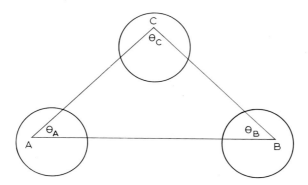

introduced as proposed by Axilrod and Teller (1943), and discussed by Sinanoğlu, Abdulnur and Kestner (1964).

$$E_3(ABC) = \frac{3}{2} \frac{\alpha_A \alpha_B \alpha_C}{R_{AB}^3 R_{BC}^3 R_{AC}^3} \varDelta (1 + 3 \cos\theta_A \cos\theta_B \cos\theta_C), \qquad (11)$$

where $\varDelta$ is derived from the mean molecular excitation energy, which may be taken as ionization potential I, and is given by

$$\varDelta = \frac{I_A I_B I_C (I_A + I_B + I_C)}{(I_A + I_B)(I_B + I_C)(I_A + I_C)}. \qquad (12)$$

For a collection of molecules, the total E_3 is obtained by summation of equation (11), over all triplets. Sinanoğlu et al. consider how much the attraction between molecules A and B, $E_2(AB)$ is affected by the presence of a third molecule C. This is given by

$$E_3(ABC)/E_2(AB). \qquad (13)$$

In the case where the molecules are similar (A=B=C) and equidistant ($\theta_A = \theta_B = \theta_C$ and $R_{AB} = R_{AC} = R_{BC}$), then $E_3(ABC)/E_2(AB) \cong \alpha/R^3$, thus for $\alpha = 4\text{Å}^3$ and $R = 4\text{Å}$, molecule C affects the interaction of A and B by 6%.

This example shows that even in the case of London–Van der Waals interactions between three similar molecules, the formulation becomes extremely complex, and also involves the use of isotropic, atomic polarizabilities instead of molecular polarizabilities, which result in very crude approximations. Although theoretical methods (e.g. De Voe and Tinoco 1962) permit better estimates to be made of molecular polarizability, as yet little data is available for theoretical studies of cell contact phenomena which involve macroscopic, multimolecular situations.

If the London–Hamaker approximation,

$$V_A = -Aa/12H, \qquad (8)$$

is to be used in biological calculations, and at the moment we have little else, then it is necessary to have some idea of the value of the effective Van der Waals constant A. Experimental attempts to evaluate A come from studies of colloidal stability, and studies of interfacial forces.

The approach of Verwey and Overbeek (1948) and Derjaguin and Landau (1941) shows that the potential energy of interaction V, between spherical colloidal particles is given by

$$V = V_R + V_A.$$

From experimental studies of flocculation of particles, it is possible to measure the so-called stability ratio W, which is the amount by which a predicted number of particle collisions is reduced. Then, according to Wilkins et al. (1962)

$$W = 2a \int_{2a}^{\infty} \exp(V/kT \cdot dR/R^2), \qquad (14)$$

where a is the radius of particles, and R the distance between them at which lasting contact is made. Thus, from value of V_R, calculated from measurements of electrophoretic mobility, approximate estimates may be made of A. Wilkins and Ottewill attempted to evaluate A for polymorphonuclear leucocytes on the basis of flocculation experiments and obtained estimates of 10^{-14} to 10^{-15} ergs. Similar values were obtained by the same authors for stearic acid and arachidic acid particles in water; and for water in oil emulsions by Alberts and Overbeek (1960). On the other hand, these values are different from the measurements on other lyophobic systems quoted by Wilkins et al., which gave values of 10^{-12} to 10^{-13} ergs.

Fowkes (1964a,b) has described a technique, whereby from knowledge of surface energies at interfaces, it is possible to calculate the London dispersion force contribution to surface free energy γ^d, and thereby evaluate A. In water, the calculated value of A ranged from 10^{-14} ergs for polyethylene and polystyrene and 10^{-15} for paraffin wax to 10^{-16} for polytetrafluorethylene.

An alternative to the 'microscopic' London–Hamaker approach to the problem of Van der Waals interactions comes from a macroscopic view, according to the theories developed by Lifshitz (1955), Pitayevskii (1960), Dzyaloshinski and Pitayevskii (1959) and reviewed by Dzyaloshinski et al. (1961). The obvious mathematical difficulties inherent in either approach are magnified by lack of knowledge about the molecular structure of the cell periphery. An excellent appreciation of the forces between molecules for those who are not theoretical physicists, has been given by Derjaguin (1960), and will be quoted extensively. In the case of two molecules radiating electromagnetic vibrations, forces between them will depend on variation in electrical current according to Ampère's Law, and variation in charge according to Coulomb's Law.

According to the London theory, the force between two molecules is given by C/R^7, where the constant C depends on a number of molecular electric properties including their polarizability. By polarizability is meant the degree to which an electrical field distorts a molecule changing the position of its electrons relative to the nuclei of its constitiuent atoms. As the polarizability of individual molecules are unknown, London's formula will not permit absolute values of intermolecular forces to be calculated with any degree of accuracy. Derjaguin points out that the London theory is neither applicable for large distances of separation between molecules nor for very small ones. In common with other electrostatic theories, London's regards forces as being instantaneously communicated between molecules, although in fact electromagnetic radiation travels at the speed of light. Derjaguin quotes an analogy from Lebedev, to illustrate the importance of the speed of radiation. If molecules are considered as small radio antennae in which oscillating charges cause the emission of electromagnetic waves, the vibrations from one antennae will cause the charges in another to oscillate, and in turn emit signals which are received back by the first. The two antennae thus interact by exchanging radiation, and the strength of the interaction varies with the phase of the arriving waves and the oscillating charges relative to one another; if the waves and charges are in phase, the stronger the interaction. As this phase relationship depends on the distance between the antennae and the frequency of the waves, it can be seen that in this model at least, it will depend on wavelength.

The radiation emitted by molecules has a wave length of the order of $0.1\,\mu$; therefore, in the case of molecules separated by $0.1\,\mu$ or less, there is the possibility of considerable phase-shift in the radiation exchanged between them. Casimir and Polder (1948) took cognizance of phase-shift in deriving an electromagnetic theory of molecular forces based on quantum mechanics. In this, it is considered that the radiation is emitted discontinuously in quanta, or photons, and also that molecules are capable of interacting without either the emission or absorption of energy by exchanging 'virtual' photons. At distances of about $0.1\,\mu$, the theory of Casimir and Polder evaluates the attractive forces between molecules as K/R^8; allowance for phase-shift thus leads to force decreasing with the eighth power of intermolecular distance, as distinct from the seventh power given by London. The constant K, which is different from London's C, also contains a term for molecular polarizability, and cannnot be directly evaluated.

Thus, the London approach can be taken to apply when the distances between interacting molecules are small enough to make phase-shifts negligible, as possibly is the case in interactions between bodies separated by $8\,\text{Å}$ or less. On the other hand, the Casimir–Polder approach appears applicable where phase-shifts cannot be ignored, at distances possibly in excess of $1,000\,\text{Å}$. In addition, Henniker (1949) considers that short-range forces may be serially transmitted over long distances by successive polarization of neighbouring molecules. The application of both theories so far ascribed to the biological situation, is severely limited, because both pertain to small numbers of isolated molecules, as distinct from condensed bodies containing many, close-packed, interacting molecules. Lifshitz (1956) developed a theoretical approach for determining the molecular interactions of two macroscopic bodies, which depends only on their macroscopic properties and ignores the individual molecules. This approach is of considerable interest in the biological field, since macroscopic properties are more amenable to measurement. Lifshitz considered two closely spaced bodies, and calculated the electromagnetic fields in the space between and around them by charge fluctuations in various regions of the bodies. From the difference between field strength in the gap between the bodies and in the surrounding space, the force can be calculated. Although the considerations were first developed along the lines of classical electromagnetic theory, they were later extended by Dzyaloshinski and Pitayevskii by use of quantum field theoretical methods to the treatment of interactions in inhomogeneous media.

Although the formulae are very complicated they contain experimentally measurable quantities, in contrast to those discussed earlier. To calculate the force it is necessary to know only the wavelengths absorbed by the materials in the infra-red and ultra-violet regions and their polarizabilities or dielectric permeabilities as determined on macroscopic specimens. Experimental tests of the Lifshitz theory were made by measuring the attraction between various plates separated by small distances *in vacuo*, and attached to an incredibly sensitive balance by Derjaguin et al. (1956) and later by Block et al. (1960). Although in the early experiments, the measured forces were very much larger than predicted, later experiments in which the electric charge was removed, gave results consistent with theory. For gaps ranging from 0.2 to 0.4 μ, the measured forces, which depended on the materials composing the plates, varied from 0.002 to 0.0002 dynes. At this order of separation, the Casimir–Polder formulae fitted the results better than London's.

Derjaguin (1960) remarks that whereas it is impossible to make the mathematical jump from the 'microscopic', bimolecular, London–Hamaker approach to the real, macroscopic situation, the reverse is possible; the calculation of the attraction between two molecules may be taken as a special limiting case of the Lifshitz theory. For distances small in relation to the wavelength of their main absorption lines, the force reduces to the London inverse seventh-power relationship, and for greater distances to the Casimir–Polder inverse eighth-power law. At small distances for macroscopic bodies, the energy of attraction varies inversely as the distance separating them

$$\left(V_A = -\frac{1}{H} \cdot \frac{Aa}{12} \right);$$

at large distances there appears to be a good deal of uncertainty. As discussed earlier, the attraction between two bodies is not simply the sum of the attractions between all pairs of their constituent molecules, even on the macroscopic scale.

4.1.3 Long-range interactions

It may reasonably be asked at this stage whether there is any direct evidence at all demonstrating long-range interactions in cell contact phenomena. Rosenberg (1962) has made an ingenious attempt to demonstrate long-range interactions between cultured human conjunctival cells and stainless steel, tantalum quartz, 'mylar' and polytetrafluorethylene base surfaces. The surfaces were covered with steps of known thicknesses of a mixed film of stearic acid/barium stearate by successive dipping through a film of this mixture, maintained at a surface pressure of 29 dynes/cm in a Langmuir trough, according to the technique devised by Blodgett (1935). The films were deposited in bilayers; a monolayer of approximately 24Å depth was deposited on each upward and downward motion of the base through the film on the trough. Two parameters of cellular interaction were measured as a function of the thickness of film interposed between the cells and the bases, namely the time courses of cell attachment and of cell spreading. With increased thickness of interposed film, both the rates of attachment and spreading progressively decreased and the rates varied with the nature of the underlying base surface. The fall off in rates with interposed film thickness was most rapid on bases of stainless steel, intermediate for quartz, and least rapid on the plastic bases. By means of this technique, interactions between cells and base layers could apparently be observed up to distances of 1,400 Å. Rosenberg has discussed the possible objections to interpretation of the observations in terms of long-range interactions between the bases and cells. These include 'skeletonization' of the interposed film by interactions with protein in the medium, as suggested by the work of Sher and Sobotka (1955), and the changes in molecular arrangement induced in the film by sterilization with ultra-violet radiation, which was part of his technique. Rosenberg does not think that either of these interactions would affect the interposed films significantly. Another artefact not discussed by Rosenberg, has been considered by Schaefer (1941) in connection with the lack of close agreement between X-ray and optical measurements of mono-layer thickness. Harker (cited by Schaefer) has suggested that as layers are progessively added to previously deposited films, some of their constituent molecules would move from the topmost into underlying layers, tending to form crystals. However, this objection would make little difference to the distances involved, since under the conditions described, the discrepancy would only result in an overestimate of film-thickness by 2.8 to 4.2%. In addition to the possibility of long-range interactions, Rosenberg also considers permeability of the films, surface inhomogeneities at molecular level in the base material and a combination of long-range and co-operative short-range forces. If Rosenberg's films are continuous, I would incline to regard the experiments as indicating the existence of long-range interactions between cells and bases but, as pointed out by Rosenberg, the question of whether these are of the direct type as postulated by Derjaguin, Lifshitz and their colleagues, remains open.

Other work in favour of long-range interactions comes from Rothen's (1957) work, which he interprets to indicate interaction between enzymes and their substrates when separated by films, Rothen's earlier work was subject to much criticism on the grounds that his results could be interpreted in terms of holes in the films separating the reagents, and/or enhanced diffusion in two-dimensional systems. However, neither of these two objections can adequately account for Rothen's most recent data.

4.1.4 Combined interactions of V_A and V_R.

Ignoring for the moment the retardation effects (Casimir–Polder) in Van der Waals attractions, it is seen from equation (8) that V_A decreases inversely as the distance between particles ($1/H$), whereas V_R decreases exponentially with distance (equation 6). The total energy of interaction, as a function of distance between particles is therefore expected to follow the scheme shown in fig. 4.2, in which a potential energy barrier ('maximum') to contact lies between two attractive 'troughs', the primary, short-range minimum, and the secondary, longer-range minimum.

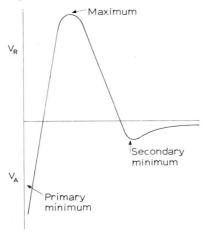

Fig. 4.2. Scheme of total energy of interaction between two particles as a function of the minimum distance between their surfaces.

Essentially then, factors reducing the potential energy repulsion barrier will facilitate the closer approximation of cells, thereby permitting the closest parts of their peripheries to enter the primary minimum, and contact will be made. It will also be appreciated that the existence of secondary minima also raise the possibility that if the separation of particles is such that they lie in each other's secondary attractive troughs, then the particles can adhere in a sense, even though they are in fact separated by a potential energy barrier.

4.1.5 Factors affecting V_A

From consideration of the nature of Van der Waals interactions, it is expected that not much change will result in V_A from alteration of any of the terms in equation (8) in physiological context. Alteration of cellular radius of curvature will certainly produce a proportional reduction in V_A. However, as both V_A and V_R are directly proportional to radius of curvature, such alteration will *in toto* simply change the energy scale shown in fig. 4.2, rather than to alter V_A/V_R relationships. If a more dynamic view is taken, then reduction in radius of curvature of approaching cell parts when they are in the region of the potential energy maximum will energetically facilitate their transit through this region, as will shortly be discussed. Having passed through the maximum, if the cell probe now expands its radius of curvature, the attractive forces will increase proportionately.

Tissue cells normally adsorb material from their environment. It is of relevance therefore, that Vold (1961) has specifically considered the effect of adsorption of concentric shells of material on the Van der Waals interaction of spherical colloidal particles. In all cases, the interaction energy was attractive, regardless of the Van der Waals constants for the particles, media or adsorbed material. For values of Van der Waals' constants between 2×10^{-13} to 8×10^{-12}, which are higher than the 10^{-14} ergs expected for cellular material, and on the assumption that $10kT$ (say 5×10^{-13} ergs) are sufficient to prevent thermal redispersion of a flocculated system, Vold showed that particles of up to 500 Å radius can be stabilized by absorbed layers thicker than 20 Å. This result assumes that the particles cannot desorb the adsorbed materials. It is not possible to draw conclusions about the numerical extrapolation of Vold's work to cell contact; however, as the radius of cell probes or microspikes (vide infra) is less than 500 Å, and the thickness of adsorbed protein which goes to form a solvate shell may well lie between 5 and 20 Å, her findings appear relevant. It therefore seems likely that adsorbed material can appreciably affect the Van der Waals interactions bewteen cell probes, and that stabilization will be most effective when the Van der Waals constant for the adsorbed material is either greater or less than the constants for both the cell and the medium as a whole.

Curtis (1960) made the suggestion that owing to their rheological properties, cell surfaces could undergo an areal expansion due to the shearing associated with active cell movement. This expansion would result in appreciable reduction in charge density, and V_R, but no significant change in Van der Waals' V_A. Hence, when two cells meet, the effective shear due to the interaction of their peripheries will lead to membrane expansion, and contact will be made easier. Experiments made to demonstrate that apparent increase in surface area is associated with reduction in surface charge density (electrophoretic mobility) have been unsuccessful, in both the case of cells swollen osmotically (Patinkin and Doljanski 1965), and cultured cells fixed in the rounded and spread states (Nordling and Mayhew 1966). In these cases, increases in cell volume could be achieved without true surface expansion because of the probable wrinkled nature of the cell periphery, (Pulvertaft and L. Weiss 1963) in a manner analogous to the way in which the volume of air enclosed by concertina bellows can vary, while the bellows' surface area remains constant. Thus, Curtis' hypothesis is not substantiated by experimental evidence.

4.1.6 Factors affecting V_R

From the consideration of equation (6), it can be seen that factors reducing the repulsive potential energy barrier to cell contact are:
(a) Reduction in the Debye–Hückel parameter $1/\kappa$,
(b) Reduction in dielectric constant of the medium D,
(c) Reduction in radius of curvature, a of appoaching cell processes,
(d) Reduction in surface potential ψ_0, of approaching cells.
Before these factors are discussed, it should be noted that there are great difficulties in defining distance terms in the various equations. Before two bodies can be said to be in contact with each other, their boundaries must be spatially defined and, as has been noted in the early chapters, such a definition cannot be made precisely in the case of living cells. It would appear that measurrements taken between the outer parts of the trilaminar structures representing the peripheral zone of cells, in conventional electron micrographs are not reliable, since quite apart from fixation artefacts, there is an external 'fuzzy' layer which can be visualized by means of special techniques (Bennett 1963; Fawcett 1965; Ito and Revel 1964; Kaye and Pappas 1962; Staubesand 1963; Cotran 1965). Although this layer appears to be only a few Ångstrom units thick, such small distances could be extremely important in any theoretical treatment of cell contact.

In the calculation of V_R (equation (6)), distances refer to the spatial separation of the planes of charged groups. However, when the London–Van der Waals free energy of attraction is considered, the London dispersion forces act between all atoms; thus, the estimate of distance again becomes rather vague because of the difficulties inherent in defining spatial limits to the cell.

(a) *the Debye–Hückel parameter*
Calculations of $1/\kappa$ in regard to erythrocytes suspended in univalent electrolyte solutions have been made by Heard and Seaman (1960), using the formula

$$1/\kappa = 3.05\, I^{-\frac{1}{2}} \quad \text{at} \quad 25\,^{\circ}\text{C}, \tag{15}$$

where according to Lewis and Randall (1921):

$$I = \tfrac{1}{2} \sum c_i z_i^2, \tag{16}$$

where c_i = ionic concentration, and z_i = valency. Heard and Seaman compute that at $25\,^{\circ}\text{C}$, an erythrocyte suspended in 1M uni-univalent electrolyte is surrounded by a diffuse double-layer approximately $3\,\text{Å}$ thick, whereas at 10^{-3}M, the thickness increases to approximately $100\,\text{Å}$. Thus the value of $1/\kappa$ is dependent on ionic concentration and valency, and it is to be expected that if other things remain constant, decrease in $1/\kappa$, brought about by increase in ionic concentration and/or valency, will facilitate flocculation.

Kruyt and Klompé's (1942) data on the amounts of ions of different valencies required to flocculate negatively charged AgI sols, illustrates the effect of valency well. They found that concentrations of 140 mM per litre of $NaNO_3$ were required for flocculation, compared with 2.38 mM $Ca(NO_3)_2$; 0.067 mM $Al(NO_3)_3$ and 0.013 mM $Th(NO_3)_4$. This point has also been demonstrated in the adsorption of phage to bacteria by Beumer et al. (1957) and in the adsorption of virus to monolayers of embryonic chick cells (Allison and Valentine 1960). However, Allison and Valentine showed that if the ionic concentration was increased beyond a certain point (10^{-2}M for Ca^{++} and Mg^{++}; e. 10^{-3} M for Al^{+++}) virus adsorption was suppressed, and suggested that cation-binding to both surfaces results in increased repulsion (Stern 1924), and that this is consistent with their previous suggestion (Valentine and Allison 1959) that ionic size as well as charge determines contact of viruses with cells. The previously discussed work of Haydon and Taylor (1960) relates ionic size to adsorption, and ionic adsorption would influence the nature of the double-layer by its effect on charge. This in turn might affect adsorption. It should not be forgotten that high concentrations of divalent and trivalent cations are sometimes toxic for cells (Pulvertaft and L. Weiss 1963), and that changes in the peripheries of cells exposed to toxic agents which affect adsorption might well not be directly related to the changes predicted by lyophobic colloid theory.

(b) *Dielectric constant*

The dielectric constant D, of a medium may be defined as the ratio of the capacity (C) of a condenser containing the medium between its plates to that of the same condenser *in vacuo* (C_0): $D = C/C_0$. This definition of dielectric constant is strictly relevant only to static electric fields which at most, change slowly with time. It must be remembered that fields produce polarization of the medium by displacing positive and negative charges relative to one another, and that such polarization affects the original electrical field by giving rise to new electrical forces. This is particularly well seen in the passage of light waves through a medium, where the rapid oscillations of approximately 10^{14} per second will impose vibration on the charges, and give marked variations in dielectric constant and the connected refractive index. It can be appreciated from equation (6) that when the electrical interactions between two electrically charged cells are considered, the dielectric constant of the separating medium can be of considerable importance.

An important study of the effect of the dielectric constant of the medium on the agglutination of antibody-coated human erythrocytes has been made by Pollack et al. (1965). The electrophoretic mobilities of erythrocytes were measured in imidazole buffers of various known ionic strengths, dielectric constants and viscosities. It was shown at ionic strengths of 0.08 that after corrections were made for viscosity, the electrophoretic mobilities increased with dielectric constant (D): $-1.36\,\mu\text{sec}^{-1}\cdot\text{volts}^{-1}\cdot\text{cm}$ (Sucrose; $D=69$); $-2.1\,\mu\text{sec}^{-1}\cdot\text{volts}^{-1}\cdot\text{cm}$ (5% Ficoll; $D=152$); $-3.27\,\mu\text{sec}^{-1}\cdot\text{volts}^{-1}\cdot\text{cm}$ (10% PVP; $D=430$) and $-3.34\,\mu\text{sec}^{-1}\cdot\text{volts}^{-1}\cdot\text{cm}$ (10% Dextran; $D=483$). Thus, from consideration of the Helmholtz–Smoluchowski equation for electrophoresis,

$$V = \frac{\zeta D}{4\pi\eta},\qquad(17)$$

where $V=$ electrophoretic mobility; $\zeta=$ zeta-potential; $\eta=$ viscosity in the plane of shear, it can be seen that if corrections are made for viscosity,

$$\zeta \propto V/D,$$

and that the calculated ζ-potentials decrease with increase in dielectric constant, i.e. at $D=483$ (10% Dextran) $\zeta \propto 0.0069\,\text{mV}$, whereas at $D=69$ (Sucrose) $\zeta \propto 0.02$ mV. If as a first approximation ζ is equated with surface potential ψ_0, reference to equation (6) will suggest that the effect of decreasing ψ_0 should be to promote haemagglutination – as was in fact observed. Equation (6) also indicates that increasing the dielectric constant of the medium should by itself increase the potential energy of repulsion, V_R, thereby reducing haemagglutination. However, it must be remembered that changes in ψ_0 will produce correspondingly greater effects than changes in dielectric constant, since in computing V_R, ψ_0^2 is used.

As the nature of the cellular peripheral zone is undetermined, and as ionic concentrations and the presence of water structures particularly in the regions of charged groups may be different from those in the bulk phase of the medium, it may be asked whether the space separating the charged groups of cells should be regarded as containing three dielectrics, as distinct from one. These would consist of one narrow zone immediately surrounding each cell, separated by a zone of bulk dielectric constant, which becomes progressively narrower as contact proceeds. Obviously the narrower the immediate zone becomes, the more important would be the dielectric properties of the zones immediately surrounding the cells. The situation is depicted in fig. 4.3 where x_1, and x_3 are the widths of the zones close to the cellular periphery, x_2 is

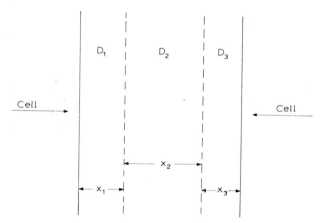

Fig. 4.3.	Diagram indicating that three dielectric constants D_1, D_3 and D_2 may be involved in the two pericellular zones x_1 and x_3, and in the intermediate zone x_2 respectively, when two cells approach each other.

that of the intermediate zone, and D_1, D_3 and D_2 are their respective dielectric constants. It would appear unlikely that differences between ionic concentration near to the charged groups and in the bulk phase of the medium will affect dielectric constant substantially, since as shown by Hasted et al. (1948), the observed dielectric constant for aqueous solutions of sodium chloride at 21 °C varies from 65.2 at 2M, 67.4 at 1M, 72.8 at 0.5M to 80 for pure water, and it is expected that the differences of interest in the physiological situation might fall between the values of 73 and 80. The presence of structured water around the cell is by no means proven to be different from that of the bulk phase, and there is absolute uncertainty about its dielectric constant, or spatial dimensions. If it is present, it is conceivable that its dielectric properties will be different from that of the bulk phase (Grant 1965; Schwan 1965).

The effect of electric fields on the dielectric constant of water is discussed by Haydon (1964). Malsch (1928) found that some experimental data could be fitted to the expression

$$D = D_0 + \alpha E^2 , \qquad (18)$$

where D is the dielectric at a field strength of E e.s.u., D_0 is the dielectric constant at zero field strength and α is a constant of approximate value -3×10^{-6}. In his survey of the literature, Haydon suggests that Booth's (1951) estimate of $D \sim 60$ for water at the high field strength in a double-layer of $\sim 3 \times 10^6 \text{V cm}^{-1}$, is reliable. He couples this to Grahame's (1950) finding that the relationship between surface charge density and surface potential is not very sensitive to change in dielectric constant, and concludes that if only water is involved, 'dielectric saturation is unlikely to be very important in experimental investigations of diffuse layers'.

In addition to the possible asymmetric distribution of ions and structured water in the region of charged groups at the cell periphery, the concentration of adsorbed macromolecules may also be different from that in the bulk-phase, and may also affect the dielectric constant in this region.

(c) *Radius of curvature of contracting cells*

Examination of equation (6) shows that the potential energy barrier to cell contact may be effectively reduced by decrease in the radius of curvature of the parts of the cells (probes) approaching each other. The question of the importance of radius of curvature in cell contact was raised by Bangham and Pethica (1960), Pethica (1961), Bangham (1964); and L. Weiss (1964a) has suggested that the non-adhesiveness of erythrocytes in physiological environments, may be due to their inability to put out low radius of curvature probes. Although not establishing a causal relationship, the relevance of this suggestion has received support from Lesseps' (1963) and Taylor and Robbins' (1963) electron micrographs of contacting cells, which show that approach is made via low radius of curvature probes. The difficulties of estimating the radius of curvature is well illustrated in the case of *Chaos chaos*, where by light microscopy the radius of its pseudopods are in the region of $15\,\mu$. However, Pappas (1959) has demonstrated fibrous plasmalemmal extensions in these organisms having diameters of 40–60 Å, ignoring preparative artefacts; and L. Weiss (1964a) has pointed out that contact among these amoebae may possibly involve the extensions. Thus, in this case the value to be substituted in equation (6) would lie between 15μ and 30Å!

(d) *Surface potential,* ψ_0

Electrophoretic mobility measurements, as discussed in chapters 2 and 5 show that the charge at cell surface may change considerably with physiological activity of the cell. It is expected that the higher the charge density of areas of cells making contact, the greater the potential energy barrier. However, the heterogenous nature of the cell periphery does not allow us to determine whether cells make contact at their charged areas, or between them. This question of discreteness of charge becomes of importance for mammalian cells at distances less than about 8Å which is the Debye–Hückel parameter, and is illustrated in fig. 4.4.

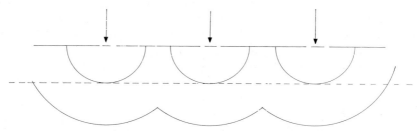

Fig. 4.4. Diagrammatic representation of discrete and indiscrete fields, on moving out from the plane of the charges indicated by the arrows. The dotted line will be approximately 8Å from the plane of the changes in physiological environment.

4.1.7 Secondary minima

It should be made quite clear that I am not discussing the feasibility of secondary minima; theory clearly points to their existence. The point at issue is not their existence, but rather their relevance to cell contact and adhesion.

Overbeek (1952) notes the retardation correction to the London–Van der Waals forces would tend to reduce or destroy the secondary minimum, but 'as the magnitude of this retardation is still less predictable than the value of the London force', evaluation of secondary minima can only be performed by examination of the rather sparse experimental data. Although many attempts have been made to demonstrate secondary minima with particles of sizes of biological interest, the sensitivity of these experiments is determined by the value of the attractive energy of the secondary minima in relation to the Brownian motion of the particles (say $3/2 \cdot kT$, where k is Boltzmann's constant). In effect, owing to the distribution of Brownian energy around the mean, the secondary minimum must be more than several kT 'deep' if particles are to be held apart in a system stable enough for measurement. As secondary minima are not usually demonstrable, with some possible exceptions which will be discussed, it must be assumed that quantitatively they are small in terms of kT. In fact Overbeek observes that the secondary minimum will not be deep enough to prevent flocculation.

Von Buzagh (1929, 1930) described experiments in which quartz particles were allowed to settle onto a glass plate while suspended in different electrolyte solutions; the plate could be inverted to determine the numbers of particles adherent to the glass. It was noted that particles much less than 3μ in diameter fell off the glass, presumably because the secondary minimum was not deep enough to counteract Brownian motion; particles greater in diameter than 3μ fell off because they were too heavy, whereas particles of 3μ diameter remained adherent. The adherent particles were separated from their glass substratum by fluid, since they were observed to possess lateral Brownian motion. These experiments could therefore be interpreted in terms of secondary minima between glass and 3μ quartz particles, in very dilute electrolyte solutions (e.g. 1.0 mM NaCl; cf. 0.145 M NaCl in physiological saline). Other experimental evidence in favour of secondary minima is due to van den Tempel (1958) who optically measured the thickness of an aqueous film between paraffin-oil droplets with a zeta-potential of 100 mV, in the presence of 0.01 M sodium dodecyl sulphate and sodium chloride up to concentrations of about 0.1 M. Under these conditions, the globules flocculated, which is to say their energies of attraction and repulsion balanced, even when separated by aqueous films 100Å thick, when closer approach is prevented by a potential energy barrier. When the aqueous film ruptures coalescence of the drops occurs. It should be emphasized that these experiments were carried out in uni-univalent electrolyte, in concentrations somewhat less than physiological, and that the zeta-potential of the oil droplets is 100 (100mV), compared with cells (c. 20mV). Thus, flocculation at distances of 100Å cannot be extrapolated numerically to the biological situation, as proposed by Curtis (1960). In an interesting paper, this author suggested that using the DLVO-theory of interactions, cells could form stable adhesions when separated by 100–200Å, without the presence of cementing material. In favour of this suggestion Curtis quotes electron microscopic data showing a separation of this order between the trilaminar structures of adjacent cells. As described in chapter 1,

the interpretation of trilaminar structure is currently impossible; without
special staining methods, quite apart from preparative artefacts, measurement of the separation between trilaminar structures cannot in my opinion,
give useful support for a theory such as Curtis'.

Pethica (1961) has attempted to put real values into the various equations
for V_R and V_A using the London–Hamaker approach for a cell of radius
10^{-4} cm, and A as 10^{-14} ergs,

$$V_A = -\frac{10^{-10}}{12H} \quad \text{or} \quad \frac{V_A}{kT} = -\frac{10^3}{5H}.$$

Dispersion forces, according to these values, only exceed $10kT$ for separations of 20 Å or less. Therefore, stable contacts between cells separated by
100–200 Å as suggested by Curtis seem most unlikely energetically. It may
also be mentioned that in the case of polymorphonuclear leucocytes, which
were flocculated by a variety of ions of different valency and strength, Wilkins et al. (1962) found no evidence for the existence of secondary minima
greater than $3kT$, which is, according to current concepts, insufficient to
give flocculation stability. It therefore seems extremely unlikely that secondary potential energy minima can play a significant role in cell contacts;
their magnitude would be insufficient to withstand Brownian motion,
quite apart from the largely unknown locomotor energy of crawling cells.

At this stage, an operational definition of cell contact may be given as
occurring when parts of cells have approached closer together than the peak
of the potential energy barrier between them. This peak will, in mammalian
physiological environment, exist at less than approximately 10 Å from the
plane of the charged groups at the cell periphery. Contact proper will occur
at the range of distances lying between where the balance of repulsion,
due to overlap of electron orbitals and attractive forces, prevents cell parts
moving closer together, and the balance of energies of attraction (V_A) and
electrostatic repulsion (V_R) prevent the cells moving apart. This type of
contact will occur at separations of between 3 to 6 Å. These contact regions
are shown in fig. 4.5.

4.1.8 Cellular locomotor energy

So far in the DLVO-approach to cell contacts, cells have been treated as inert
particles subject to Brownian motion and to gravity. Although this approach
is to some extent applicable to cell suspensions and other model systems,
in many of the 'real' situations described in chapter 4, the effective unit is

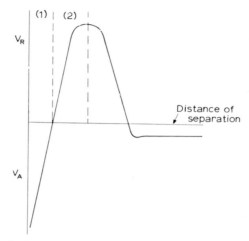

Fig. 4.5. Cell contact defined in terms of interaction energies of cells, as a function of distance; (1) region of true contact; (2) region of operational contact.

a crawling cell. An attempt was made (Weiss 1964a) to evaluate the loco-motor energy of crawling cells in relation to potential energy barriers, in an effort to determine whether either had biophysical significance. Allen and his colleagues had been studying the movements of the giant amoeba *Chaos chaos*, along tubes of 50 to 100 μ diameter. When these organisms plugged the tubes, their crawling movements could be stopped by hydro-static pressures of 10–20 mm water. These pressures are much too low to affect sol–gel transformations, and indicate that the total locomotive force exerted by an amoeba in a tube of 50μ radius is approximately 0.15 dynes, which corresponds to a locomotor pressure of approximately 2×10^3 dynes/cm^2. Under these conditions, with amoebae in Prescott and James' (1955) solution of low ionic strength (KCl, 6 mg/l; CaHPO$_4$, 4 mg/l; MgSO$_4$, 2 mg/l), they had a mean electrophoretic mobility of $-2.73\,\mu\sec^{-1}\cdot$ volts$^{-1}\cdot$cm, which corresponds (see chapter 5) to a zeta-potential of -35 mV. The hypo-thetical case was considered in which two such organisms were crawling towards each other, with their opposing faces flat and parallel, and carrying diffuse electrical double-layers, in uni-univalent electrolyte concentration of 1.5×10^{-4} M, which is equivalent to Prescott and James' solution. Under these conditions, the 'electrostatic pressure' P, opposing mutual contact at distance H, is given approximately by:

$$P = 64nkT\alpha^2\,e^{-2\kappa H}$$

where n = number of ions per ml (Overbeek, 1952).

$$\alpha = \left(\frac{e^{\varepsilon\psi_0/2kT} - 1}{e^{\varepsilon\psi_0/2kT} + 1}\right) \tag{19}$$

ε = electronic charge = 4.84×10^{-10} e.s.u., and the other symbols have their usual meaning. Assuming ψ_0 may be replaced by $\zeta(-35\text{mV})$, the maximum value of the pressure corresponding to V_R, is $P = 8.6 \times 10^4 \text{dynes/cm}^2$. This is an overestimate since only V_R is considered at zero separation ($H = 0$) instead of the interaction $V_R + V_A$; and also, at zero separation the value for V_R is higher than at the separation of 6 to 8 Å where the peak maximum is thought to be located.

It was concluded that the locomotor pressure of 2×10^3 dynes/cm^2 is certainly appreciable in relationship to the recognized overestimate of the electrostatic barrier at 8.6×10^4 dynes/cm^2. If, instead of the consideration of flat plates, allowance were made for low radius of curvature probes, then locomotor pressure might well more nearly approach V_R in magnitude. Unfortunately, no data are presently available for the locomotor energy of mammalian cells. However, if the energetic considerations applicable to *Chaos chaos* have any general relevance, they clearly point to the limitations and dangers of treating contact between actively moving cells in the same manner as contact between inanimate particles, in which the only movements are Brownian or gravitational.

4.2 Cell adhesion

The possible forces of adhesion which can exist between cells have been summarized and discussed by Pethica (1961). It is proposed to first classify the various forces, and consider them in terms of available biological data.

4.2.1 Forces of adhesion

(1) *Chemical bonds.* According to Pauling (1960), chemical bonds exist between atoms or groups of atoms, when the aggregate has sufficient stability to make it convenient for the chemist to consider it as an independent molecular species. Chemical bonds include:

(a) *Electrostatic bonds,* including ionic bonds, due to electrostatic attraction between two atoms or groups of atoms in which the electronic structure is essentially independent. The most important electrostatic bond is the ionic bond, which is due to coulombic attraction between ions of opposite net charge.

Werner (1920) pointed out that metal ions can combine with a characteristic number of atoms or groups of other molecules. The number, the coordination number, is usually six for the alkaline earths including calcium and magnesium. In aqueous solution, these ions can be surrounded by six water molecules in a structure composing the first coordination shell. Morgan and Drew (1920) used the term chelate to refer to the coordinating atoms which are linked to the binding molecule (the ligand) to form a ring structure. Rubin (1963) in his brief review, represents chelation of a hydrated metallic ion, M, with hydrated anions, A — A, as

$$M(H_2O)_x^{+n} + (H_2O)_y A - A(H_2O)_y^{-2m} \rightarrow$$

$$(H_2O)_z M \begin{pmatrix} A \\ \\ A \end{pmatrix} n - 2m + (x + 2y - z) H_2O.$$

An ingenious mechanism for cell adhesion has been advanced by Rappaport and Howze (1966) and Rappaport (1966), in which negatively charged groups at the cell periphery are coordinated about monovalent cations, particularly potassium. It was observed that tissues could be dissociated into single cells by exposing them to solutions of sodium tetraphenylboron (TPB), which complexes K^+ and certain quarternary ammonium compounds, but not Na^+ or divalent or trivalent cations (Flascka and Barnard 1960). Cells were also dissociated by picrate and perchlorate, but not by K^+-neutralized picrate; also the dissociation with TPB was inhibited by excess KCl but not by choline-Cl. The evidence therefore suggests that cell separation can be brought about by removal of potassium. Rappaport considers that the situation may be analogous to that in mica for example, where negatively charged layers are held together by coordination about K^+, and the type of coordinate depends on the coordination number of the cation. In contrast to Na^+ which has only one configuration in which 6 anions are symmetrically oriented around it, K^+ forms a number of complexes differing in the number of anions and spatial arrangements (Pauling 1960). Such K^+ coordinates according to Rappaport, would be able to exchange any of their sites not permanently occupied by cellular anionic sites, with mobile anionic ligands such as H_2O, Cl^-, OH etc., which can bind cells to each other directly, or through the agency of intermediate intercellular macromolocules. A particularly interesting extension of this coordination hypothesis is that it provides a possible coupling mechanism between a dynamic approach to cell adhesion and electrolyte exchange. Rappaport is also of the opinion that such a coordination mechanism requires the opposing surface to be approximately 5 Å from one another at coordination sites. As the various reagents used including TPB, are probably producing effects on the cells other than those observed, it will doubtless be as difficult to unequivocally prove this attractive and novel hypothesis, as it would be to disprove it.

(b) *Covalent bonds*, in which a pair of electrons are shared by two atoms.

(c) *Hydrogen bonds* occur when an atom of hydrogen is shared by two strongly electronegative atoms, specifically oxygen, nitrogen, nitrogen or fluorine. The hydrogen atom has only one stable electronic orbital (Is) and can therefore form only one covalent bond. The hydrogen bond is therefore a resonant structure. Hydrogen bonds play a part in maintaining water structures (Pauling 1959; Bernal 1965). Hydrogen bonds lie in the range of 2 to 10 kcal/mole, and are therefore well-suited for a range of reactions taking place at 37 °C where they can form and break with small activation energies. Although the hydrogen-bonded water structures are not strong enough to withstand vaporization, hydrogen-bonded structures of greater strength may be formed between carboxyl groups:

$$R-C \underset{O \ldots HO}{\overset{OH \ldots O}{<}} \!\!\!> C-R$$

According to Bernal (1959), the strength of the hydrogen bond is determined by another atom, the so-called proton-activator, which is usually covalently or ionically linked to the oxygen, nitrogen or fluorine. The proton activator determines the covalent character of the hydrogen bond, in that the length of the bond and its strength vary with the polarizing power of the activator. Small highly charged ions give rise to short hydrogen bonds of the acid type, whereas large, weak cations such as the alkali metals and the tetra-alkyl ammonium ions give long hydrogen bonds. In polymerized structures, hydrogen bonds play an important part in determining secondary structure and in linking polymers together.

All of the chemical bonds described act over the range of approximately 2 to 3.1 Å.

(2) Van der Waals interactions, which have been discussed will be mainly effective over about 3 to 4 Å. The term 'hydrophobic bond' (Kauzmann 1959) describes the tendency of non-polar parts of proteins etc. to orient away from an aqueous phase, and thus cohere by means of non-polar inter-

actions. These 'bonds' are discussed briefly by Salem (1964) who notes that their stability is due to a favorable entropy effect. If CH_2 in water is taken as a typical non-polar group, then London–Van der Waals dispersion (CH_2/CH_2) interactions will occur, and electrostatic and dispersion water/water interactions will take place. The only significant CH_2/water interactions are also of the dispersion type as polarization forces are negligible. Longuet–Higgins (1964) showed that in the case of energies, W, between interacting pairs A and B,

$$W_{A \leftrightarrow A} + W_{B \leftrightarrow B} > 2W_{A \leftrightarrow B}.$$

Hence, the total potential energy of the system will be larger if the interactions between like pairs (i.e. water/water and CH_2/CH_2) are kept at a maximum. Salem therefore considers that 'homophilic' bonding is a suitable descriptive alternative term to 'hydrophobic' bonding.

(3) As bonding between proteins at the cell periphery, perhaps through intermediate molecules, is possibly of some importance in cell adhesion, the forces holding protein molecules together may be very briefly considered. Richards (1963) describes how a computer was programmed with the atomic coordinates of myoglobin, and instructed to print out the distances between all pairs of atoms in two groups; those more than 2 and less than 3.1Å apart, and those 3.1 to 4Å apart. The sheets pertaining to the first groups which corresponded to hydrogen bonds and salt links gave a pile one quarter of an inch high, while the sheets of the second group, which indicate 'apolar' bonds, gave a pile of sheets two inches high! This is taken to indicate their relative importance in maintaining protein structure. For further discussion of the importance of the interaction between water and the non-polar groups of protein in maintaining structure the reader is referred to the review of Richards (1963), Kauzmann (1959) and Klotz (1960).

(4) Electrostatic attractions between surfaces of like charge, have also been discussed by Pethica (1961), and were described by Bierman (1955) and Derjaguin (1954).

When two parallel flat plates with potentials ψ_1 and ψ_2 of the same sign are separated by a univalent electrolyte solution, an attraction will result between them when the distance between the plates is less than:

$$\left(\frac{DkT}{8\pi Ne^2} \right)^{\frac{1}{2}} \cdot \log e \left(\frac{\tanh Z_2/4}{\tanh Z_1/4} \right), \qquad (20)$$

where $Z_1 = \varepsilon\psi_1/kT$ and $Z_2 = \varepsilon\psi_2/kT$ (Bierman 1955). $M = \bar{\mu} \times 10^{-3}N$, where $\bar{\mu}$ is the molarity of the electrolyte, N is Avagadro's number and ε is electronic charge. According to Pethica (1961), with cells of surface potential -25 to -15 mV, in isotonic saline at 25 °C, attractions occur between them at something less than 4Å separation.

(5) L. Weiss (1960) discussed cellular adhesion in terms of surface energy and contact angles in an attempt to stress the point well-known in engineering practice, that the greater the true area of contact (i.e. wetting) between adherends, the greater the work of adhesion. Pethica has pointed out that the use of 'interfacial tension' and 'angle of contact' by myself in this connection was wrong, and that Helmholtz free energy per unit-area of cell (F) should be used. The complexity of the processes involved are illustrated by Taylor's (1962) failure to correlate cell adhesion assessed by cell-spreading, to the contact angle of water with their substrata. It therefore seems that surface energies cannot at the moment be treated in a precise manner, but this does not mean that they are not involved.

Many experiments have been described relating the adhesion of cells to a number of different substrata, with and without the addition of sera or various proteins to the medium. In very short-term experiments Taylor (1961) found that cell-spreading is slower in the presence of serum than in its absence. On the other hand, longer-term experiments indicate that cell adhesion to glass (L. Weiss 1959a) and to various gels (L. Weiss 1959b) is promoted in the presence of serum, and L. Weiss (1959a) and Puck et al. (1956) have shown species variation among the sera in the promotion of cell-spreading. In addition, the α-globulin fraction was invoked in adhesive activity by Lieberman and Ove (1957, 1958) and L. Weiss (1959a), and fetuin by Fisher et al. (1958). Although these and similar experiments have technical interest, they do not, in my opinion, shed much light on the actual mechanisms of cell adhesion.

An important conclusion to be drawn from this very brief survey of adhesion mechanisms is that they all operate over, at most, several Ångstrom. Thus, for any or all of these mechanisms to come into play, it would be expected from what has been said about contact, that parts of cells would have to traverse the potential energy maximum which tends to keep them apart. It is clear that the position of the potential energy maximum relative to the approaching cell processes is critical; if it lies between the processes then contact and adhesion as defined here cannot occur. If the potential energy maximum no longer separates the cell processes, then contact has occurred, and if the requisite conditions are met, adhesions can also be formed. The potential energy maximum is thought to occur, very approximately, at 10Å separation, and the spatial relationships of two rather vague cell peripheries have to be defined with respect to this maximum. As the light microscope cannot give this information, and as the preparative artefacts and limitations associated with electron microscopy preclude its use in this circumstance, the statement 'cells make contact or not' is meaningless in a precise physical context. In my opinion, the best test for contact and adhesion between cells is not simple observation with any form of microscope, but to note if one cell moves when the other pulls, or is pulled way from it.

4.3 Cell separation

4.3.1 The separation process

The assumption is usually made in cell biology that cell adhesion and cell separation are thermodynamically reversible. In this section it is proposed to show that adhesion and separation are probably not quantitatively reversible, and to look into some of the factors affecting the separation process.

The problem can initially be illustrated by the simple analogy of the removal of a surgical dressing from a wound: sometimes pieces of tissue remain stuck to the dressing; sometimes fragments of the dressing remain adherent to the wound, but clean separation at the wound/dressing interface is improbable. If this analogy is applicable to the separation of cells from other cells or non-cellular substrata, then the plane of separation will be spatially different from the interfacial plane of adhesion.

A clear discussion of the improbability of true adhesional failure at an interface is given by Bikerman (1961), in his monograph on adhesive joints. Bikerman's statistical approach to the problem as applied to the interfacial boundary between a cell and its substratum is summarized in fig. 4.6.

If stress is applied to the interface at X, separation will be initiated where local stress exceeds local strength. The plane of separation proceeds to the right of the figure between an atom of the cell A, and an atom of its substratum, S. As the separation proceeds, in the simplest case, its plane can now proceed in three directions, at the interface A/S, as previously, or between two cell atoms A/A, or two substratum atoms S/S. When there is no weighting of pathways, the probability of the separation continuing in the interfacial plane A/S is 1/3; and the probability of interfacial separation

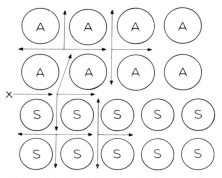

Fig. 4.6.   The propagation of the plane of separation between the atoms of two adherends
A and S. Although the plane may start at the interface, X, as each pair of atoms is 'passed'
three possibilities for the direction of the plane of separation occur.

extending over n atoms is $(1/3)^{n-1}$. Thus, in the case of separation extending
between 11 atoms, the probability of it lying in the interfacial plane is only
about 1 in 59,000. In a three-dimensional model, instead of three possible
pathways for the plane of separation at any one point, there will be seven,
and in this case the probability of interfacial separation will be even less,
according to $(1/7)^{n-1}$. If, instead of individual atoms, polymers are considered,
where it is energetically easier for separation to occur in the intermolecular
plane than the intramolecular, then separation can be visualized as weighted
in favour of extending into intermolecular planes, generally away from the
interface. From these arguments it seems unlikely that cell separation can
occur cleanly over the total areas of cell adhesion.

If a cell separates from its substratum, then in gross terms, the plane of
separation will run through the material having the lowest cohesive strength
(L. Weiss 1961a). This is illustrated diagrammatically in fig. 4.7.

A cell (white) is shown adherent to a substratum (black) by podial projections (a). When the cell separates, the plane of separation could be infacial
as shown in (b), but from the discussions already given, this is considered
an improbable event. If the cell podia are weaker than the substratum as
shown in (c), then fragments of cell are left behind. This is expected in the
case of cell detachment from glass for example. On the other hand, if, as
shown in (d), the substratum has less cohesive strength than the corresponding adherent parts of the cell, then fragments of the substratum will
separate with the cell. If one cell separates from another, and both their
peripheries have similar cohesive strengths, then separation will be accomplished by ruptures occurring within both cell peripheries as shown in (e),

leading to effective interchange of peripheral materials between the cells.

An attempt was made to provide experimental verification for the cohesional-failure theory of cell separation, by culturing cells on glass, detaching them by shearing forces transmitted through their culture fluid by use of a shearing machine (L. Weiss 1961a), and then examining the glass for visible evidence of cellular fragments (L. Weiss 1961b). Light microscopy, including phase-contrast and polarization optics, and various stains failed to reveal the presence of cell fragments. Secondary cultures of trypsinized cells were then grown in serum-free medium, on the same sites from which the primary cultures had been detached. It was shown that these cells were less easily detached from their substrata, than secondary cultures adherent to control sites. It was concluded that the trypsinized cells in serum-free medium were detectors for material left behind when cells were detached from glass.

A somewhat naive attempt was made to relate some of the experimental data, obtained in the above experiment, to the plane of separation between cells and glass. The force per cm^2, F, resisting separation across an adhesive interface is given by

$$F = W/(3 \times 10^{-8}) \text{ dynes/cm}^2,$$

where W is the work of adhesion, and 3×10^{-8} represents the distance over

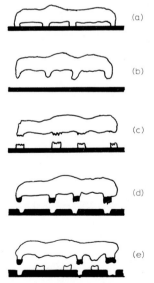

Fig. 4.7. The effect of cohesive strength of the cell periphery and the substratum to which it adheres, on the location of the plane of separation.

which the force would have to act to break the adhesive bonds. It was next assumed that in the case of complete wetting the work of adhesion between the cell and glass is numerically twice the surface tension, γ at the cell periphery. While a value for γ is not known, and as pointed out by Pethica (1961), the values usually quoted for cells indicate cell deformation rather than surface tension, a very low value of 0.15 dynes per cm was taken in an effort to minimize any estimates of work of adhesion. Therefore, the force of adhesion was given as:

$$F = \frac{W}{3 \times 10^{-8}} = \frac{2\gamma}{3 \times 10^{-8}} = \frac{2 \times 0.15}{3 \times 10^{-8}} = 10^7 \text{ dynes/cm}^2$$

of areas of true contact between cell and glass.

Ambrose's (1961) observations with the surface contact microscope had led him to suggest that true contact between cells and their glass substrata, at the level of a few Ångstrom, may only exist over 1 % of the total surface area opposed to the glass. It was therefore assumed that the force of adhesion was 10^5 dynes/cm^2 of cell surface presenting to the substratum. Note was made of the work of Bangham and Razouk (1937), which shows that the work required to separate a solid and liquid surface in the case of complete wetting, is better given by:

$$W = 2\gamma + \pi_e,$$

where π_e is the spreading pressure of the material at the surface of the cell. Although no estimate was given of π_e in my own work, it was observed that if it were considered, then the estimate of the force of adhesion would have to be increased. Pethica (1961) has raised the point that, except in the case of pure liquids, it is doubtful whether surface tensions can be substituted for considerations requiring excess interfacial Helmholtz free energy per unit area, however in the case of the estimate given, where a very low value for γ was used, it seems unlikely in the absence of contradictory evidence, that the value of 10^5 dynes/cm^2 was too *high*. The experimental data (L. Weiss 1961b) showed that cells may be detached from glass by shearing pressures of less than 10 dynes/cm^2. This could then be interpreted to indicate that either the estimate of F was in error by 4 orders of magnitude or, alternatively, separation of the cells from glass did not occur at the adhesive interface between them. As the estimates of F were expected to be low rather than high, and as material could be detected with cellular 'amplifiers', the second alternative was considered most likely. A more precise mathematical treatment has been given for better defined physical systems by Tabor (1951), who takes account of both free surface energies and spreading pressures, and concludes that separation does not occur in the interfacial plane.

A more direct demonstration that cellular material was left behind on glass, when cells were detached from it, was given by L. Weiss and Coombs (1963). The sites from which the cells were removed was examined for the species-specific antigens normally located at the cell periphery by means of a slight modification of the mixed-agglutination test developed by Coombs (1961). It was demonstrated, as shown in fig. 4.8, that 16C rat fibroblasts and HeLa cells left behind rat and human species-specific antigens respectively. An actual experimental result is shown in fig. 4.9.

It should be made clear at this juncture that the ruptures referred to when cells were separated from glass were not lethal when produced by the shearing technique used, which is described in chapter 5. The materials left on the glass are not to be confused with leakage products from the cells, since if cells were cultured in hanging drops, when they were not in direct contact with glass, no material could be demonstrated.

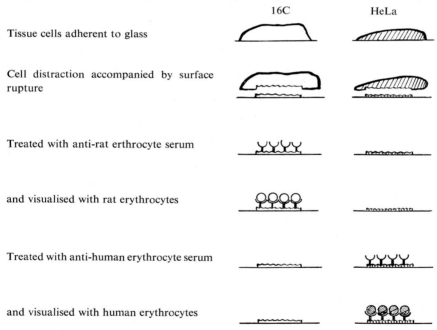

Fig. 4.8. Diagrammatic illustration of the recognition of species-specific antigenic material ruptured off cell peripheries, when the cells were distracted from glass. (From L. Weiss and Coombs,(1963), by permission of the Editors of 'Experimental Cell Research').

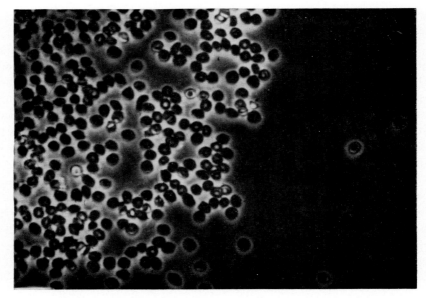

Fig. 4.9.   Human erythrocytes adhering to a patch (on the left) from which a circular microculture of HeLa cells was sheared, after which the whole field was first treated with antihuman erythrocyte serum and then washed. The perimeter of the circular patch is sharply defined. (From L. Weiss and Coombs (1963), by permission of the Editors of 'Experimental Cell Research').

Amoeboid movement of cells, regardless of the locomotive mechanisms, is dependent on them making and breaking contacts with the surface over which they crawl. From what has been stated, it would be expected that cells crawling over glass should leave tracks behind them, consisting of material ruptured off their peripheries. Although such tracks have been known under these circumstances for some time, this particular interpretation of their appearance dates from the experiments described earlier (L. Weiss 1961a,b). Moscona (1960), among others, has observed tracks of 'filmy substance' by phase-contrast microscopy, which are large blebs resembling the membrane-bounded, cytoplasmic packets torn from macrophages in the process of clasmacytosis (Jacoby 1965). The presence of tracks was shown in the case of HeLa cells crawling over glass, by radioautographic techniques on cells previously labelled with ^{35}S-methionine (Pelc and Micou, unpublished data). Little and Edwards (1962) observed under the electron microscope, 'mucous-like' trails, and 'quite large pieces' of cytoplasm left behind by fibroblasts crawling over formvar grids. L. Weiss and Lachmann

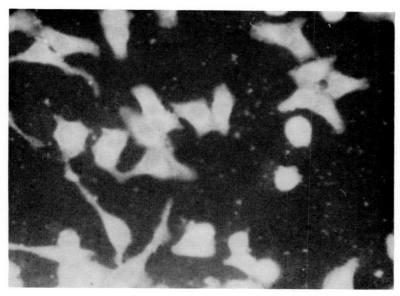

Fig. 4.10. HeLa cells surrounded by discrete patches of fluorescent 'labelled', species-specific antigenic material. (From L. Weiss and Lachmann (1964) by permission of the Editors of 'Experimental Cell Research').

(1964) demonstrated, by the use of immunofluorescent techniques, that HeLa cells crawling over glass left species-specific antigenic tracks, as shown in fig. 4.10.

In contrast to all other observers who looked for tracks, Curtis (1964) was unable to detect them by the technique of reflexion–interference microscopy. The vagaries of this technique with surfaces of biological interest (L. Weiss 1957) would lead me to suspect the method, rather than the theory being tested.

Grobstein (1961) observed that in primary, embryonic-induction systems, inductor spinal cord left inducing material behind on millipore membranes, to which it was adherent and later detached. This raises the question of whether the exchanges of peripheral material, postulated when one cell separates from another as in active movement, could result in intercellular exchange of information. It is of interest in this context that L. Weiss and Mayhew (1966) have demonstrated that cells labelled with tritiated uridine leave RNA 'foot-prints', when detached from glass. Although the informational content of this RNA is unknown, it is an interesting speculation that RNA is a peripheral component of some cells, and that the association between lymphoid cells and macrophages, for example, may result in RNA being torn off the macrophages by the lymphoid cells, and to thereby act as the source of the RNA required by the latter, before they can manufacture antibodies.

It must be emphasized that cell separation from glass, whether active or passive, does not give quantitative information which can readily and unequivocally be extrapolated to *in vivo* systems. However, the cell/glass system, at least as used by my colleagues and myself, had given qualitative data on cell separation, which indicates that in the weighted case of separation of cells of relatively low cohesive strength from their glass substrata, material is left behind. This suggests very strongly that separation of adherent cells, with their indistinct, merging, hydrated peripheral zones, is most unlikely to occur at their mutual adhesive interfaces. This spatial difference between adhesion and separation, indicates that the two processes cannot be considered simply as the reverse of one another, and that cell separation should be considered in terms of factors influencing *cohesive* strength.

4.3.2. *Factors influencing cohesive strength*

The same forces are involved in cohesion of a cell to itself, and in its adhesion to another cell. Since separation will occur when cohesive or adhesive failure takes place, the question arises of why cohesive failure should occur more readily than adhesive failure. Some of the possible explanations are to be found in a consideration of the factors influencing cohesive strength.

Theories of strength of materials have been discussed at an elementary level by Hartog (1961), including the following:

(1) The maximum-stress theory, which simply states that an element within a macroscopic structure will fail when the maximum principal stress exceeds a given critical value. This theory is invalid because it predicts that pure shear, pure tension and pure compression, having the same maximum principal stress, should lead to the same estimate of shear-stress in a material. This is not the case with ductile structures.

(2) The maximum-strain theory states that an element will fail when the maximum strain in any direction exceeds a critical value. A structure being extended in one direction will diminish in a direction normal to this. Thus, a tensile stress in one direction leads to compression stress at right angles to it, and different strains can result in the same maximum stress.

(3) The maximum-shear-stress theory, states that cohesive failure will occur in an element when a critical shear-stress is exceeded, and implies that

an element will not fail when the three principle stresses applied are equal, or nearly so. This theory apparently has been confirmed experimentally in the case of ductile materials, where the material 'slips' along the planes of maximal shear.

Shear-stresses will cause cohesive failure in materials needing twice that amount of tensile stress. In the case of cells which are actively or passively separated from substrata, it therefore seems of importance to know what type of stress is applied.

The theory of mechanical breakdown in relation to molecular orientation in high-polymeric solids has been dealt with by Hsiao (1959). On theoretical grounds, increase in uni-directional orientation is expected to be associated with increase in fracture strength. This theory is well substantiated by experimental data on drawn polystyrene and stretch-oriented polyethylene. If macromolecules in the cell periphery are stretch-oriented as a result of a separation movement, then as a cell process lengthens it will, up to a point, become harder to break. This would be expected to result in the formation of long, thin tenuous strands, such as often observed.

When the theoretical cohesive strengths of materials are calculated from bound energies, as tabulated by Cottrell (1958) for example, they are invariably found to be much higher than the strengths observed by experiment. Experimental estimates of cohesive strength in polymeric films are extremely difficult to make, as discussed by Brunt (1964); nonetheless the general statement holds good. Thus, the rupture strength of sodium chloride crystals is calculated to be 200–400 kg per mm^2, and is observed to be only 0.6 kg per mm^2. Some glasses have observed strengths of 3.5 to 8.5 kg per mm^2 as opposed to calculated values of well over 1,100 kg per mm^2 (Houwink 1937). It is generally considered that these enormous discrepancies between observed and calculated cohesive strengths in materials are due to structural inhomogeneities (Griffith 1924), or 'Lockerstellen' as suggested by Smekal (1933) for crystals and by Houwink (1936) for resin macromolecules. These inhomogeneous regions would constitute a potential weakness, when force is applied, because they initiate sites of local stress concentration (Orowan 1949). This is well demonstrated on a macroscopic scale by photoelastic stress analysis, when local stress concentrations can be seen around stuctural inhomogeneities (Frocht 1941). Even in homogeneous materials, the direction of the plane of separation while it is actually occurring, is determined by local stress distribution.

On the apparently reasonable assumption that heterogeneity favours structural weakness, and hence separation, a number of attempts have been made to increase the heterogeneity which undoubtedly exists within the cell periphery, and to correlate this with the ease of cell separation from glass substrate *in vitro*. Cell detachment was studied as (a) a function of environmental temperature, (b) division-rate and, (c) following the induction of pinocytosis (L. Weiss 1964b).

(a) Replicate cultures of rat fibroblasts were incubated for 24 hours at 37 °C, when half were transferred to an incubator at 30 °C. Viable cell counts made at 1, 2 and 3 days after transfer showed that as expected, the cells incubated at 37 °C were multiplying faster than those grown at 30 °C (fig. 4.11). Comparable cultures maintained at 37 °C and 30 °C were exposed to similar shearing pressures, at the same time intervals after transfer, and the percentages of cells detached were determined and compared as shown in table 4.1.

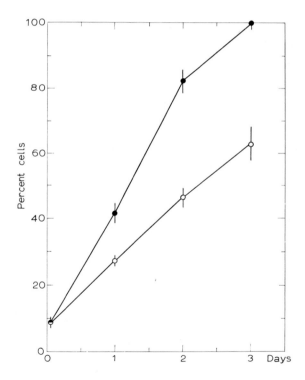

Fig. 4.11. Cells in replicate cultures incubated at 30° (○—○) and 37° (●—●) expressed as a percentage (± S.E.) of the number present in the 3-day cultures maintained at 37°. (From Weiss (1964b) by permission of the Editors of 'Experimental Cell Research').

TABLE 4.1

Percentage of cells detached by similar shearing pressures together with results of *t*-test

Time after transfer, days	Per cent cells detached ± S.E. incubation temperature		*t*-Tests ('30 °C' vs. '37 °C')		
	30 °C	37 °C	*t*	*df*	*p*
1	9.7 ± 2.1	22.6 ± 3.2	3.6	39	0.001
2	32.9 ± 7.1	45.5 ± 4.7	6.1	33	0.001
3	100	100	–	–	–
3[a]	17.3 ± 3.1	29.8 ± 3.4	3.2	80	0.01–0.001

[a] As all cells were detached by the shearing stresses as large as those applied at 1 and 2 days, a smaller stress was applied in this group, viz. 150 revolutions at 150 r.p.m. (at 30 °C) with 0.05 cm separation.

The results show that significantly more cells are detached at the higher temperature, when multiplication was proceeding at a higher rate. The differences were higher than could be accounted for by the numbers of cells in mitosis at the different temperatures.

(b) It is well known that chick embryo extract has both growth-promoting and, as the concentration rises, growth-inhibitory effects (Parker 1929). Cultures of fibroblasts previously established on glass were exposed to increasing concentrations of chick embryo extract for periods up to three days, and their numbers (indicating multiplication) were determined simultaneously with the percentage detached from glass by similar shearing pressures. The results shown in fig. 4.12 indicate that as the multiplication rates increase, the percentage of cells detached increases; and that as the multiplication rates decrease, a smaller percentage of cells is detached.

(c) After culturing cells on glass for 24 hours in serum-free synthetic medium, bovine serum was added to give a final concentration of 15%. Within 15 minutes pinocytosis was marked. The detachment of cells from glass was subsequently measured and compared in cultures 15 minutes after adding serum and in controls at different shearing pressures directly proportional to the speeds shown in table 4.2. A full description of the shearing technique is given in chapter 5. It is seen that significantly more cells were detached in the cultures exhibiting pinocytosis.

This group of experimental results indicates that under conditions of increased activity, cells are more easily detached from glass. While not providing unequivocal proof, the results suggest that the increased peripheral activity in terms of diffusion and increased passage of metabolites,

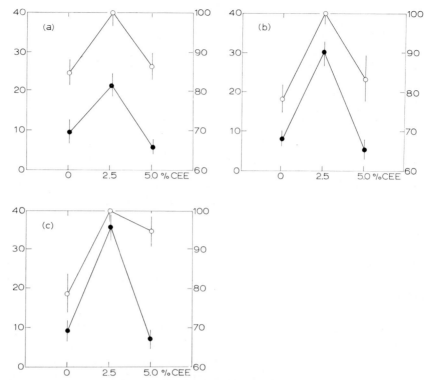

Fig. 4.12.   Percentage ($\pm$ S.E.) of cells detached (●—●, left-hand ordinate), and cell numbers (○—○, right-hand ordinate) expressed as a percentage of the maximum number of cells in the group after 1 (A), 2 (B) and (3) days in media containing the amounts of chick embryo extract (CEE) indicated. (From L. Weiss (1964b) by permission of the Editors of 'Experimental Cell Research').

TABLE 4.2

Percentage of cells ($\pm$ S.E.) detached from glass 15 min after adding serum and in control cultures, after shearing at the speeds indicated for 60 sec at 37°C

Shearing speed r.p.m.	Per cent cells detached ($\pm$ S.E.) + serum	control	t	t-Test df	p
150	54.7 ± 2.5	3.20 ± 3.5	5.17	48	0.001
200	49.3 ± 3.3	33.2 ± 3.9	3.16	61	$0.01\ p\ 0.001$
250	88.4 ± 2.9	43.5 ± 3.9	9.47	34	0.001
300	96.8 ± 0.64	91.3 ± 1.5	3.3	16	$0.01\ p\ 0.001$

(From Weiss (1964b) by permission of the Editors of 'Experimental Cell Research').

including active transport and pinocytosis, could be promoting structural weakness by virtue of induced increase in structural heterogeneity. Additional evidence in favour of this hypothesis, in the special case of separation of malignant cells from primary tumors, is discussed in chapter 7.

The cohesive strength of the cell periphery can be reduced by enzyme activity. If the model system of cells adherent to glass is considered, then if cell detachment is facilitated by enzyme activity, it could be argued that the enzymes are acting at the glass/cell adhesion interface, or within the peripheral zone of the cell, thereby reducing its cohesive strength, or in both of these regions. In the present context the term 'cell/glass' interface is a misnomer, since substances present in the medium, including serum protein, adsorb to the glass before the cells settle and adhere to it; therefore the situation is better represented as cell-adsorbed protein etc./glass interfaces, and when such a system is incubated with a proteolytic enzyme for example, activity directed towards the adsorbed protein could also facilitate cell detachment.

It is well-known among cell culturists that certain enzymes, particularly those having proteolytic activity, facilitate the detachment of cells from glass. G. Easty et al. (1960) attempted to quantitate the facilitation of cell detachment with a variety of enzymes, by enumerating the cells detached from the walls of glass tubes, following controlled-centrifugation. They interpreted the facilitation of cell detachment as indicating that the enzymatic substrates were involved in cell adhesion proper, and were parts of a two-dimensional surface. They did not consider that their enzymes might be acting on material adsorbed to the glass, and, at that time, the possibility of cohesive failure had not been appreciated. Later experiments (L. Weiss 1963a) confirmed and extended the observations of Easty et al.; that a variety of enzymes would indeed facilitate the detachment of cells from glass, but rather different interpretations were given to the observations.

The failure of enzymes to facilitate cell detachment from glass does not necessarily mean that no enzymatic substrate is available either in the cell periphery, or in the adsorbed material interposed between it and the glass; the substrate may be an important functional constituent of the cell periphery, but may be relatively unimportant as regards its cohesive strength. Another possible cause for the failure of enzymes to facilitate cell detachment, in spite of the presence of substrate in the peripheral zone, is steric hindrance; as in the case of ovine salivary-gland mucoprotein (Gottschalk 1960), in which tryptic digestion of the peptide backbone is sterically hindered by sialic acid containing prosthetic groups.

Differences in the degree of facilitation of detachment of different cells by the same enzyme can be interpreted in at least three ways;

(1) There are differences in the amounts of enzyme-dissociable groups at the peripheries of various cells.

(2) There are different degrees of steric hindrance to enzyme action.

(3) The enzyme may not be able to reach peripheral regions opposed to the glass, because of morphological impedance to diffusion.

Differences in the percentages of cells detached would not simply reflect the areas of different cells, since the same distractive pressure per unit area was applied to all the cells tested.

TABLE 4.3

Percentage ($\pm$ S.E.) of different types of cell detached following incubation with trypsin (Difco 1:250) dissolved in calcium, magnesium-face Tyrode's solution, and exposure to a shearing pressure of approximately 3.7 dynes / cm^2 for 2 min. 16C and 16R are strains of foetal rat fibroblasts; BKB were an established line of calf kidney cells; HLM were isolated from human foetal liver and HeLa were of a 'wild' type. (From L. Weiss (1963a) by permission of the Editors of 'Experimental Cell Research')

Percent trypsin to which cells were exposed at $20 \pm 1\,°C$ for 10 min	16C	BKB	16R	HeLa	HLM
0	34.3 ± 3.9	10.9 ± 2.6	83.3 ± 6.0	41.1 ± 4.5	–
0.001	41.7 ± 3.9	–	78.3 ± 6.1	46.7 ± 5.0	15.0 ± 3.4
0.01	–	–	77.6 ± 3.2	–	79.5 ± 2.3
0.05	69.2 ± 2.2	9.2 ± 2.5	87.3 ± 1.1	61.1 ± 5.1	–
0.1	89.8 ± 0.55	4.5 ± 2.3	96.6 ± 0.22	98.9 ± 0.14	88.7 ± 1.8
1.0	95.0 ± 1.5	11.7 ± 5.5	98.0 ± 1.5	100 ± 0.0	100 ± 0.0

Trypsin facilitates the detachment of HeLa cells from glass, however, as shown in table 4.3, the degree of facilitation is different. Thus, calf kidney cells (BKB) were relatively insensitive compared to one strain of foetal rat fibroblasts (16C). If tryptic activity were simply confined to the adsorbed material interposed between the cells and glass, provided that the trypsin freely diffused in this region, it would have been expected that the enzyme would facilitate the detachment of the different types of cell to the same degree. The fact that it did not suggested strongly that part of the cell periphery proper was involved in the detachment effect. When the sites from which trypsin-treated cells had been sheared free, were examined by the modified double-mixed agglutination test (L. Weiss and Coombs 1963), it was clearly shown that human-specific antigenic material was left behind by HeLa cells (but not 16C cells) as shown in fig. 4.13. This showed that trypsin facilitated HeLa cell detachment by acting initially in the cell periphery, deep to its species-specific antigens.

The comparative weakness of the agglutination test, when compared with sites of cells which were removed without prior incubation in trypsin, also suggests that trypsin also acts on the proteinaceous material adsorbed to glass; however, the described experiments did not permit us to determine whether this takes place at the same time as its activity within the cell periphery, or before or after the cells were detached.

TABLE 4.4

Percentage ($\pm$ S.E.) of cells detached after exposure to crude neuraminidase or Hanks' solution alone (control), and shearing pressures. The numbers of separate cultures examined for each mean value is given in parentheses. Note that similar results have since been obtained with pure enzyme. (From L. Weiss (1963a) by permission of the Editors of 'Experimental Cell Research')

Shearing pressures in dynes/cm^2		16C	BKB	16R
3.7 (for 2 min)	Exptl.	51.9 ± 2.4 (16)	6.0 ± 1.7 (16)	74.1 ± 4.9 (7)
	Control	3.7 ± 1.7 (8)	7.9 ± 1.7 (8)	18.0 ± 2.9 (11)
12.2 (for 1 min)	Exptl.	40.3 ± 5.7 (8)	2.2 ± 0.8 (15)	56.2 ± 2.6 (8)
	Control	12.8 ± 0.9 (25)	7.5 ± 3.0 (8)	22.4 ± 4.0 (8)
36.5 (for 1 min)	Exptl.	42.2 ± 2.1 (24)	16.9 ± 5.3 (12)	89.2 ± 1.7 (8)
	Control	22.1 ± 1.9 (40)	20.1 ± 4.9 (11)	41.8 ± 3.6 (16)

Neuraminidase also aids cell detachment from glass (L. Weiss 1961c, 1963a), and different cell types show a different degree of facilitation (table 4.4). The fact that a difference was obtained again provides some argument against the site of action being on sialoprotein adsorbed from the culture medium. It is known from the evidence given in chapter 1 and 6 that the carboxyl groups of surface sialic acids are oriented outwards into the electrokinetic surface of cells in general, and that reduction in electrophoretic

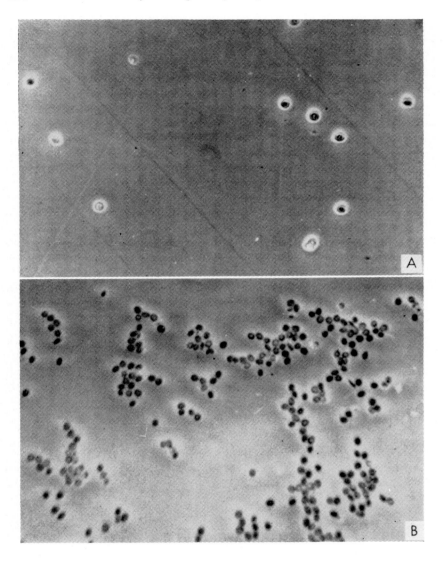

Fig. 4.13. A. A negative mixed agglutination test in which a few human erythrocytes are seen adhering to an area of glass treated with anti-human erythrocyte serum, after shearing off a culture of 16c rat fibroblasts. B. A positive reaction (cf. fig. 4.9) showing human erythrocytes adhering to a site, treated with anti-human erythrocyte serum, from which HeLa cells were previously sheared after incubation with trypsin. (From Weiss and Coombs (1963) by permission of the Editors of 'Experimental Cell Research').

mobility following incubation of cells with neuraminidase is brought about
by hydrolytic cleavage of the glycosidic bond joining the keto group of
N-acetyl-neuraminic acid to an amino sugar, such as D-galactosamine
(Gottschalk 1957). It therefore follows that as neuraminidase cannot act
in the plane of the carboxyl groups of sialic acid, at the cell-substratum
interface proper, it is acting more deeply than this, within the 3-dimensional
peripheral zone, where it produces its effects. An obvious experiment to
relate neuraminidase activity and cell detachment would be to determine the
facilitation of detachment by this enzyme on cells having different sialic
acid-dependent electrophoretic mobilities.

The last enzyme to be considered from the quoted series of experiments
is hyaluronidase, which did not facilitate the detachment of cells from glass.
The interest of this negative finding which merely quantitated common
experience, lies in the fact that my colleagues at the Strangeways Research
Laboratory provided me with two strains of foetal rat dermal fibroblasts
with which to work. By treating the original 16C strain with cobalt salts
for some months, a new variant 16R arose, which produced hyaluronic acid
in vitro (Daniel et al. 1961). It was argued that if hyaluronic acid is found
in the culture medium of 16R cells, at some stage it must be in the region of
the cell periphery, and at that time can probably be regarded as a constituent of the peripheral zone. The persistent failure of potent staphylococcal
and testicular hyaluronidase to facilitate detachment of 16R could not be
attributed to the inaccessibility of the enzymatic substrate, since incubation
for 60 minutes at 37° followed by exposure of the cells to high shearing
pressures, which are extreme treatments, also produced no demonstrable
effects. It was, therefore, concluded that enzymatic degradation of hyaluronic acid at the peripheries of 16R cells produced no appreciable diminution
in their cohesive strength, and that in this situation, hyaluronic acid is not
an important structural unit in the purely mechanical sense.

In addition to the extrinsic enzymes discussed, intrinsic enzymes released
by the cells themselves can also facilitate cell separation. As discussed in
chapter 2, the acid hydrolases released from activated lysosomes would be
expected to function optimally in the region of negatively charged groups,
on account of the higher hydrogen ion activity around them (ΔpH) than in
the environmental bulkphase. Following earlier work, an attempt was made
to correlate lysosome activation with facilitation of cell detachment from
glass. Initial experiments (L. Weiss 1962) showed that significantly more cells
were detached from glass, following pretreatment with excess vitamin A,
than in the controls. It is known that treatment of this type activates the

lysosomal enzymes (Lucy et al. 1961), but it was not known what else the excess vitamin did to the cells at the time of the detachment experiment.

The work described in chapter 2, showed that antisera, prepared against fractions rich in various subcellular organelles, cause the release of lysosomal enzymes from cells, on the evidence of loss of Gomori-positive staining and direct assay of culture media (L. Weiss and Dingle 1964). An attempt was next made to relate the loss of Gomori-positive staining to the facilitation of cell detachment from glass, with the viewpoint that as the lysosomal enzymes left the cell to appear in the culture medium they might well degrade its peripheral region, thereby facilitating cell detachment (Weiss 1965b). As the main interest was in living cells, the rat fibroblasts (16C) used in these experiments were exposed to low concentrations of rabbit antiserum which studies on over 2,000 cultures had previously shown to produce only small amounts of lethal damage. It was also known from the work previously quoted, and from other experiments made by Fell and L. Weiss (1965a), that the activation of lysosomal enzymes could be prevented or retarded by the presence of $10 \mu g/ml$ of hydrocortisone hemisuccinate in the culture medium. The cytotoxic effects of antiserum were only partially abolished by hydrocor-

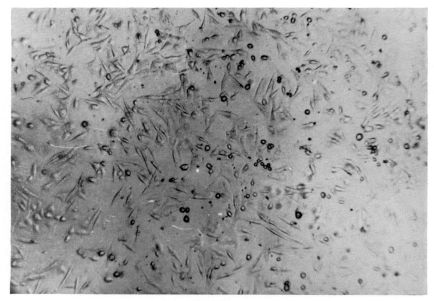

Fig. 4.14.   16C fibroblasts incubated in synthetic medium 199 + antiserum for 1 hour at 37°C, and stained by a modified Gomori technique after fixation in formalin. No acid phosphatase is demonstrable.

tisone. Consequently, the effects of synthetic medium 199 containing anti-serum, were compared with a control medium which contained hydrocor-tisone in addition to antiserum. The dramatic differences between exposure to the two media are seen in phase-contrast photomicrographs (figs. 4.14 and 4.15), which respectively show the disappearence of Gomori-positive staining in morphologically intact cells treated with media containing anti-serum alone, and the marked Gomori-positive staining following incubation under similar conditions but in the presence of hydrocortisone.

16C cells were sheared from glass by exposure to a calculated shearing pressure of 14 dynes per cm^2 for 1 minute, after varying exposure to media containing antiserum, with and without the addition of hydrocortisone. The results shown in fig. 4.16 indicate that exposure to antiserum facilitates cell detachment, and that this effect is inhibited by the presence of hydrocor-tisone.

The fact that no morphological evidence of cytopathic change was seen after exposure to the low concentrations of antiserum, although signifi-cant facilitation of detachment had occurred after two minutes, did not of course preclude sub-microscopic lethal changes, which, in themselves,

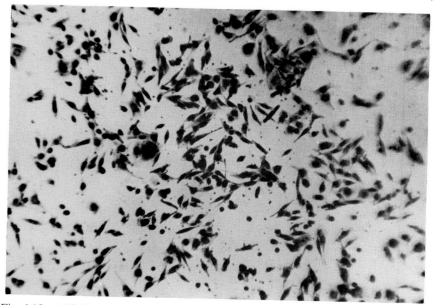

Fig. 4.15. 16C fibroblasts incubated in synthetic medium 199 + antiserum + 10 μg/ml hydrocortisone hemisuccinate for 1 hour at 37°C, and stained as in fig. 4.14. Cells showed marked positive Gomori staining.

might have promoted detachment. However, although as shown in fig. 4.16, hydrocortisone completely inhibits facilitation of cell detachment over the times studied, it only partially inhibits cell death under these conditions. The results were therefore taken to imply that cells were detached from glass more easily following exposure to antiserum, due to enzyme activity in their peripheries. Other experiments showed that the uptake of vital dyes into these cells was retarded by hydrocortisone, and it was suggested that it might act by reducing the permeability changes produced in membrane systems, which in turn trigger off lysosomal activation.

It was also shown that if lysosomal extracts from rat liver were added to cell cultures, their detachment from glass was significantly facilitated, compared with cultures treated with boiled enzyme. This suggests that enzymes released from one type of cell can facilitate the separation of neighbouring cells.

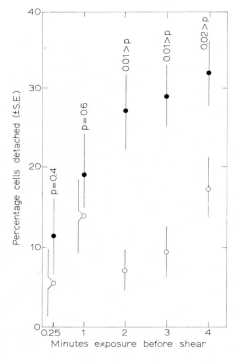

Fig. 4.16. Percentage of cells ($\pm$ S.E.) detached from glass by a shearing pressure of approximately 14 dynes/cm^2, after exposure to the media for the times indicated. ● $= 2.5\%$ antiserum; ○ $= 2.5\%$ antiserum $+ 10\,\mu$g/ml hydrocortisone.

It is freely admitted that some of the experiments on factors that affect cell separation could be interpreted as being mediated through changes at adhesive interfaces as distinct from changes occurring in the cohesive strength of the peripheral zone in depth. However, some of the work quoted clearly indicates that cell separation does not occur in the same spatial plane as cell adhesion. Quite apart from its theoretical interest, this hypothesis would suggest that such interfacial properties of cells as their electrophoretic mobility, while directly influencing cell contact and probably adhesion, will not directly influence cell separation by electrostatic repulsion. Electrical charge in the cell periphery could conceivably promote cell separation by virtue of optimizing the low pH requirements for released acid hydrolases through the ΔpH effect.

It is considered that in both designing experiments on intercellular relationships, and in interpreting experimental data, the differences between contact, adhesion and separation of cells must be borne in mind.

4.4 *Specificity of cell contact phenomena*

The experimental data discussed in chapter 3 show that different cells may interact differently with one another, indicating specificity in contact interactions. The discussions in this chapter indicate that contact interactions should be considered in terms of cells or their parts making contact, adhering and separating from each other. These processes will now be examined with a view to indicating how specificity can occur in each of these defined phenomena.

It will be appreciated that of the three processes discussed, contact and adhesion at least, involve consideration of distances of separation of only a few Ångstrom, and that owing to the uncertainty of the spatial definition of cell peripheries at this level due to limitations in both semantics and techniques, much of this discussion can only be at the theoretical level.

4.4.1. *Specificity in contact*

Two cells make contact with one another when they have approximated closely enough to form adhesive bonds of the types described earlier. Specificity in contacts between cells themselves, or between cells and intercellular material would therefore be concerned with their approach up to the distance required for adhesion. Contact specificity can be considered as determining

whether cells made contact or not, that is in terms of an all-or-none phenomenon, or alternatively to act as a mechanism whereby potentially adherent
or non-adherent chemical species are aligned, relative to one another.

All-or-none contact specificity could arise if the energies of repulsion
between parts of two cells were so high compared with the energies of attraction, that the total interaction energy maximum exceeded the cellular locomotor energy and the energy associated with Brownian motion, V_{LB}. In
order to account for specificity in contact between, say, two cells of type x,
and non-contact between two cells of types x and y, their respective total
interaction energies V^{xx} and V^{xy} must be considered, namely:

$$V^{xy} = V_R^{xy} + V_A^{xy} + V_{LB}^{xy}, \quad \text{and} \quad V^{xx} = V_R^{xx} + V_A^{xx} + V_{LB}^{xx}.$$

In other words, contact between cells x and y does not occur because com-
pared with each other, V_R^{xy} is too high, and/or V_A^{xy} is too low and/or V_{LB}^{xy} is
too low. By similar reasoning, contact between cells x and x does occur,
because comparatively V_R^{xx} is low, and/or V_A^{xx} is high, and/or V_{LB}^{xx} is high.
Considerations of the energy of attraction, V_A, in terms of Van der Waals'
interactions, would lead to the assumption that, by their very nature, unless
the cells had different atomic density or their constituents markedly differed
in polarizability etc., then when cells are separated by distances dictated
by the potential energy maxima, contact specificity is not explicable in
terms of attractive interactions by themselves. Little or no information is
available about the locomotor energy of whole cells, or more importantly
about the locomotor and Brownian contribution to the locomotor energies
of fine cellular probes. Measurements on cellular velocities *in vitro* reveal
little difference between cells, and the masses of them and their probes
would not appear to be sufficiently different to account for specificity in terms
of $\frac{1}{2}mv^2$. However, it must be emphasized that *in vitro* measurements of
velocities may be misleading. Thus, from this line of reasoning, it would
be expected that if all-or-none contact specificity exists, the key lies in energies of repulsion, and the equation (6) governing them:

$$V_R = \frac{1}{2}Da\psi_0^2 \log e(1 + \exp^{-\kappa H})$$

must be re-examined.

It may be stated immediately that it is extremely unlikely that variations
in bulk-phase dielectric constants are connected with contact specificity,
and no information is available on the dielectric constants in the outermost
parts of cells. From what has been said of the Debye–Hückel parameter,
$1/\kappa$, it can be seen that this term is sensitive to both ionic concentrations

and valencies, and that local differences in these could conceivably affect the height of the potential energy maximum. However, it must be remembered that in the case of mammalian cells at least, the ionic strengths of their environmental fluids are so high in colloid terms, that it seems unlikely that local fluctuations in different cell types could materially affect V_R. The radius of curvature, a, of parts of cells making contact is important, and it is to be expected that cells able to put out low radius of curvature probes (below a maximum of about 0.2μ) would be more likely to effectively reduce the potential energy repulsion barrier to contact than those which could not. If macroscopic determinations of cell deformability do in fact reflect on a cell's ability to put out projections of low radius of curvature as suggested (L. Weiss 1965b, 1966), then it is possible that such measurements would correlate with contact specificity. On the one hand, macrophages which can make contact with many types of cell on the evidence of their active, infiltrative movements through tissues are very deformable (L. Weiss et al. 1966); on the other hand, murine ascites tumour cells of both Sarcoma 37 and Ehrlich type, which are also infiltrative, possess peripheries which are very much more difficult to deform (L. Weiss 1965b). Electron and phase-contrast microscopy of different cell types shows that many are capable of extending small probes; while there are good reasons for correlating the extension of such projections with contact, there is, in my opinion, no evidence at present for invoking them in specificity of the type being discussed. It is well-known that different cell types have different electrophoretic mobilities and hence different net charge densities at their surfaces. It could reasonably be argued that as surface potential is squared in equation (6), small differences in this parameter could produce marked differences in V_R, which could be reflected in all-or-none specificity of contact. If this were so, it would be expected that the higher the value of ψ_0 in equation (6), the less likely would contact be. Thus, to account for specificity in these terms, in the case of cells of type x which do not make contact with cells of type y, the charge density on y would have to be higher than on x. Sparse personal data on different cellular electrophoretic mobilities in relation to contact suggests that at the moment such simple direct correlations do not apply. There is, of course, no question that cells will not make contact with surfaces carrying very high negative charge, but within the physiological range of average charge density such a naive macroscopic approach appears unlikely.

It was noted (L. Weiss 1963b) that calculations based on measurements of electrophoretic mobility can at best give information on charge density;

they cannot give data on charge distribution. If the bound ionogenic groups
are arranged in zones of higher charge density than the average for the
whole cell, and if due to the mutual electrostatic repulsion and hence high
resistance to deformability (L. Weiss 1965b) these high charge density zones
are found at the tips of cell processes, then much higher potential energy
maxima will be encountered by processes tending to make contact than
calculated from average data. If all-or-none contact specificity exists, it
might conceivably be explained in these terms (fig. 4.17).

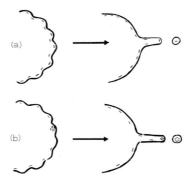

Fig. 4.17.   The surfaces of cells A and B carry the same density of charged groups, and
would have the same electrophoretic mobilities. When low radius of curvature projections
are put out to make contact with another cell over the whole probe tip surface, V_R in the
case of cell B, will be 36 (i.e. $6^2:1^2$) times as high as for cell A owing to the higher charge
density of the probe-tip.

As the distance from charged surface groups increases, thermal motion
of ions becomes progressively more important and the concentration of
anions and cations approaches equality, in contrast to the asymmetrical
distribution close to the charged surface. Thus, as shown in fig. 4.4, discreteness of charge patterns would be lost further out than about 10Å from
charged surfaces in physiological environments. Therefore, if charged groups
are to play a part in producing the type of specificity in contact, whereby
definite areas of the cell periphery are aligned in a particular relationship
to one another, this would not become operative until they were closer than
at most 10Å. Charged groups could act by determining either where contact
could take place, or, alternatively, where it could not. The attractions between
negatively and positively charged groups could, for example, promote their
alignment to form an adhesion. On the other hand, the mutual repulsion of
two negatively charged groups would tend to prevent alignment unless for

example, they somehow or other came close enough together to permit calcium-bridging between them. Such a scheme based on overlapping patterns of calcium-binding anionic groups has been proposed by Steinberg (1958), but as suggested by this author, very regular patterns are required. I find it difficult to understand how Steinberg's hypothesis can account for specificity, since any cell with a greater density of suitable anionic groups, could form calcium-bridges with all of the available sites in cells containing fewer anionic groups.

Another way of looking at contact specificity is to suggest that charged groups bring about alignment of non-charged areas of cell surface. These non-charged areas could then form or not form, any of the requisite adhesive bonds of the types already described. A third choice is that the charged groups on two opposing cells align, not with each other, but with uncharged regions. These various possibilities are shown in fig. 4.18. It must be emphasized that at the moment not only are we unable to choose between any of the possibilities, but we do not know in fact whether specificity in contact, as defined here, exists at all.

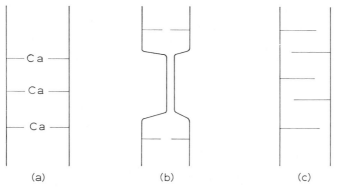

(a)   (b)   (c)

Fig. 4.18.   The different types of alignment at contact produced by negatively charged groups (⊢): (a). Exact opposition with calcium-bridging for example. (b). Opposition of charged groups which are kept apart by repulsion, allowing contact to be made between uncharged areas. (c). Interdigitation of charged groups allowing the opposition of charged and non-charged areas.

4.4.2. Specificity in adhesion

It is not proposed to deal with specific chemical bond formation between cells which have made contact. Obviously at this level specificity can be conferred by whether or not opposed groups can form adhesive bonds of the types referred to earlier. The questions be to considered here will be specificity in adhesion due to shape, London–Van der Waals' and other charge fluctuation forces, and surface-energy relationships.

The Tyler–Weiss hypothesis (Tyler 1947; P. Weiss 1950) suggests that adhesions may be analogous to antibody/antigen (Ab/Ag) reactions. Many types of cell adhesion cannot be said to resemble Ab/Ag reactions because of their lack of specificity; however, it is of course true that the specific contact between antibody and antigen is charge-dependent as evidenced by its sensitivity to pH and ionic strength. Pressman (1963) reviews some of the evidence suggesting that antibody molecules are formed by folding of parts of the polypeptide chain of a gamma-globulin molecule so that it forms a structure complementary in shape to the antigenic region against which it is directed. The resulting close fit of the Ab/Ag complex allows the various amino acid residues present to participate in the adhesive bonds described by Pauling et al. (1943), and earlier in this chapter. It is well-known that cells may be agglutinated with a high degree of specificity, by antibodies directed against their peripheral components. However, similar mechanisms for specificity in cell adhesion would require complementary antibody and antigen sites on like cells. In the absence of evidence for the existence of such complementary sites, I do not think that the Tyler–Weiss hypothesis is relevant to adhesive specificity between cells, except in the possible case of some spermatozoa/ovum interactions. The main value of this hypothesis, in my opinion, has been to stress the need for close approximation of cells before short-range adhesive bonds can come into play.

A more precise appreciation of complementarity in relation to the general Van der Waals interactions is due to Jehle and his colleagues (Jehle et al. 1965; Jehle et al. 1964), following on Pauling's (1957) calculations of the energy advantages inherent in close fit. Possibly of more immediate interest is the remarkable property of charge fluctuation interactions to favour the association of like molecules as nearest neighbours, in mixtures of molecules in a liquid medium. All charge fluctuation forces participate in self-recognition, those due to quantum mechanical fluctuations and those due to thermal fluctuation of which the Kirkwood–Shumaker (1952) forces are most important. Jehle et al. start by considering the London-type interactions $\Delta A_{I, II}$ between a pair of isolated molecules I and II:

$$\Delta A_{I, II} = (A_{I, II})_R - (A_{I, II})_\infty, \qquad (21)$$

where $(A_{I, II})_R$ is the energy at distance R separation, and $(A_{I, II})_\infty$ the energy at infinity. The interactions are also proportional to the product of the molecular polarizabilities, $-\alpha_I \alpha_{II}$.

If in a mixture of molecules of types I and II a pair of like molecules II, II come together, then molecules of type I must make room for them. This results in two less I, II pairs and one more I, I pair. The rearrangement energy for the 4 pairs, which is derived from equation (21) is given by:

$$\Delta_4 A_{I, II} = \Delta A_{I, I} + \Delta A_{II, II} - 2\Delta A_{I, II} \tag{22}$$

and

$$\Delta_4 A_{I, II} \propto - (\alpha_I - \alpha_{II})^2 \leqslant 0.$$

This inequality implies a preferential association of like molecules, and has been noted by Hamaker (1937) and De Boer (1936). Jehle et al. note that this preference, as stated, would be weak; however, in the case of two different types of molecules in a suspending medium, composed of a third molecular species, the preference is greater. These authors consider that charge-fluctuation forces could well play a role in shifting of adhesive junctions.

A theory for specificity in cell adhesion is due to Steinberg, (see Steinberg 1964 for review) and is based on the thermodynamic principle that the free energy of any system tends to a minimum. If two pairs of cells of types x and y are considered, which will adhere to each other to form x–x, y–y, or x–y doublets, and the adhesive energy in each case is W_x, W_y or W_{xy} respectively. On the assumption that these simple relationships can be applied in this way to very complex systems, the probability of any particular type of doublet being formed will depend on the energy relationships. Thus, the most stable, and hence probable, ultimate association will be the one where the work of adhesion is highest. Note that as in like doublets, four cells are involved (x–x and y–y), to compare the adhesive energies with W_{xy} this sum must be divided by 2.

If $W_{xy} > \frac{1}{2}(W_x + W_y)$, the highest energy of adhesion will be favoured, resulting in unlike cells adhering to each other, i.e. x–y and y–x.

If $\frac{1}{2}(W_x + W_y) > W_{xy}$, the highest energy of adhesion will again be favoured, resulting on this occasion, in like cells adhering to each other, i.e. x–x and y–y.

Thus cellular segregation occurs not only when the heterotypic (x–y) adhesions are the weakest of the three possible associations, x–y, x–x or y–y; but also, and most importantly in this argument, when the x–y adhesions are weaker than the *average* of the other two, i.e. $W_{xy} < \frac{1}{2}(W_x + W_y)$. In other words, segregation may occur in the case where, for example, $W_x > W_{xy} > W_y$, as long as the relationship $W_{xy} < \frac{1}{2}(W_x + W_y)$ holds.

An interesting development of Steinberg's work comes from additional mixtures of cells. Thus, if in the case of mixed cultures of x and y cells, the x cells come to surround a central mass of y cells; and if in mixtures of y and z cells the y cells come to surround a central mass of z cells, then it can be predicted, and confirmed experimentally, that in a mixture of x and z, the x cells will surround a central mass of z cells which enables correct predictions of their positions within mixed aggregates. Fenn (1922, 1923), Ponder (1927), Mudd et al. (1934) attempted to analyze phagocytosis of bacteria and related phenomena in terms of surface tension or energy. L. Weiss (1960) attempted to use similar considerations in describing some aspects of cellular adhesion, and pointed out many possible analogies from work done on glue and synthetic adhesives, which seems to fit in with Young's equation for three-phase systems where surface tensions are related through the angle of contact. Pethica (1961) has reasonably criticized this use of contact angles, and points out that instead of surface tension, the interfacial Helmholtz free energy per unit-area (F) should be used. In the case of cells, F cannot be measured. Pethica therefore considered that the treatment of cell adhesion as a wetting phenomenon 'is probably unfruitful'. However, Steinberg has considered the surface energy relationships of cells in mixed aggregates by treating them initially as fluid drops where surface tension may be substituted numerically for the quantity F. He concludes that in the case of cell types x and y, if $W_x > W_y$ (and assuming that segregation will occur, i.e. $\frac{1}{2}(W_x + W_y > W_{xy})$ then y cells will come to surround a central mass of x cells, which have the stronger adhesions between them.

Steinberg covers the remaining case of where mixtures of two cell types do not arrange concentrically, but form two separate aggregates (as in the case of amphibian, epidermal and neural cells), as being due to both homotypic adhesions, W(epiderm) and W(neural), being greater than heterotypic, W(epiderm-neural), adhesion. This somewhat rare exception does, of course, require a preferential higher adhesive strength between like cells.

Abercrombie (1964), in reviewing the various theories accounting for cell segregation, makes the important point that a precise physical analogy is not required to translate surface/energy relationships in fluids to cell movements, and that 'any cellular behaviour, or combination of kinds of behaviour which sufficiently reduces the probability of separation of cells once collision has occurred, will, in theory, serve instead of adhesion'. Work already described also suggests that the separation of cells cannot be predicted, except by coincidence, in their true interfacial properties such as adhesion, and there are also serious difficulties in the way of directly measuring cell adhesion as distinct from cell separation (see chapter 5). Thus Steinberg's hypothesis based on adhesive strengths has not yet been tested by direct measurement.

4.4.3. Specificity in separation

From what has been said about contact, cells could separate after apparent contact had been made or after making real contact with each other. By apparent contact is meant that although by microscopy the cell surfaces are in contact, there is still a potential energy maximum between them; true contact on the other hand, means that the cells are no longer separated by a repulsion barrier. Energetically, separation of cells which have made real and apparent contact will be different.

The separation of cells which have made apparent contact, which is analogous to flocculation, is perhaps covered by the theories of repeptization. It is a common observation that suspensions of coarse particles of greater diameter than one micron may be repeptized by shaking. Overbeek (1952b) explains repeptization in terms of the shearing motion of the suspended fluid brought about by agitation. This force which tends to separate two neighboring particles is proportional to the radius of the particles (Stoke's Law) and to the distance between their centers, which accounts for the difference in velocity of the fluid. Thus, the attractive force holding the particles in the flocculated state is inversely proportional to their radius, whereas the shearing force distracting them is proportional to the square of the radius. Separation of this type does not involve the separating cell processes retraversing a potential energy barrier, and the energy involved is concerned with the small secondary minimum; cohesive failure or micro-ruptures would not result from this sort of separation phenomenon. It is expected that any specificity in this process would be found in the ability of the cells to move to other regions where they could make true contact, as demonstrated by Carter (1965) in the case of cultured cells moving in a direction dictated by their ability to form more adhesions. This type of 'specificity' might be the explanation for the way in which filopodia explore the surfaces of other cells by progressively making and breaking apparent contacts. This process is not specificity of separation, but should be considered as all-or-none specificity of contact, together with the factors directing movement of the cells or their projections, away from the areas of apparent contact. Presumably this type of contact inhibition could be explained by differential adhesions directing movement away from contact regions, as sug-

gested by P. Weiss and Garber (1952) in terms of 'herniations' of the cell
periphery, or by Steinberg in terms of free surface energy relationships.

Specificity in the separation of cells, or their processes, after these have
made true contact, are thought to involve cellular interactions which facilitate cohesive failure. These interactions can therefore involve weakening of
the peripheral zones of one or both cells involved, and/or increases in distractive energies by the cells. It has been argued that structural weakness and
hence separation could be facilitated by heterogeneities produced in the
peripheral zone of cells by increased metabolic activities as well as inherent
structural weaknesses. It seems possible that different combinations of contiguous cells could have different metabolic activities by virtue of contact.
Contact between like cells leads to inhibition of growth in monolayers;
and it is known that a number of mucopolysaccharides and related substances can block mitosis in a number of different cells (e.g. Lippman 1965).
Work on interacting embryonic cell systems (e.g. Dodson 1963) shows that
proximity between two cell types can result in the formation of 'specific'
intercellular materials. It therefore seems possible that the type of peripheral
material lying between various cell combinations as well as the induction
of weakness in it, can in some way be dependent on the cell types in contact,
and that these complex processes may in turn affect cell separation.

It is known from studies on the cellular reactions involved in the immune
response, (see chapter 9) that lysis of target cells can occur when they make
contact with lymphoid cells. Such cytolysis results in the liberation of lysosomal acid hydrolases, which would be expected to facilitate cell separation
by enzymatic degradation of their peripheral regions. It is to be conjectured
that sublethal enzyme release of the type referred to earlier, may be triggered
off by contact between unlike cells thereby aiding their separation. Lysosomal
activation can be brought about by many different physical and chemical
agents acting on membrane systems which presumably produce permeability
changes in them. At the moment it is not possible to suggest any definite
mechanisms whereby 'specific' stimuli in contacting cells may activate the
sublethal release of lysosomal or other enzymes; however, work is currently
proceeding along these lines.

4.5 *Conclusions*

It will be appreciated that most of the current ideas on 'specificity' in contact reactions between cells are, at best, working hypotheses. It seems reason-

able to consider contact, adhesion and separation as separate processes; but it should be made clear that even if specificity exists in all three of these processes, there is a good deal of overlap. In my opinion, a glaring deficiency in our generally sparse knowledge, is almost complete ignorance of the factors regulating active cell movements, and the values of locomotor energies to ascribe to cells and their processes. Finally, as very small distances and regions are involved in considerations of potential energies of attraction and repulsion etc. there are very few experimental biological data presently available with which to check the theoretical approach.

References

Abercrombie, M. (1964). Arch. Biol. (Liège) **75**, 351

Albers, W. and Overbeek, J. Th. G. (1960). J. Colloid Sci. **15**, 489

Alexander, A. E. and Johnson, P. (1950). Colloid science. Oxford, Clarendon Press

Allison, A. C. and Valentine, R. C. (1960). Biochim. Biophys. Acta **40**, 400

Ambrose, E. J. (1961). Exptl. Cell Res. Suppl. **8**, 54

Axilrod, B. M. and Teller, E. (1943). J. Chem. Phys. **11**, 299

Bangham, A. D. (1964). Ann. N. Y. Acad. Sci. **116**, 945

Bangham, A. D. and Pethica, B. A. (1960). Proc. Roy. Phys. Soc. (Edinburgh) **28**, 73

Bangham, D. H. and Razouk, R. I. (1937). Trans. Faraday Soc. **33**, 1459

Bennett, H. S. (1963). J. Histochem. Cytochem. **11**, 14

Bernal, J. D. (1959). In, D. Hadži, ed., Hydrogen bonding. Pergamon Press, London, p. 7

Bernal, J. D. (1965). Symp. Soc. Exptl. Biol. **19**, 17

Beumer, J., Dirkx, J., and Beumer-Jochmas, M. P. (1957). Nature **180**, 83

Bierman, A. (1955). J. Colloid Sci. **10**, 231

Bikerman, J. J. (1961). The science of adhesive joints. Academic Press, New York and London, p. 125

Block, W., De Jongh, G. V., Overbeek, J. Th. G. and Sparnaay, M. J. (1960). Trans. Faraday Soc. **56**, 1597

Blodgett, K. B. (1935). J. Ann. Chem. Soc. **57**, 1007

Booth, F. (1951). J. Chem. Phys. **19**, 391, 1327, 1615

Brunt, N. A. (1964). Kolloid Z. Polymere **199**, 13

Burzagh, A. von (1929). Kolloid. Z. **47**, 370

Burzagh, A. von (1930). Kolloid. Z. **51**, 105, 230

Carter, S. B. (1965). Nature, **208**, 1183

Casimir, H. G. B. and Polder, D. (1948). Phys. Rev. **73**, 360

Chapman, D. L. (1913). Phil. Mag. **25**, 475

Coombs, R. R. A. (1961). Cancer Res. **21**, 1198

Cotran, R. S. (1965). Lab. Invest. **14**, 1826

Cottrell, T. L. (1958). The strengths of chemical bonds. 2nd ed. Academic Press, New York

Curtis, A. S. G. (1960). Am. Nat. **94**, 37

Curtis, A. S. G. (1962). Biol. Rev. **37**, 82

Curtis, A. S. G. (1964). J. Cell Biol. **20**, 199

Daniel, M. R., Dingle, J. T. and Lucy, J. A. (1961). Exptl. Cell Res. **24**, 88

De Boer, J. H. (1936). Trans. Faraday Soc. **32**, 21, 118

Debye, P. (1920). Physik. Z. **21**, 178

Debye, P. (1921). Physik. Z. **22**, 302

Debye, P. and Hückel, E. (1923). Physik. Z. **24**, 185

Debye, P., and Hückel, E. (1924). Physik. Z. **25**, 97

Derjaguin, B. (1934). Kolloid Z. **69**, 155

Derjaguin, B. (1940). Trans. Faraday Soc. **36**, 203

Derjaguin, B. V. (1954). Discussions Faraday Soc. **18**, 85

Derjaguin, B. V. (1960). Scientific American, **203**, 47

Derjaguin, B. V., Abrikossova, I. I. and Lifshitz, E. M. (1956). Quart. Rev. **10**, 295

Derjaguin, B. V. and Landau, L. (1941). Acta Physicochim. U.R.S.S. **14**, 633

De Voe, H. and Tinoco, I. (1962). J. Mol. Biol. **4**, 500

Dodson, J. W. (1963). Exptl. Cell Res. **31**, 233

Dzyaloshinski, I. E., Lifshitz, E. M. and Pitayeskü, L. P. (1961). Advan. Physics **10**, 165

Dzyaloshinski, I. E. and Pitayevskü, L. P. (1959). Soviet Phys. JETP **9**, 1282

Easty, G. C., Easty, D. M. and Ambrose, E. J. (1960). Exptl. Cell Res. **19**, 539

Eisenchitz, R. and London, F. (1930a). Z. Physik **60**, 491

Eisenchitz, R. and London, F. (1930b). Z. Physik **63**, 245

Fawcett, D. W. (1965). J. Histochem. Cytochem. **13**, 75

Fell, H. B. and Weiss, L. (1965). J. Exptl. Med. **121**, 551

Fenn, W. O. (1922). J. Gen. Physiol. **4**, 373

Fenn, W. O. (1923). J. Gen. Physiol. **5**, 143

Fisher, H. W., Puck, T. T. and Sato, G. (1958). Proc. Natl. Acad. Sci. (U.S.) **44**, 4

Flascka, H. and Barnard, A. J. (1960). In, Advan. in analytical and chemical instrumentation, Vol. I. Interscience, New York

Fowkes, F. M. (1964a). Advan. Chem. **43**, 99

Fowkes, F. M. (1964b). Ind. Eng. Chem. **56**, 40

Frocht, M. M. (1941). Photoelasticity. Chapman Hall, London

Gittens, G. J. and James, A. M. (1963). Biochim. Biophys. Acta **66**, 237

Glaeser, R. M. (1963). The electric charge and surface properties of intact cells. Office of Technical Services, Washington

Gottschalk, A. (1957). Biochem. Biophys. Acta **23**, 654

Gottschalk, A. (1960). Nature **186**, 949

Gouy, G. (1910). J. Phys. **9**, 457

Gouy, G. (1917). Ann. Phys. **7**, 129

Grahame, D. C. (1947). Chem. Rev **41**, 441

Grahame, D. C. (1950). J. Chem. Phys. **18**, 903

Grant, E. H. (1965). Ann. N. Y. Acad. Sci. **125**, 418

Griffith, A. A. (1924). Proc. Intern. Congr. Appl. Mech. (Delft), p. 55

Grobstein, C. (1961). In, La culture organotypique. Colloque Intern. CNRS, Paris, **101**, 169

Hamaker, H. C. (1937). Physica **4**, 1058

Hartog, J. P. D. (1961). Strength of materials. Dover Publications, New York

Hasted, J. B., Ritson, D. M. and Collie, C. H. (1948). J. Chem. Phys. **16**, 1

Haydon, D. A. (1964). In, J. F. Danielli, K. G. A. Pankhurst and A. C. Riddiford eds., Recent progress in surface science. Academic Press, New York and London, p. 94

Haydon, D. A. and Taylor, F. H. (1960). Phil. Trans. Roy. Soc. A **253**, 255

Heard, D. H. and Seaman, G. V. F. (1960). J. Gen. Physiol. **43**, 635

Henniker, J. C. (1949). Rev. Mod. Phys. **21**, 322

Houwink, R. (1936). Trans. Faraday Soc. **32**, 122

Houwink, R. (1937). Elasticity, plasticity and the structure of matter. Cambridge University Press p. 33

Hsiao, J. (1959). J. Appl. Phys. **30**, 1492

Ito, S. and Revel, J. P. (1964). J. Cell Biol. **23**, 44A

Jacoby, F. (1965). In, E. N. Willmer, ed., Cells and tissues in culture. Academic Press, London and New York, Vol. 2 p. 1

Jehle, H., Parke, W. C., Shirven, R. M. and Aein, D. K. (1964). Biopolymer. Symp. **1**, 209

Jehle, H., Parke, W. C. and Salyers, A. (1965). In, B. Pullman, ed., Electronic aspects of biochemistry. Academic Press. New York and London, p. 313

Kauzmann, W. (1959). Advan. Protein Chem. **14**, 1

Kaye, G. I. and Pappas, G. D. (1962). J. Cell Biol. **12**, 457

Keesom, W. H. (1921). Physik. Z. **22**, 129, 643

Kirkwood, J. G. and Shumaker, J. B. (1952). Proc. Nat. Acad. Sci. (U.S.) **38**, 855, 863

Klotz, I. M. (1960). Brookhaven Symp. Biol. **25**

Kronig, R. de L. and Kramers, H. A. (1928). Z. Physik **48**, 174

Kruyt, H. R. and Klompé, M. A. M. (1942). Kolloidchem. Beihefte **54**, 484

Lesseps, R. J. (1963). J. Exptl. Zool. **15**, 171

Lewis, G. N. and Randall, M. (1921). J. Am. Chem. Soc. **43**, 1112

Lieberman, I. and Ove, P. (1957). Biochim. Biophys. Acta **25**, 449

Lieberman, I. and Ove, P. (1958). J. Biol. Chem. **233**, 637

Lifshitz, E. M. (1955). Zh. Eksperim. Theor. Fiz. **29**, 94

Lifshitz, E. M. (1956). Soviet Phys. JETP **2**, 73

Lippman, M. (1965). Trans. N. Y. Acad. Sci. **27**, 342

Little, K. and Edwards, J. H. (1962). J. Roy. Microscop. Soc. **81**, 23

London, F. (1930). Z. Physik. Chem. **222**, B 11

London, F. (1942). J. Phys. Chem. **46**, 305

Longuet-Higgins, H. C. (1964). J. Chem. Phys. **61**, 13

Longuet-Higgins, H. C. (1965). Discussions Faraday Soc. **40**, 7

Lucy, J. A., Dingle, J. T., and Fell, H. B. (1961). Biochem. J. **79**, 500

Malsch, J. (1928). Physik. Z. **29**, 770

Morgan, G. T. and Drew, H. D. K. (1920). J. Chem. Soc. **117**, 1456

Moscona, A. A. (1960). In, D. Rudnick, ed., Developing cell systems and their control. Ronald Press, New York, p. 45

Mudd, S., McCutcheon, M. and Lucké, B. (1934). Physiol. Rev. **14**, 210

Nordling, S. and Mayhew, E. (1966). Exptl. Cell Res. **43**, 72

Orowan, E. (1949). Rept. Progr. Physics. **12**, 185

Overbeek, J. Th. G. (1952a). In, H. R. Kruyt, ed., Colloid science. Elsevier, Amsterdam and London. Vol. I, p. 324

Overbeek, J. Th. G. (1952b). In, H. R. Kruyt, ed., Colloid science. Elsevier, Amsterdam and London, Vol. I, p. 337

Overbeek, J. Th. G. and Lijklema, J. (1959). In, M. Bier ed., Electrophoresis. Academic Press, New York and London, p. 1

Pappas, G. D. (1959). Ann. N. Y. Acad. Sci. **78**, 448

Parker, R. C. (1929). Arch. Exptl. Zellforsch. **8**, 340

Patinkin, K. and Doljanski, F. (1965). J. Cell. Comp. Physiol. **66**, 343

Pauling, L. (1957). Festschrift Arthur Stoll. Birkhäuser, Basel, p. 597

Pauling, L. (1959). In, D. Hadži, ed., Hydrogen bonding. Pergamon Press. London, p. 1

Pauling, L. (1960). The nature of the chemical bond. 3rd ed. Cornell University Press

Pauling, L., Campbell, D. H. and Pressman, D. (1943). Physiol. Rev. **23**, 203

Pethica, B. A. (1961). Exptl. Cell Res. Suppl. **8**, 123

Pitayevskii, L. P. (1960). Soviet Phys. JETP **10**, 408

Pollack, W., Hager, H. J., Reckel, R., Toren, D. A., and Singher, H. O. (1965). Transfusion **5**, 158

Ponder, E. (1927). Protoplasma **611**

Prescott, D. M. and James, T. W. (1955). Exptl. Cell Res. **8**, 256

Pressman, D. (1963). In, Conceptual advances in immunology and oncology. Harper and Row, New York, p. 290

Puck, T. T., Marcus, P. I. and Cieciura, S. J. (1956). J. Exptl. Med. **103**, 273

Pulvertaft, R. J. V. and Weiss, L. (1963). J. Pathol. Bact. **85**, 473

Rappaport, C. (1966). Proc. Soc. Exptl. Biol. Med. **121**, 1022, 1025

Rappaport, C. and Howze, G. B. (1966). Proc. Soc. Exptl. Biol. Med. **121**, 1010, 1016

Richards, F. M. (1963). Ann. Rev. Biochem. **32**, 269

Rosenberg, M. D. (1962). Proc. Natl. Acad. Sci. (U.S.) **48**, 1342

Rothen, A. (1957). Rev. Sci. Instr. **28**, 283

Rubin, M. (1963). In, R. H. Wasserman, ed., The transfer of calcium and strontium across biological membranes. Academic Press, New York and London, p. 25

Salem, L. (1964). In, B. Pullman, ed., Electronic aspects of biochemistry. Academic Press, New York and London, p. 293

Schaefer, V. J. (1941). J. Phys. Chem. **45**, 681

Schwan, H. P. (1965). Ann. N. Y. Acad. Sci. **125**, 344

Seaman, G. V. F. and Cook, G. M. W. (1965). In, E. J. Ambrose, ed., Cell electrophoresis, J. and A. Churchill, London, p. 48

Sher, I. H. and Sobotka, H. (1955). J. Colloid Sci. **10**, 125

Sinanoğlu, O., Abdulnur, S., and Kestner, N. R. (1964). In, B. Pullman, ed., Electronic aspects of biochemistry. Academic Press, New York and London, p. 301

Smekal, A. (1933). Physik Z. **34**, 633.

Staubesand, J. (1963). Z. Zellforsch. **58**, 915

Steinberg, M. S. (1958). Am. Natl. **92**, 65

Steinberg, M. S. (1964). In, M. Locke, ed., Cellular membranes and development. Academic Press, New York, p. 321

Stern, O. (1924). Z. Elektrochem. **30**, 508

Tabor, D. (1951). Rep. Progr. Appl. Chem. **32**, 621

Taylor, A. C. (1961). Exptl. Cell Res. Suppl. **8**, 154

Taylor, A. C. (1962). In, Biological interactions in normal and neoplastic growth. Little, Brown and Company, p. 169

Taylor, A. C. and Robbins, E. (1963). Develop. Biol. **7**, 660

Tyler, A. (1947). Growth, Suppl. **10**, 7

Van den Tempel, M. (1958). J. Colloid Sci. **13**, 125

Valentine, R. C. and Allison, A. C. (1959). Biochim. Biophys. Acta **34**, 10

Verwey, E. J. W. and Overbeek, J. Th. G. (1948). Theory of the stability of lyophobic colloids. Elsevier, Amsterdam, London, New York

Vold, M. J. (1961). J. Colloid Sci. **16**, 1

Wang, S. C. (1927). Physik Z. **28**, 663

Weiss, L. (1957). M. D. Thesis. University of Cambridge

Weiss, L. (1959a). Exptl. Cell Res. **17**, 449

Weiss, L. (1959b). Exptl. Cell Res. **17**, 508

Weiss, L. (1960). Intern. Rev. Cytol. **9**, 187

Weiss, L. (1961a). Exptl. Cell Res. Suppl. **8**, 141

Weiss, L. (1961b). Exptl. Cell Res. **25**, 504

Weiss, L. (1961c). Nature **191**, 1108

Weiss, L. (1962). J. Theoret. Biol. **2**, 236

Weiss, L. (1963a). Exptl. Cell Res. **30**, 509

Weiss, L. (1963b). J. Gen. Microbiol. **32**, 331

Weiss, L. (1964a). J. Theoret. Biol. **6**, 275

Weiss, L. (1964b). Exptl. Cell Res. **33**, 277

Weiss, L. (1965a). Exptl. Cell Res. **37**, 540

Weiss, L. (1965b). J. Cell Biol. **26**, 735

Weiss, L. (1966). J. Cell Biol. **30**, 39

Weiss, L. and Coombs, R. R. A. (1963). Exptl. Cell Res. **30**, 331

Weiss, L. and Dingle, J. T. (1964). Ann. Rheumat. Diseases **23**, 57

Weiss, L. and Lachmann, P. J. (1964). Exptl. Cell Res. **36**, 86

Weiss, L. and Mayhew, E. (1966). J. Cell Physiol. **68**, 345

Weiss, L., Mayhew, E. and Ulrich, K. (1966). Lab. Invest. **15**, 1304

Weiss, L. and Woodbridge, R. F. (1967). Fed. Proc. **26**, 88

Weiss, P. (1950). Quart. Rev. Biol. **25**, 177

Weiss, P., and Garber, B. (1952). Proc. Nat. Acad. Sci. (U.S.) **38**, 264

Werner, A. (1920). In, Neuere Anschauungen auf dem Gebiete der anorganischen Chemie. Vieweg, Braunschweig

Wilkins, D. J., Ottewill, R. H. and Bangham, A. D. (1962). J. Theoret· Biol. **2**, 176

CHAPTER 5

Some methods of studying the periphery of viable cells

5.1 Cell electrophoresis

5.1.1. Theoretical considerations

The velocity of cells suspended in fluid, through which a direct current passes, may be measured with respect to the cathode, and expressed in terms of micra per sec per volt/cm of potential gradient. When a cell moves in fluid it takes with it part of its electrical double-layer, and the plane between that part of the fluid moving with the cell, and the fluid of the bulk-phase proper, is known as the hydrodynamic slip plane. Measurements of electro-phoretic mobility reflect the (zeta)-potential at the slip plane, and it will be appreciated that these zeta-potentials are a composite measurement of both true surface potential of the cell due to its charged groups and possibly ad-sorbed ions, and the contribution from that part of the ionic double-layer enclosed between the plane of the bound charges and the hydrodynamic slip plane. From a knowledge of experimentally determined values of cellular electrophoretic mobility, calculations may be made of zeta-potential, and the average, net, surface-charge density.

The theory and formulation of the factors governing the calculations of zeta-potential and surface charge density will not be discussed here, and the reader is referred to the works of Abramson et al. (1942), Stern (1956), James (1957) and Brinton and Lauffer (1959).

In the case of animal cells, and probably bacteria, electrophoretic mobility V, is related to zeta-potential ζ, by the Helmholtz–Smoluchowski equation

$$V = \frac{\zeta D}{4\pi\eta},\tag{1}$$

where D is the dielectric constant of the suspending fluid and η its viscosity.

Brinton and Lauffer point out that use of the Helmholtz–Smoluchowski

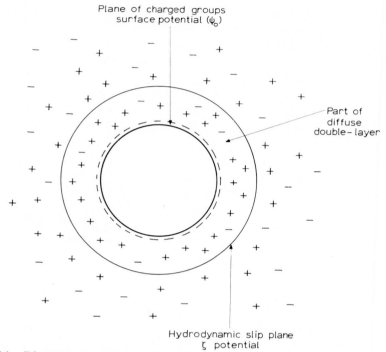

Fig. 5.1. Diagrammatic representation of electrokinetic planes of a moving cell. Emphatically not to scale.

equation depends on understanding of a number of assumptions which are made in its derivative, and these assumptions will be discussed.

(a) The product of the Debye–Hückel constant, (expressed in cm^{-1}) and the radius of curvature of the particles, (expressed in cm) should give a large dimensionless number, i.e. $\kappa a > 100$. In the physiological situation where $1/\kappa$ is very approximately $10\,\text{Å}$, and $\kappa = 10^7 \text{cm}$, values of radius of curvature down to about 10^{-5} cm (i.e. $0.1\,\mu$), will give rise to a value of $\kappa a > 100$. The question of whether the detailed geometry of the cell surface permits the use of the Helmholtz–Smoluchowski equation, or whether the cell surface should in effect be regarded as consisting of many low radii of curvature particles much smaller than $0.1\,\mu$ radius, is problematical. In general it can be expected that when $a > 1/\kappa$ the hydrodynamic slip plane will be smooth. Henry's (1931) corrected formula in cases where $100 > \kappa a > 0.1$,

$$V = \frac{\zeta D}{6\pi\eta} f(\kappa a),\qquad (2)$$

where $f(\kappa a)$ varies between 1 and 1.5, (Abramson et al. 1942) suggests that in extreme cases where $f(\kappa a) = 1$, calculations of ζ from electrophoretic mobility using the Helmholtz–Smoluchowski equation (1), could, according to Brinton and Lauffer, lead to values which are only 66% of the real zeta-potential as given by equation (2).

However, as noted by Glaeser (1963), careful consideration of the work of Henry (1931) and Overbeek (1952), on the derivation of the electrophoresis equation (2), shows that it is the gross radius which is the relevant quantity.

(b) It is assumed that the conductivity of the surface is no different from that of the bulk-phase. Although it is known that anions tend to concentrate at interfaces, it would reasonably be expected that for increased ionic concentration to produce a significant increase in conductivity, the environmental concentration of univalent electrolyte would have to be lower than 1 mM.

(c) It is also assumed that the dielectric constant and viscosity in the double-layer are the same as in the bulk-phase proper. As discussed in chapter 4, this may be an unwarrantable assumption, and that if structured water is present in this region, the dielectric constant may vary between values of about 30 for water in this state and about 180 for serum.

(d) It is assumed that the electric field of the double-layer and the applied electric field are additive, in spite of the distortion of the applied field by the particle. This is not apparently a major objection, since, as shown by Henry (1931), potentials are generally additive.

For spherical particles, having zeta-potentials of less than 25mV, their surface charge density σ, is given by:

$$\sigma = \frac{D\zeta}{4\pi}\left(\frac{1 + \kappa a}{a}\right). \tag{3}$$

In the case of cells, where as previously discussed $\kappa a > 100$, this approximates to

$$\sigma = \frac{D\zeta}{4\pi} \cdot \kappa, \tag{4}$$

where

$$V = \frac{\zeta D}{4\pi\eta}, \tag{1}$$

$$V = \frac{\sigma}{\eta\kappa}. \tag{5}$$

In the case of cells having zeta-potentials in excess of 25mV, in the presence of polyvalent electrolytes, where $\kappa a > 100$,

$$\sigma = \sqrt{\frac{NDkT}{2000\pi}} \cdot \sqrt{\left[\sum c_i \exp(-2_i e\zeta/kT) - 1\right]} \qquad (6)$$

N = Avagadro's number, k = Boltzmann's constant, T = absolute temperation, c_i = *molar* concentrations, z_i = valency of ions, e = electronic charge (Abramson et al. 1942).

In enumerating values of σ and ζ from mobility measurements, V should be expressed in CGS-units as $cm^2 \cdot sec^{-1} \cdot abvolts^{-1}$, instead of the usual $\mu sec^{-1} \cdot volts^{-1} \cdot cm$. In these units, $V = 300$, 10^{-4} (μsec^{-1})·(volts$^{-1} \cdot cm$).

From the discussion of the assumptions made in formulating values for net surface charge density and zeta-potential, together with the experimental difficulties in evaluating other factors in the derived equations, it is apparent that values given for σ and ζ may be considerably in error. At the present time it appears that cellular electrophoretic mobilities may be measured and expressed in absolute values for stated environmental conditions such as pH, temperature, viscosity, ionic strength etc., and that mobilities measured under these conditions may be compared with one another. When the assumption can be made that other factors in equations (1) and (5) remain constant, comparisons may be made of surface charge densities and zeta-potentials of cells on the basis of measurements of electrophoretic mobility, even though the absolute values are not known.

In order to determine the nature of ionizable groups at the electrokinetic surface of the cell, their ionization may be varied by altering the pH of the suspending fluid, and gross cellular isoelectric points may be determined, as described by Bangham and Pethica (1960) and others. Alternatively, attempts have been made to 'neutralize' specific negatively charged groups with various metal ions in order to identify them *in situ* (Bangham et al. 1958a; Bangham and Pethica 1960; Brinton and Lauffer 1959). Unfortunately, this latter method is much less specific than originally thought. Attempts to assess the depth of cellular-charged groups from the hydrodynamic slip-plane have been made by Heard and Seaman (1960), by measuring the mobilities of erythrocytes in media of differing ionic strengths in which the tonicity was maintained with sorbitol. The effective thickness of the double-layer $1/\kappa$ at 25° is given by:

$$1/\kappa = 3.05 I^{-\frac{1}{2}}, \qquad (7)$$

where $I = \frac{1}{2}\sum_i c_i z_i^2$ (Lewis and Randall 1921) (8) and c_i and z_i are ionic concentration and valency respectively. It is seen that as the ionic strength is decreased, $1/\kappa$ increases and therefore progressively more of the more deeply located charged groups, with respect to the hydrodynamic slip-plane, will be revealed by increased cellular electrophoretic mobility.

Pulvertaft and L. Weiss (1963) studied the effects of brief exposure to the solutions of varying pH and ionic strength and constitution described by the above-mentioned authors, on cells from embryonic mice filmed *in vitro*. It was observed that the different suspending fluids fell into three broad groups:

(1) Those that killed the cells and left them in a deformed state including unbuffered 'physiological' saline (0.145M NaCl at pH 5.5); 0.145M NaCl + NaOH pH 9.1 to 10.8; aqueous sorbitol solutions and sorbitol in 0.00145M and 0.0145M NaCl, and 0.1M Cu^{++}.

(2) Those that killed the cells without producing obvious deformation, including 0.145M NaCl + HCl from pH 2.7 to 5.0, and 0.01M La^{+++}.

(3) Those that produce no visible effect during 15 minutes, including 0.145M NaCl buffered to pH 7.0 with $NaHCO_3$; 0.067M phosphate buffer at pH 7.3; 0.0001M uranyl nitrate and 0.01M Th^{++++}. The question asked was not whether the various electrophoresis fluids were harmful to cells, but rather whether the various solutions produced changes in cellular electrokinetic properties over and above those expected of inert particles, on which double-layer theories are based. It was thought that the solutions of group (1), which produced viscous exudation from the exposed cells, might well produce changes in viscosity at the slip-plane reflected in equation (1); also, solutions of groups (1) and (2), which obviously caused cellular trauma, would lead to a cellular micro-environment more nearly resembling the bulk-phase in other properties than that of living cells. The overall conclusion was that although the complexity of the situation precluded dogmatic opinions, when cells were electrophoresed in the solutions of the first two groups, there is a possibility of error due to biological artefact.

5.1.2 *Practical considerations*

5.1.2.1 *Stationary level*
In the electrolyte solutions in common use, the walls of the glass electrophoresis cell carry a negative charge, which attracts positively charged ions. These cations flow towards the cathode when a voltage is applied across the ends of the cell, in an electro-osmotic stream. In a closed system, consisting of a single cell, fluid flows back down the centre of the cell in a reverse direction to the electro-osmotic flow, in order to prevent net flow of fluid (fig. 5.2). It can be appreciated that the observed mobility (V_{obs}) of a nega-

tively charged particle lying within the electro-osmotic stream will be less (towards the anode) than its true mobility (V) by the velocity of endosmotic flow ($V_{\text{e.os.}}$). By the same token, the observed mobility of a particle lying towards the centre of the electrophoresis cells will be greater than its true mobility, by $V_{\text{e.os.}}$ (fig. 5.2).

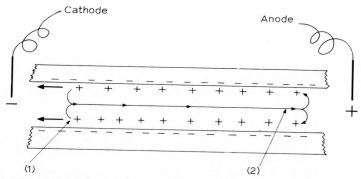

Fig. 5.2. Electro-osmotic flow in an electrolyte solution within a capillary tube along which there is a potential difference. (1) Direction of electro-osmotic flow (opposite direction to a negatively charged particle $V_{\text{obs}} = V - V_{\text{e.os.}}$). (2) Return flow (same direction as a negatively charged particle $V_{\text{obs}} = V + V_{\text{e.os.}}$).

Somewhere across the electrophoresis cell there must be a plane between the fluid moving along its wall and that moving along its central region, where no fluid movement occurs. This region is termed the 'stationary level' and is the region of the electrophoresis cell, in which the electrophoretic mobilities of particles may be measured, as indicated in fig. 5.3.

The location of the stationary level, with respect to a closed cylindrical cell, is discussed by Seaman (1965) as follows

$$V_{\text{e.os.}} = \frac{P}{4\eta}(r^2 - \tfrac{1}{2}R^2), \tag{9}$$

where, $P =$ hydrostatic pressure gradient, parallel to the axis of the electrophoresis cell, $R =$ radius of the electrophoresis cell, $r =$ distance from the axis of the electrophoresis cell, $\eta =$ bulk viscosity of suspending fluid. The velocity of the suspending fluid, V_s, at the surface of the electrophoresis cell, where $r = R$, is given by:

$$V_s = PR^2/8\eta, \tag{10}$$

therefore

$$V_{\text{e.os.}} = V_s(2r^2/R^2 - 1). \tag{11}$$

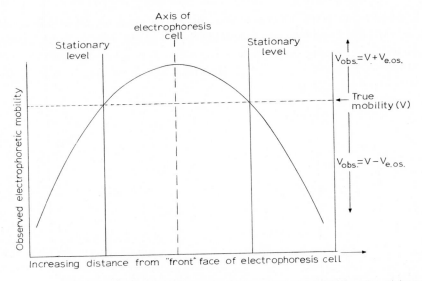

Fig. 5.3. The observed parabolic distribution of electrophoretic mobilities of particles at different depths within an electrophoresis cell.

Substituting in the equation

$$V_{\text{obs}} = V - V_{\text{e.os.}} \tag{12}$$

$$V_{\text{obs}} = V - V_{\text{s}} + V_{\text{s}}(2r^2/R^2). \tag{13}$$

At the stationary level, when $V_{\text{e.os.}} = 0$, and $V_{\text{obs}} = V$; from equation (13), $V_{\text{s}} = V_{\text{s}}(2r^2/R^2)$. Therefore, $2r^2 = R^2$ and $r = (R/2)^{\frac{1}{2}} = 0.707R$. In other words, the stationary level within the electrophoresis cell is, $0.707R$ from its axis, or $0.293R$ from its inner wall. In practice therefore, the microscope on the electrophoresis apparatus is focussed by means of a micrometer, at a plane $0.293R$ from the inner wall of the electrophoresis cell, which is itself located by means of scratches produced deliberately or accidentally during manufacture.

Seaman (1965) notes that although there is no exact solution to the hydrodynamic equations governing the location of stationary levels in rectangular electrophoresis cells, at width/depth ratios greater than 20:1, they are located at 0.21 and 0.79 of total cell depth.

5.1.2.2 Henry's correction

When a cylindrical cell apparatus containing a cell suspension is set up, immersed in a bath of fluid, the distance of the stationary level from the outer face of the optical flat ground out of the capillary tube is the practical distance required. This may be calculated by use of Henry's (1938) correction as follows:

$$\frac{\mu_1}{pR - \mu_1\,kR/\mu_2} = \frac{\mu_3}{qR - kR} + \frac{\mu_2 - \mu_3}{R},$$

where pR is the distance the microscope must be advanced in microns, indicated on the micrometer adjustment, from the position focus for the front optical flat, to the stationary level.

μ_1 = refractive index of fluid in the water-bath
μ_2 = refractive index of the glass capillary
μ_3 = refractive index of suspending medium
R = internal radius of capillary
kR = minimum thickness of glass of ground front of tube
qR = the actual distance to the stationary level.

As noted by Seaman (1965), although Henry's correction for a cylindrical chamber in air may amount to about $0.1R$, for a chamber in water as is the case in modern apparatus, the correction is less than $0.01R$, and may be neglected.

A very useful experimental method for locating the stationary level has been described by Bangham et al. (1958a) in which the charge on the electrophoresis cell wall is altered by allowing it to adsorb haemoglobin from lyzed erythrocytes at about pH 9.0 and pH 6.5, and then measuring depth/velocity curves for erythrocytes in dilute haemoglobin solutions at these two pH values, bearing in mind that the mobilities of washed human and sheep erythrocytes are constant over the range pH 5 to 9 in the presence and absence of haemoglobin. The two curves are plotted in the same graph, when their intercept indicates the stationary level (fig. 5.4).

5.1.2.3. Determination of electrophoretic mobilities

Particles are timed to cross a given number of squares in a calibrated graticule placed in the eyepiece of a microscope, focussed on the stationary level, when a known voltage gradient is applied. Transit time should, ideally, not be less than 5 sec because of observer errors in starting and stopping the stopwatch, and not greater than 20 sec because then particles may move appreciably from the stationary level. Each particle should be timed in both directions by reversing the current. Seaman (1965) considers that the applied potential gradient should lie between 2 to 5 volts/cm.

In my own laboratory, we have found it convenient to prepare conversion

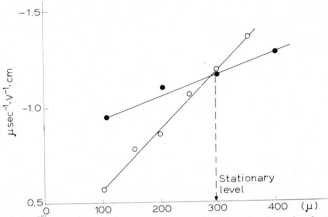

Fig. 5.4.   Electrophoresis cell depth/mobility curves of erythrocytes in electrolyte containing haemoglobin at *p*H 5.0 (●—●) and *p*H 8.5 (○—○). The intercept indicates the
stationary level. Abscissa: distance from inner face of cylindrical electrophoresis tube.
Ordinate, cell mobility.

tables for individual electrophoresis cells, with which the times taken for
individual particles to cross a given number of eyepiece squares, at predeter-
mined voltage gradients, can be directly converted to mobilities expressed
as μ sec^{-1}·volts^{-1}·cm.

The various types of apparatus are well described by Abramson et al.
(1942), Brinton and Lauffer (1959), Seaman (1965), Furhmann and Ruhenstroth-Bauer (1965) and Lukiewicz and Korohoda (1965). My own comments
will be limited to two types used in this laboratory, which are the cylindrical
cell apparatus designed by Bangham et al. (1958a), and commercially available from Rank Bros. Bottisham, Cambridge, England, and the rectangular
cell apparatus developed by Ruhenstroth-Bauer and his colleagues (vide
Fuhrmann and Ruhenstroth-Bauer 1965), and available commercially through
Carl Zeiss, Oberkochen, Germany.

Seaman (1965) has listed some of the general points about cell design
which include:

(a) Ease of construction and replacement. The cylindrical cell, which is
made from capillary tubes which are manufactured to high degrees of
accuracy, is much easier and cheaper to make and replace than rectangular
cells.

(b) The cell should be easy to clean and fill. Corners and joints lead to
inadequate cleaning, with the risk of contamination of the specimens being

measured, and also to trapping of air bubbles. In our own experience, trapped air bubbles are more of a problem in the rectangular than the cylindrical cells, although the apparatus developed by Zeiss enables the rectangular cell to be rocked in a vertical axis.

(c) The cell should be thin enough to permit the heat produced, when current flows (Bangham 1961) to be rapidly dissipated. In both of the pieces of apparatus described, the cells are immersed in water baths. I would not use a non-thermostated cell.

The big advantage of the Zeiss apparatus is that as the cell is constructed of optical flats, phase-contrast microscopy can be used for viewing the specimens. This is invaluable for organelles, and ghosts, as well as helping in cell identification.

In our own experience it is desirable to be able to fill the apparatus without disturbing the electrodes; in addition, the introduction of small volumes of cell suspension is aided by having separate filling ports. Cylindrical electrophoresis cells, with essentially separate compartments, have been described by Seaman and Heard (1961) and by Häyry and Saxén (1965), and are standard equipment on the Zeiss apparatus.

5.1.2.4. Electrode systems

The choice of electrodes is governed to some extent by the dimensions of the apparatus and the ionic strength of the suspending fluids, in so far as these affect current density at the electrodes. Thus, in a constant voltage apparatus, changes in resistance, due to polarization at the electrodes, which may be manifest in the late stages by visible gas bubbles, lead to variations in field strength in the part of the cell in which measurements are made. Polarization changes are aggravated by high current density at the electrode surface, and may be overcome by having electrodes with large surface areas. The platinum electrodes used by us are cylindrical and, more importantly, platinized (Findlay 1949), which vastly increases their surface area. Thus, although there may be theoretical objections to platinum electrodes due to their increased tendency to polarize as compared with $Cu/CuSO_4$ (Abramson 1929), or Ag/AgCl (James 1957) electrodes, this objection does not seem valid in practice, when platinum electrodes are used in the small-bore cylindrical cell. As platinum electrode systems are simpler, and do not result in the liberation of toxic ions, such as Cu^{++}, or Ag^+, which require the interposition of sintered glass, millipore, agar or gelatin plug filters, their practical advantages outweigh the theoretical objections to their use with living cells.

5.1.2.5. Timing

For small numbers of measurements a stopwatch reading to 1/10 sec is adequate. However, for large numbers of readings, a stopwatch is slow and tedious. We have developed a print-out stopwatch, accurate to 1/10 sec, which is started by a push-button which, on pressing again, stops the timing mechanism, prints out the time and zeroes itself, all within 1/5 sec. By use of such machines we are able to make many more measurements in a given time, with far less fatigue than previously.

5.1.2.6. Cell sedimentation

A cell moving in the plane of the stationary level in an electrophoresis chamber is subject to an electrical field-producing movement in a horizontal plane in the direction of the voltage gradient, and a gravitational field tending to produce movement in a vertical plane. The direction of movement of the cell, as observed in the microscope, will thus be upwards at a varying angle to the horizontal, which will depend on the mobility vector and the gravitational vector, as influenced by cellular buoyancy, which will depend on the density of the suspending fluid.

Since the gravitational and mobility vectors are orthogonal, the gravitational vector has no component in the horizontal direction. Therefore, the time taken to traverse distances measured horizontally will not be influenced by gravity and will be the same for the same cell, regardless of the direction of its motion in the electrophoresis chamber (fig. 5.5).

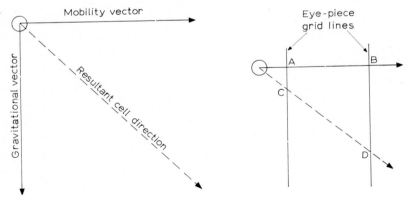

Fig. 5.5.   Movements of a cell in terms of mobility and gravitational vectors. Although in terms of distance, CD > AB, the times taken for cells to traverse AB and CD are the same, because the cellular velocity along path CD is greater than along path AB.

Sedimentation may be retarded by suspending the cells in a mixture of 50% Hanks' saline and 50% of a 4.3% aqueous sucrose solution. Tests with ascites tumour cells have revealed no differences in aerobic and anaerobic metabolism between cells suspended in sucrose/Hanks' and Hanks' saline alone.

5.2 The assessment of cell adhesion

No methods are currently available for the unequivocal measurement of the energy of cell adhesion; however, some cell properties which are expected to be associated with adhesiveness may be measured. Some of these will be described.

5.2.1. Adhesion number

This technique is a development of those well-known in colloid science in which particles are allowed to settle on to a plate and are then counted. The plate is then inverted, the remaining particles are counted, and expressed as a percentage of the total previously present.

As I have used the technique any culture vessel having a flat transparent bottom may be used. This is inscribed with small circles having a diameter of about 3 mm. A cell-suspension of density such that 200 to 300 cells will settle over one inscribed circle is introduced into a number of vessels. At given times, the cells over the circles are counted with an inverted microscope, the vessel is inverted, and the remaining cells counted. The standard Sykes–Moore culture vessels, which are essentially two circular coverslips separated by an O-ring gasket are very suitable, as are 'Perspex' slides of the type shown in fig. 5.6.

Some typical results obtained by use of this method are shown in fig. 5.7a and b, which were part of some studies on the adhesion of cells to glass at different temperatures, in the presence and absence of serum.

5.2.2. Cell spreading

This may be determined by counting the total number of cells over a given area of substrate, and then rejecting those with a circular outline as non-spreaders. An example of this procedure is given in fig. 5.8 which shows the effect of serum on the spreading of fibroblasts cultured at various temperatures. Although there is no difficulty in enumerating well-spread cells,

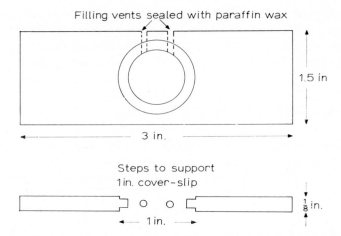

Fig. 5.6. Perspex (Lucite) chamber for determination of adhesion number of cells to glass. Standard 1″ diameter coverslips are held to the recessed steps by means of sparsely applied silicone grease.

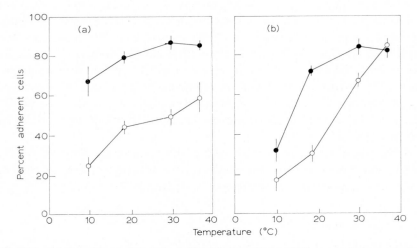

Fig. 5.7. (a) Percentage of foetal rat fibroblastic cells ($\pm$ S.E.) remaining attached to glass following inversion 110 (○—○) and 280 (●—●) minutes incubation in medium 199, at the indicated temperatures. (b) Percentage of cells ($\pm$ S.E.) remaining, following inversion after 75 (○—○) and 265 (●—●) minutes incubation in medium 199 + 15 % bovine serum at the temperatures shown. (From L. Weiss (1964) Exptl. Cell Res. **33**, 277, by permission of the Editors.)

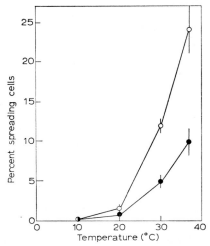

Fig. 5.8. Percentage ($\pm$ S.E.) of spreading foetal rat fibroblasts after 280 minutes incubation at the indicated temperatures in medium 199 only (○—○) and in medium 199 + 15% bovine serum (●—●). (From L. Weiss (1964) Exptl. Cell Res. 33, 277; by permission of the Editors).

particularly when these have fibroblastic morphology, it is sometimes difficult to judge minimal degrees of flattening of cells. In addition, this procedure only permits an all-or-none type of enumeration.

Spreading rates may be determined by taking photomicrographs of cells at various time intervals, projecting the photographic negatives and measuring face-on areas with a planimeter. The technique which I have found most useful consists of an inverted phase-contrast, photo-microscope which has a stage modified to take a rotating disc which accepts six Sykes–Moore chambers at its periphery. In this way, six cultures may be observed in rapid sequence. Dr. G. O. Gey has for many years used a system similar to this, which is entirely automated; the disc carrying the cultures is continuously rotated and they are photographed by exposure to brief high intensity light flashes, recorded on a 35 mm cinecamera.

5.2.3. 'Dynamic' adhesiveness

The adhesion of cells transported in the blood stream to the vascular endothelium is considered to be an important step in the metastatic process. For this reason, it is of interest to determine the adhesion of cells to the walls of model flow labyrinths. A useful system is the perfusion of columns of glass beads with suspensions of cells. This has been used to study the inter-actions of leucocytes (Garvin 1961) and platelets (Hellem 1960) with the column. However, these authors have not clarified the relationship between the perfusion method, the adhesive properties of the cells and the quantities measured. Blumenson (1967) has made an intensive mathematical analysis of the passage of cells through bead columns. Firstly, in such columns, assuming a close packed configuration of the beads, a cell passes through two types of void space sequentially – a tetrahedral space enclosed by four beads whose centres form the vertices of a tetrahedron, and an octahedral space enclosed by six beads whose centres form the vertices of an octahedron. Where r is the radius of the beads, the maximum radius of a cell fitting into a tetrahedral void is $0.22r$, and $0.41r$ for a octohedral void. The maximum radius for a cell leaving either void, through spaces at their sides, is $0.15r$ for both types. In passing through a pair of void spaces of volume $0.53r$, the total surface area exposed to a cell is approximately $4r^2$.

A measured quantity of cell suspension is layered on top of a water-jacketed column of beads, from which it drips out through a 27-gauge needle. Known number of drops of cell suspension are collected into diluent, in numbered jars, and cell counts are made on a Coulter Counter.

The following quantities are determined:

r – radius of the beads,

V – void volume of the packed beads,

L – height of the bead column,

$10V$ – volume of 10 drops of emergent cell suspension,

i – number of cells in $10V$ ml of suspension added to the column,

G – generic number of a collection jar,

$T(G)$ – number of cells in the Gth jar,

D – number of the collection jar such that $T(G) = T(D)$ for all jars after the Dth,

N – largest integer less than or equal to $L/2r$,

M – largest integer less than or equal to $5VL/rV$.

The dynamic adhesivity of a cell passing through a microchamber consist-ing of both a tetrahedral and octahedral void is related to:

s – probability that a cell entering a microchamber never leaves it,

$c, c+d$ – two types of delay (relative to fluid velocity) which a cell can experience in a microchamber which it enters and eventually leaves,

p – probability that this cell experiences a delay of c,

$1-p$ – probability that this cell experiences a delay $c+d$.

The purpose of this type of experiment is to evaluate s, d and p, from the determined quantities relating to the column, and the input and output of cells going through it. Blumenson considers a set of $M(N+1)$ numbers

$$m + N(1 + c) + kd, \quad \text{where} \quad m = 1, ..., M; \; k = 0, 1, ..., N,$$

for each m and k, M can be divided into the number in this equation a certain number of times, with a remainder. For each integer G and each m, let $K(m, G)$ denote the set of k selected from 0, 1, ..., N for which this division gives either a whole part equal to G-1 and a positive remainder, or else a whole part equal to G and a zero remainder. $1(m, G)$ is defined as

$$1(m, G) = \sum_{K(m, G)} C(N, k) \, p^{N-k}(1 - p)^k,$$

where $C(N, k)$ is the binomial coefficient, $N!/k!(N-k)!$ Then, when $G < D$:

$$T(G) = uM^{-1} \sum_{H=1}^{G} \sum_{m=1}^{M} 1(m, H),$$

where the number of cells collected in the Gth jar entered the bead column during collection into the Hth jar, and $u = (1-S)^N i$. When $G \leq D$, $T(G) = u$. The values for $K(m, G)$, $1(m, G)$ and $T(G)$ are computed electronically from the equations given.

If N, u and i are known, then s may be evaluated from $S = 1—(u/i)^{1/N}$, U (the asymptotic value of $T(G)$) is obtained experimentally from determination of D, which is the first jar, after which all collection jars contain the same number of cells.

Thus, by simple experiments, the pattern of emergence of cells from glass bead columns can give quantitive information on 'dynamic' adhesion. We are currently using the technique to give information on the interactions of cells with beads having polar and non-polar surfaces, and their modification by environmental fluids. In addition, we hope to evaluate whether fibrin only influences cell trapping in microchambers by mechanical means.

5.2.4. Cell agglutination

Standard agglutination experiments provide a useful index of cell adhesion, which is inversely proportional to some function of the percentage of free cells remaining, in comparable experiments. The free cells may be enumerated by direct or electronic counting, and the size of aggregates may be determined directly, from photomicrographs or electronically. Specific techniques are described by Armstrong (1966) and Wilkins et al. (1962).

5.3 The measurement of cell detachment

From the discussions in chapter 4, it will be appreciated that any quantitative test involving cell detachment from any other cells, or non-cellular substrata, is a measurement of cell separation which probably may not be equated with cell adhesion. Many tests described in the literature as measuring adhesion are thus probably incorrectly described.

In the past, cells have been detached from glass tubing by a stream of fluid at known hydrostatic pressure by Dan (1947), or detached from the walls of glass culture vessels by shaking (L. Weiss 1959) or by centrifugation (Easty et al. 1960). Cells have been scraped off epithelial sheets by Herrmann and Hickman (1948), pulled apart from each other with microneedles (Coman 1944) or shaken free of standard tissue blocks by McCutcheon et al. (1948), in a quantitative manner. All of these techniques may be classified as peeling tests, in which two adherends are peeled apart.

Peeling tests are discussed at some length by Bickerman (1961), and Spies (1953) has made a detailed mathematical analysis of them, in the special case of bonded metal joints. Of interest here is Spies' conclusion that the value of numerical data from such tests is limited by knowledge of the rheological properties of the adhesive. Thus, peeling tests are sensitive to cohesive strength, but peeling strength also increases with elasticity of the adhesive.

In classical rheology, materials may be characterized as elastic or Hookean, plastic or St. Venant, viscous or Newtonian, or mixtures of these. When such ideal materials are deformed by loading, it is theoretically possible to calculate their properties under no load, i.e. in the ground state, by extrapolation (fig. 5.9). Unfortunately all real materials are rheologically anomalous, which in effect means that extrapolation of their properties from one set of deforming conditions to another is not possible, as discussed by Weis-

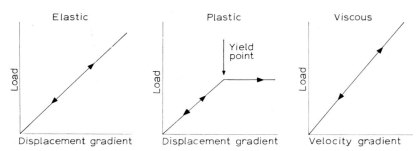

Fig. 5.9. The behaviour of 'ideal' bodies under load.

senberg (1948). This concept is well illustrated by a consideration of thixo-tropy and dilatancy. Thixotropy may be defined as reversible, isothermal gel–sol transformations produced by mechanical working (Peterfi 1927), and dilatancy as the increased resistance to shearing as strain or rate of strain increases (Jobling and Roberts 1959). If there are thixotropic and dilatant elements in the periphery of a cell, then the former would tend to undergo gel–sol transformation and weaken on application of distractive force, while the latter would show increased resistance to deformation; and both of these processes would be expected to be rate-dependent. Experiments in which ascites sarcoma 37 cells were deformed into micropipettes (L. Weiss 1966) showed that when negative pressure was applied at a rate of 3 cm H_2O per sec, approximately 15 cm H_2O were required to produce a standard hemi-spherical bulge; on the other hand, only about 5 cm H_2O of negative pressure was required when applied at a rate of 0.2 cm per sec. This demonstration of bulk dilatant properties indicates the necessity in distraction experiments, of knowledge of not only peak force, but also the rate at which it is applied. The rheological considerations also suggest that quantitative expressions of separation in cell populations should be given over a range of distractive forces.

An attempt was made (L. Weiss 1961a) to overcome some of the diffi-culties mentioned in estimating the forces required to distract cells from non-cellular substrata, by the use of shearing pressures transmitted through fluid. Cells are grown on the flat glass bottoms of specially made stainless steel culture vessels of the type shown in fig. 5.10. A rotating steel cylinder fixed to a modified vertical drill press, as shown in fig. 5.10, is lowered into the fluid covering the cells, and is brought to rest at a known preset distance above them by a micrometer stop. It should be emphasized that the bottom face of the rotating cylinder does not come into direct contact with the cells.

When the cells are immersed in a fluid of dynamic viscosity η poises, and separated from the bottom of the rotating cylinder by h cm, when it revolves about its centre with a linear velocity of V cm per sec, then the force, F exerted on cells growing on a narrow circular strip of substratum of width dr, distance r cm from its centre is given by

$$F = \frac{V \cdot \eta \cdot 2\pi r \cdot dr}{h}.$$

$$\text{Shear stress} = \frac{\text{Force}}{\text{Area}} = \frac{V \cdot \eta \cdot 2\pi r \cdot dr}{2\pi r \cdot dr \cdot h} = \frac{\eta V}{h}.$$

Fig. 5.10.   Shearing machine showing (a) rotating cylinder, (b) culture vessel, (c) micrometer stop, (d) tachometer, (e) revolution counter. (From L. Weiss (1961a) Exptl. Cell. Res.
Suppl. **8**,141, by permission of the Editors).

Linear velocity (V)=angular velocity (ω) × radius (r)

$$\therefore \text{Shear stress} = \frac{\eta \cdot \omega \cdot r}{h} \; \text{dynes/cm}^2.$$

In the actual experiment, small circles are engraved on the under surface of the glass disc at the bottom of the culture vessel, with their centres on a 1 cm radius from its centre. The cells adherent to the glass, or films spread over it, within the confines of the engraved circles are counted under the microscope. The cultures are then exposed to shearing pressures, and the residual cells counted. The percentage of cells detached under given conditions of shear may thus be determined.

Calculations of shearing pressures from data given in the equations are only approximate. At any speed of rotation the opposed substratum and cylinder surfaces tend to act as a centrifugal pump, and the simple direct relationship between shear stress and distance from the axis of rotation (r) is no longer strictly applicable. This system has been improved in two ways since its original description; by cutting the bottom face of the rotating cylinder to a 1° cone, and by constructing a new machine in which the culture vessel is rotated and the cylinder is kept stationary. Laminar flow of fluid is to be expected (Schultz–Grunow 1935) when the distance separating the bottom of the cylinder from the cells is less than 1/50th of the radius of the cylinder. In addition, the maximal speed for streamline-flow lies between 300–400 r.p.m. On account of the various hydrodynamic considerations, the shearing pressures are only approximately calculable, however, within the limits of accuracy of the tachometer, spacing micrometer and general engineering tolerance of other parts of the machines, the shearing pressures are reproducible.

The facilitation of cell detachment by enzymes and other agents can, under suitably controlled conditions, be used as an analytical technique for identifying components present at the cell periphery. Thus, facilitation of cell detachment by incubation of neuraminidase was used as evidence that sialic acid was present at the periphery of cultured fibroblasts (L. Weiss 1961b); and more recently, the facilitation of cell detachment by ribonuclease, together with other evidence, was taken to favour the idea that RNA is a structural constituent of the periphery of other cultured cells (L. Weiss and Mayhew 1967). This type of mechanochemical analysis must take account of the fact that proteins from the culture medium coat the glass bottoms of the culture vessels and may form an enzyme-susceptible intermediate layer between the cell periphery and the glass. Other agents such as vitamin A

(L. Weiss 1963) can probably act by entering the cells and activating the lysosomal hydrolases, which in turn can facilitate detachment by autolytic activity.

5.4 Tension at the cell periphery

Measurements of the tensions at cell peripheries have been used to elucidate their molecular architecture. Much of the earlier data has been critically and meticulously reviewed by Harvey and Danielli (1938). The clarity of this review is such, that it is surprising that confusion should have subsequently arisen over the interpretation of tensional data.

The techniques used up to that time are reviewed in detail by Harvey (1936, 1937) and Harvey and Danielli (1938) and will only be outlined. Three general techniques are of interest here:

5.4.1 Centrifugation

The assumption is made that a fluid drop becomes unstable when it is drawn into a cylinder whose length is π times its diameter, when it breaks into two spheres (Harvey 1931). The method is applicable to spherical cells containing oil globules which are less dense the average cytoplasmic contents, and other granules which are denser. The process of formation of two 'half cells' is seen under direct observation in the centrifuge-microscope (Harvey 1932).

At the moment of instability the tension T, around the circumference πD (where D = diameter) of the cylindrical cell is given in a medium of density ρ_m, by consideration of the downward component of the heavy part of volume V_H and density ρ_H, i.e. $V_H(\rho_H - \rho_M)$; and the upward component of the light (oil) part of volume V_L and density ρ_L; i.e. $V_L(\rho_M - \rho_L)$. When the half cells separate at a centrifugal force G, and where $g = 981$, then

$$\pi D T = Gg \left[V_H(\rho_H - \rho_M) + V_L(\rho_M - \rho_L) \right].$$

By use of this method, the tension at the surface of unfertilized sea urchin eggs is estimated at about 0.2 dynes/cm.

Of more value in the estimation of tensional forces in smaller cells, is a modification of the method in which oil drops are injected into cells which are then centrifuged until just before they separate into two half cells; a neck of protoplasm forms which has an internal diameter equal to the diameter of the oil drop. At this stage it is reckoned that the buoyancy of the oil is equal to the tension around the neck of protoplasm. Where the oil has a volume of V_0 and a density of ρ_o, then

$$\pi D T = Gg\left[V_0(\rho_M - \rho_o)\right].$$

By use of this modification, values where obtained of 1–3 dynes/cm for *Amoeba dubia* (Harvey and Marsland 1932), 2 dynes/cm for rabbit macrophages and 1.3 dynes/cm for frog leucocytes (Shapiro and Harvey 1936).

5.4.2. Compression methods

Initially (Harvey and Fankhauser 1933) attempts were made to measure the tension at the surfaces of cells by considering them as originally spherical, sessile fluid drops, flattened by gravity.

Where T is tension at the surface expressed in dynes/cm; g is the acceleration due to gravity; ρ is the density of the cell, and ρ_m is the density of the medium; r is the radius of the cell where it is flattened most and F is a function of distance d which is an index of vertical flattening, then (Dorsey 1928) (as in fig. 5.11) $T = g(\rho - \rho_m)r^2F$.

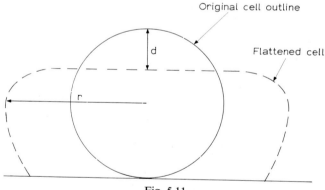

Fig. 5.11.

Using this technique values of 0.5 dynes/cm and 0.1 dynes/cm were obtained on the eggs of *Busycon canaliculatum* and *Triturus viridescens*.

For those cases where cells do not flatten enough under their own weight to enable reasonable measurements of flattening to be made, a compression device was made (Cole 1932) in which cells are flattened by gold microbeams to which weights can be added, as indicated in fig. 5.12.

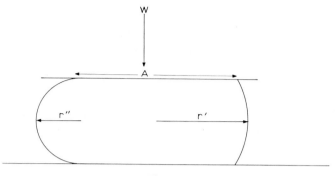

Fig. 5.12.

When weight W is applied to a measured flattened area A of a cell, to exert a pressure $W/A = P$, and then the two radii of the flattened cells are r^1 and r^{11} as shown, then

$$T = \frac{Pr^1 r^{11}}{r^1 + r^{11}}.$$

Tension/compression curves are extrapolated back to give the tension at zero compression. A value of 0.08 dynes/cm was thus obtained for the uncompressed eggs of *Arbacia punctulata*.

Rosenberg (1963) has described a technique whereby human and chick cells, cultured *in vitro*, are compressed between coverslips, and the degree of deformation required for herniation of their peripheries is measured, but apart from determining the relative extensibility of the cells, he made no attempt to calculate tensions at their surfaces.

5.4.3. Cell elastimeters

A third technique involves use of the cell elastimeter described by Mitchison and Swann (1954). Essentially, this apparatus consists of a fluid-filled micro-pipette connected to an accurately movable reservoir, by means of which cells may be sucked variable distances into the micropipette by known negative pressures, as shown in fig. 5.13.

When a cell of radius R is deformed to produce a bulge of radius r, pro-truding distance x up a tube of diameter d, then where P is the negative pres-sure and T the tension at the surface of the cells,

$$P = 2T\left(\frac{1}{r} - \frac{1}{R}\right),$$

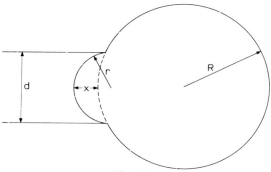

Fig. 5.13.

where

$$r^2 = \left(\frac{d}{2}\right)^2 + (r - x)^2,$$

$$P = 2T\left(\frac{2x}{x^2 + \frac{1}{4}d^2} - \frac{1}{R}\right).$$

Mitchison and Swann's technique has been scaled down by Rand and Burton (1964) to measure the mechanical properties of the erythrocyte membrane, and L. Weiss (1965) has used a similar technique to determine the deformability of tumour cells, in which approximately 5 to 20 cm H_2O pressure was required to make a hemispherical bulge into a micropipette of 5μ internal diameter. This corresponds to a tension at the cell surface of 0.3–3 dynes/cm, using the relationship $T = Pr/4$.

The difficulties with the interpretation of these types of data stem from the fact that 'tension at the cell surface' is not the same thing as cell 'surface tension'. Surface tension is the force which makes a drop of liquid tend to contract into a sphere, which behaves as though it is surrounded by a skin. If the surface contracting force is γ_0 dynes/cm in such a fluid drop, then where S is the entropy in the system, T the absolute temperature, P the pressure, V the volume, A its surface area, n the number of molecules and μ the chemical potential, then where F is the total free (Helmholtz) energy $dF = SdT - PdV + \gamma_0 dA + \mu\,dn$ (Davies and Rideal 1961). At constant temperature and volume, when the number of molecules in the system remains the same

$$\gamma_0 = \frac{\partial F}{\partial A}.$$

If γ_0 is positive, then the Helmholtz free energy F, will decraese when there is a diminution of surface area (i.e. $-\partial A$). As the surface of a stable liquid drop tends to form minimal surface area, γ_0 is in fact positive, and is the surface tension. To deform a fluid drop, such as an oil droplet, the deforming force must be greater than the surface tension, which may be measured by variations of the techniques outlined above.

When a cell membrane is deformed by applying pressure to the whole cell then the emergent data is concerned with 'tension at the cell periphery' as distinct from surface tension and is very much more complex. Thus Harvey and Danielli (1938) draw attention to the fact that the cell membrane may possess elastic and plastic properties. Cole (1932) demonstrated the elastic properties at the periphery of the sea urchin egg, but his conclusions have been recently criticized by Yoneda (1964), who considers that Cole's estimation of area of contact between cells and the compressing plate was wrong. Yoneda finds that when allowance is made for area of contact, then tension remains constant, irrespective of change in surface area. Although this finding indicates no elasticity, irregularities in the surface of any cell at the ultrastructural level make computation of its surface area almost impossible, (Weiss 1961a, 1962, Pulvertaft and Weiss 1963, Patinkin and Doljanski 1965; Nordling and Mayhew 1966) and it seems difficult to concede that the surface of the sea-urchin egg, or indeed other cells is inelastic.

From Mitchison and Swann's (1954) description of the behaviour of sea urchin eggs sucked into pipettes, it is clear that although the egg possesses elastic properties, it is not a purely elastic system. From the time taken for the cell to deform at constant pressure, and the creep of an egg into the pipette, viscous elements are also present. In addition to this, Mitchison and Swann clearly describe a yield-point, indicating a plastic element. Katchalsky et al. (1961) have demonstrated that the erythrocyte periphery may be approximately represented as a Kelvin unit, which consists of elastic and viscous elements arranged in parallel. To complicate matters still further, all materials so far examined show rheological deviations from ideal theoretical expectations (Weissenberg 1948). It is concluded that the data obtained from any type of cell deformation experiment, present an intractable mathematical problem, from the viewpoint of detailed interpretation.

References

Abramson, H. A. (1929). J. Gen. Physiol. **12**, 469

Abramson, H. A., Moyer, L. S. and Gorin, M. H. (1942). Electrophoresis of proteins and the chemistry of cell surfaces. Reinhold, New York

Armstrong, P. B. (1966). J. exp. Zool. 163, 99.

Bangham, A. D. (1961). Proc. Roy. Soc. B **155**, 292

Bangham, A. D. and Pethica, B. A. (1960). Proc. Roy. Phys. Soc. (Edinburgh) **28**, 43

Bangham, A. D., Pethica, B. A. and Seaman, G. V. F. (1958a). Biochem. J. **69**, 12

Bangham, A. D., Flemans, R., Heard, D. H. and Seaman, G. V. F. (1958b). Nature **182**, 642

Bickerman, J. J. (1961) The science of adhesive joints. Academic Press, New York and London

Blumenson, L. E. (1967). In press

Brinton, C. C. and Lauffer, M. A. (1959). In, M. Bier, ed., Electrophoresis, Academic Press, New York, p. 427

Cole, K. S. (1932). J. Cell. Comp. Physiol. **1**, 1

Coman, D. R. (1944). Cancer Res. **4**, 625

Dan, K. (1947). Biol. Bull. **93**, 274

Davies, J. T. and Rideal, E. K. (1961). Interfacial phenomena. Academic Press, London

Dorsey, W. E. (1928). J. Wash. Acad. Sci. **18**, 505

Easty, G. C., Easty, D. M. and Ambrose, E. J. (1960). Exptl. Cell Res. **19**, 539

Findlay, A. (1949). Practical physical chemistry. Longmans, Green and Co., London

Furhmann, G. F. and Ruhenstroth-Bauer, G. (1965). In, E. J. Ambrose, ed., Cell electrophoresis, Churchill, London, p. 22

Garvin, J. E. (1961). J. Exptl. Med. **114**, 51

Glaeser, R. M. (1963). The electric charge and surface properties of intact cells. Office of Technical Services, Washington

Harvey, E. N. (1931). Biol. Bull. Wood's Hole, **61**, 273

Harvey, E. N. (1932). J. Franklin Inst. **214**, 1

Harvey, E. N. (1936). J. Cell. Comp. Physiol. **8**, 251

Harvey, E. N. (1937). Trans. Faraday Soc. **33**, 943

Harvey, E. N. and Danielli, J. F. (1938). Biol. Rev. **13**, 319

Harvey, E. N. and Fankhauser, G. (1933). J. Cell. Comp. Physiol. **3**, 463

Harvey, E. N. and Marsland, D. A. (1932). J. Cell. Comp. Physiol. **5**, 255

Häyry, P. and Saxén, L. (1965). Nature **205**, 1105

Heard, D. H. and Seaman, G. V. F. (1960). J. Gen. Physiol. **43**, 635

Hellem, A. J. (1960). Scand. J. Clin. Lab. Invest. **12**, Suppl. 51

Henry, D. C. (1931). Proc. Roy. Soc. A **133**, 106

Henry, D. C. (1938). J. Chem. Soc. 997

Herrmann, H. and Hickman, F. H. (1948). Bull. Johns Hopkins Hosp. **82**, 2

James, A. M. (1957). Progr. Biophys. **8**, 96

Jobling, A. and Roberts, J. E. (1959). In, C. C. Mill, ed., Rheology of disperse systems. Pergamon Press, London, p. 127

Katchalsky, A., Kedem, O., Klibansky, H. and De Vries, A. (1961). In, A. Copley and G. W. Scott Blair, eds., Deformation and flow in biological systems. Pergamon Press, London

Lewis, G. N. and Randall, M. (1921). J. Am. Chem. Soc. **43**, 1112

Lukiewicz, S. and Korohoda, W. (1965). In, E. J. Ambrose, ed., Cell electrophoresis. Churchill, London, p. 26

McCutcheon, M., Coman, D. R. and Fontaine, B. M. (1948). Cancer **1**, 460

Mitchison, J. M. and Swann, M. M. (1954). J. Exptl. Biol. **31**, 443

Nordling, S. and Mayhew, E. (1966). Exptl. Cell Res. **43**, 77

Overbeek, J. Th. G. (1952). In, H. R. Kruyt, ed., Colloid science, Elsevier, Amsterdam, Vol. I p. 268

Patinkin, D. and Doljanski, F. (1965). J. Cell. Comp. Physiol. **66,** 343

Peterfi, T. (1927). Arch. Entwicklungsmech. Organ. **112**, 660

Pulvertaft, R. J. V. and Weiss, L. (1963). J. Path. Bact. **85**, 473

Rand, R. P. and Burton, A. C. (1964). Biophys. J. **4**, 115

Rosenberg, M. D. (1963). J. Cell Biol. **17**, 289

Schultz-Grunow, F. (1935). Z. A.M.M. **15**, 191

Seaman, G. V. F. and Heard, D. H. (1961). Blood **18**, 599

Seaman, G. V. F. (1965). In, E. J. Ambrose ,ed., Cell electrophoresis, Churchill, London, p. 4

Shapiro, H. and Harvey, E. N. (1936). J. Cell. Comp. Physiol. **8**, 21

Spies, G. J. (1953). Aircraft Eng. (March), 1

Stern, K. G. (1956). In, G. Oster and A. W. Pollister, eds., Physical techniques in biological research. Academic Press, New York, Vol. II, p. 243.

Weiss, L. (1959). Exptl. Cell Res. **17**, 499

Weiss, L. (1961a). Exptl. Cell Res. Suppl. **8**, 141

Weiss, L. (1961b). Nature **191**, 1108

Weiss, L. (1962). Biochem. Soc. Symp. **22**, 32

Weiss, L. (1965). J. Cell Biol. **26**, 735

Weiss, L. (1966). J. Cell Biol. **30**, 39

Weiss, L. and Mayhew, E. (1966). J. Cell Physiol.

Weissenberg, K. (1948). Proc. Intern. Rheol. Congr. (Holland), 1

Wilkins, D. J., Ottewill, R. H. and Bangham, A. D. (1962). J. Theoret. Biol. **2**, 176

Yoneda, M. (1964). J. Exptl. Biol. **41**, 893

PART II

The malignant cell periphery, metastasis and infiltration

Metastasis,
a short historical review

Although tumours were recognized by the Ancients, and are described in Babylonian, Egyptian and Indian writings, knowledge was confined to superficial tumours and their superficial spread, because physicians did not perform necropsies; and surgery was only done, according to the Ebers Papyrus (Bryan 1930), on lipomas.

Willis (1948) attributes the first recorded description of spread of cancer to Herodotus, who, around 520 BC, described a fungating tumour of the breast in Darius' daughter Atossa. Wilder (1956) traces the further development of the metastatic concept through Hippocrates, who in the 4th century BC, classified tumours as malignant if they showed evidence of spread and the patient died, and benign if not. Celsus (30 BC–38 AD), according to Ewing (1922), was aware of the involvement of the axillary lymph nodes in mammary cancer.

In his survey of the history of cancer, Park (1903) describes how Galen in the first century AD introduced the concept of the humoral black bile, which caused cancer wherever it gravitated. Wilder (1956) next traces the evolution of the metastatic concept to the 14th century surgeon Guy de Chanliac who advocated extensive surgery of the breast to include 'rests', and Severinus (1580–1656) removed the axillary nodes with breast tumours. There still appears no clear-cut recognition of metastasis as the spread of neoplasia from a primary focus, and Wilder points out that Morgagni (1761), who recognized cancer, described a case of carcinoma of the pylorus with hepatic involvement, yet did not link the pyloric lesions with those in the liver. John Hunter (Palmer 1835) also thought that invasive processes seem 'to have no connection whatever with the (primary) diseased part'.

The modern concept of metastasis may be attributed to LeDran, who, early in the 18th century, again according to Wilder, wrote that 'cancer is a local disease in its early stages, and that it is spread by lymphatics to regional nodes and then to the general circulation'. This concept was supported

by Peyrilhe (1735–1804). Récamier (1829) and Billroth (1855) described
infiltration of veins by cancer and recognized the same process elsewhere.
In explaining this, Récamier first used the word metastasis. The development
of the ideas of haematogenous spread in metastasis is briefly discussed by
Oniugbo (1958), who refers to an essay by Johnson (1810), in which he is
of the opinion that cancerous matter enters the 'circulating system' to produce 'a taint of the whole habit'. However, a recognition of cellular transport mechanisms being involved in the metastatic process was delayed because
of the then current concepts of oncogenesis, particularly those supported by
Virchow. The 19th century concepts of tumour pathology are elegantly
reviewed by Triolo (1965) and will not be discussed in detail here, apart
from noting that, although Virchow (1860) clearly laid the bases of cellular
pathology, following the development of the cell theory by Schwann, he
equally clearly did not understand, at least initially, the concept that secondary tumours were the result of cellular spread from a primary focus.

Oniugbo (1962) discusses the paradox that Virchow, the father of cellular
pathology, should resolutely have considered metastasis of cancer in terms
of 'morbid juices' rather than in terms of cells. Virchow's views were based
partly on the observation that the lungs at necropsy appeared to be less
frequently the site of metastases that might be expected, in terms of their
expected capacity to trap malignant cells. Virchow held the view, according
to a leader in a contemporary Lancet (1875), that metastases developed as a
result of interaction at the presumptive site between connective tissue cells
and fluids from the primary tumour. In this viewpoint Virchow was supported to some extent by Rokitansky (1854) and by Paget (1858). In view of
current knowledge of the oncogenic viruses, it is of interest to note that
Bence-Jones (1867) considered the possibility that subcellular particles could
be carried to organs to set up metastases.

The next step forward in an understanding of the metastatic process was
a demonstration by Thiersch (1865) that a number of epithelial tumours
arose from the malpighian layer of the skin. In other words, epithelium
arises from epithelium. This was taken as direct proof that Virchow's concept that all tumours arise from suitably stimulated connective tissue was
incorrect. Thiersch went further, and stipulated that epithelial tumours
found in lymph nodes must have been carried there from elsewhere, and
supported as a general case the concept that cancer is a local process which
spreads by the transport of cancer cells. It is interesting to speculate whether
this purely histological disproof of Virchow's concept would currently be
readily accepted, in view of present knowledge on cellular transformation.

On the basis of Thiersch's work, Lomer (1883) postulated that metastases result from the transport of viable tumour cells.

Waldeyer (1867, 1872) studied other epithelial tumours, and also supported Thiersch's view, and stated that the transmission of cancer occurred by means of either embolic transfer through blood and other fluids and/or through continuity of contiguity of organ structures. To Waldeyer the cancer cell was a 'parasitic germ' (entozoenkeime) capable of unlimited propagation. Billroth (1866) eventually supported this 'transplantation' theory, which he renamed an 'embolus' theory, but at the same time did not discard Virchow's humoral theory. Connheim and Maas (1877) also produced observations showing that detached fragments of neoplastic tissue distributed through the vasculature gave rise to metastases. Shortly afterwards, a number of papers (reviewed by Wilder) led to the acceptance of the essential relationship between the primary tumour and metastases arising from it.

The next question to be asked was concerned with the factors influencing the distribution of metastases from the primary tumour. In a review of sites of secondary growth in cancer of the breast, Paget (1889) made the important point that, out of 735 patients with this disease, 241 (33%) had hepatic metastases, but only 17 (2%) had splenic metastases; on the other hand, in 340 patients with pyaemia, 66 (19%) had hepatic and 39 (11%) had splenic abscesses. If the distribution of particles from the blood were merely determined by haemodynamic considerations, then Paget would have expected more metastases in the spleen. This observation was offered in support of the hypothesis that some organs were a more fertile soil for seeding with malignant cells than others. This seed and soil concept received support from others, including Bland–Sutton (1905) and Armstrong and Oertel (1919), in respect of the liver. The embolic theory, with the addition of organ selectivity, also took cognizance of Schmidt's (1903) observation that carcinoma cells from abdominal primary tumours were often found to be encapsulated and destroyed by thrombi.

Handley (1905, 1922) used Schmidt's observation as a basis of suggesting that as carcinoma cells do not excite thrombotic events in lymph vessels, dissemination of carcinoma, particularly of the breast, takes place 'almost entirely by the lymphatics and not by the blood vessels'. In the opinion of Willis (1952), Handley placed far more importance on lymphatic permeation than many pathologists are now prepared to accept. Lymphatic spread in the development of metastasis had previously been described by Klinger (1857), Hoggan (1878), Heidenhain (1889), Stiles (1899) and others; von Recklinghausen (1885) recognized retrograde lymphatic flow due to obstruction, as a possible cause of anomalous distribution of secondary deposits.

The study of metastasis historically and logically involves studies of the separation of malignant cells from the primary tumour, their movements both active and passive through the body, their lodgement in and interactions with host organs, and finally, their ability to reconstitute within the host organ a structure which often bears a histological resemblance to the primary focus. In the succeeding chapters an attempt will be made to build up a picture of these phenomena with particular emphasis on the biological and physical aspects of the processes, and their relationship to the nature of the tumour cell periphery.

References

Armstrong, G. E., and Oertel, H. (1919). Am. J. Med. Sci. **158**, 354

Bence Jones, H. (1867). Lectures on some of the applications of mechanics to pathology and therapeutics. Churchill, London, p. 258

Billroth, T. (1855). Virchows Arch. Pathol. Anat. Physiol. **8**, 268

Billroth, T. (1886). Arch. Klin. Chir. Langenbecks **7**, 848

Bryan, C. P. (1930). The Papyrus Ebers. London

Bland-Sutton, J. (1905). Lancet **1**, 1339

Celsus, De Medecina. Cited by Ewing, J. (1922). Neoplastic disease. W. B. Saunders, Baltimore

Cohnheim, J. and Maas, H. (1877). Virchows Arch. Pathol. Anat. Physiol. **70**, 161

Ewing J., (1922). Neoplastic diseases, W. B. Saunders, Phialdelphia

Handley, W. S. (1905). Brit. Med. J. **i**, 663

Handley, W. S. (1922). Cancer of the breast and its operative treatment. London

Heidenhain, L. (1889). Arch. Klin. Chir. **39**, 97

Herodotus, Thaha, Lib. III, Cap. 133. Cited by Willis, R. A. (1948). Pathology of tumours. Butterworth, London

Hoggan, G. (1878). Trans. Pathol. Soc. Lond. **29**, 384

Johnson, C. T. (1810). A practical essay on cancer. Callow, London, p. 75

Klinger, C. (1857). Virchows Arch. Pathol. Anat. Physiol. **12**, 538

Lancet (1875). Histogenesis of cancer **2**, 104

Lomer, E. (1883). Zentr. Geburts. Gynäkol. **9**, 277

Morgagni, G. (1761). De sedibus, et causis morborum per anatomen indagatis. Book II, Epis XXX Case 4. Venice

Oniugbo, W. I. B. (1958). J. Hist. Med. **13**, 529

Oniugbo, W. I. B. (1962). Bull. Hist. Med. **36**, 444

Paget, J. (1858). Lectures on surgical pathology. Republished 1953, vol. **2**, p. 580. Longman, Brown, Green and Longmans, London

Paget, S. (1889). Lancet **1**, 571

Palmer, J. F. (Ed.) (1835). The works of John Hunter. Longmans, Green and Co., London **1**, 621

Park, R. (1903). Johns Hopkins Hosp. Bull. **14**, 289.

Récamier, J. C. (1829). Recherches sur le traitment du cancer par la compression....et sur l'histoire générale de la même maladie. Vol. **2**, Paris, p. 110

Recklinghausen, F. von (1885). Virchows Arch. Pathol. Anat. Physiol. **100**, 503

Rokitansky, C. (1854). A manual of pathological anatomy. Translated by W. E. Swaine. Sydenham Society, London, Vol. 1, p. 256

Schmidt, M. B. (1903). Jena. Die Verbreitungswege der Karzinome und die Beziehung generalisierter Sarkome zu den leukamischen Neubildungen...

Stiles, H. J. (1899). Brit. Med. J. **i**, 1452

Thiersch, C. (1865). Der Epithelialkrebs namentlich der Haut...Leipzig

Triolo, V. A. (1965). Cancer Res. **25**, 75

Virchow, R. (1860). Cellular pathology. Translated by F. Chance, Churchill, London

Waldeyer, W. (1867). Virchows Arch. Pathol. Anat. Physiol. **41**, 470

Waldeyer, W. (1872). Arch. Pathol. Anat. Physiol. **55**, 67

Wilder, R. J. (1956). J. Mt. Sinai Hosp. **23**, 728

Willis, R. A. (1948). Pathology of tumours. Butterworth, London

Willis, R. A. (1952). The spread of tumours in the human body. Butterworth, London

CHAPTER 6

The periphery of malignant cells

This chapter will be concerned with possible physicochemical and functional differences between the peripheral regions of malignant cells in general and their normal counterparts. It must be constantly borne in mind that there are many different types of tumour; the International Union Against Cancer (U.I.C.C.) Illustrated Tumor Nomenclature lists 273 human neoplasms. This large number permits a great deal of individuality, as well as overlap, in the nature of tumour cell peripheries, and cautions against uncritical extrapolation of data from one type of neoplastic cell to malignant cells in general.

6.1 Chemical constitution

6.1.1. Lipids

The literature pertaining to various aspects of lipids in cancer has been reviewed up to 1955 by Haven and Bloor (1956). Among the first to analyze the lipid content of tumours were Bullock and Cramer (1914), who noted that more phospholipid was present in rapidly growing mouse mammary carcinoma than in a slower variety. Lewis (1927) observed a higher ratio of of lecithin to cholesterol in malignant ovarian and cervical tumours than in benign tumours or normal tissues from similar sites, and Yasuda and Bloor (1932) showed that the phospholipid and cholesterol content of malignant tumours was higher than their benign or normal counterparts.

The variation in lipid content in different parts of the same tumour was investigated by Bullock and Cramer (1914) who found a higher total lipid content with a lower proportion of phospholipids in the necrotic central regions of murine carcinomata. Although these observations have since been confirmed by some workers, and refuted by others, Haven and Bloor

262

(1956) consider that the results in general agree with Lang's (1939–40) suggestion that decreased cellular activity is accompanied by decreased phospholipid content, and cellular degeneration is associated with an increase in content of cholesterol esters.

Some of the changes consequent upon degeneration are reflected in the different data obtained from tumours of different age. Uramoto's (1932) studies on the Flexner–Jobling rat tumour over the 14 to 40 day period following transplantation, showed an increase in total cholesterol of 80% and a decrease in lipid phosphorus of about 35% which was most marked at the centre of the tumours. Mider et al. (1948) showed that in the case of the Walker 256 tumour the total lipid concentration decreased as the tumour increased in size. However, Haven et al. (1951) showed that the total lipid content remained constant if the rats were maintained on a high fat diet, and some of the differences in results between various workers can possibly be explained in terms of diet.

Carruthers and Davis (1961) made an interesting study of the lipid composition of the epidermis and dermis of mice at different stages of the hair growth cycle, and following the topical application of methylcholanthrene. The percentage of cholesterol and phospholipids in the epidermis progressively increased from physiological states of hair follicular activity, through hyperplasia to frank squamous cell carcinomata; in contrast, the percentage of total lipid and triglycerides progressively decreased over the same course of events, while the iodine number of the triglyceride fatty acids remained about the same. A sex difference was also noted in that the early hyperplastic male epidermis contained higher percentages of cholesterol and its esters than comparable female tissue.

Carruthers and Heining (1964) noted that in going from normal to hyperplastic to neoplastic tissues, there was no significant difference in the percentage distribution of the various classes of phospholipids. Kögl et al. (1960) noted that the benzpyrene-induced rat sarcoma, and the Brown–Pearce rabbit carcinoma contain relatively less phospholipids than heart, lung and kidney in these animals and Veerkamp et al. (1961) found that although azodye-induced rat hepatoma contained only half the amount of phospholipids as normal liver, the percentage of the various phospholipids was the same. Attempts to perform lipid analyses on sub-cellular fractions from Ehrlich ascites tumour cells have been made by Wallach et al. (1960), who found that phospholipids account for 58% of the total lipid, of which 13.7% of the phosphatides are associated with the nuclear fraction, 29% with mitochondria, 52.5% with the microsomes, and 5.4% with the supernate. The nitrogen-containing phospholipids themselves, which composed 81–93% of the total phosphatides, consisted of: lecithin 39%, phosphatidyl ethanolamine 24%, sphingomyelin 14%, and 13% indeterminate. The remainder of the phospholipids (7–19%) consisted of: phosphatidic acid 3%; inositol phosphatides 4%; acetal phosphatides 12.5%.

Although Veerkamp et al. (1961) could detect no significant differences between the phosphatide compositions of azodye-induced primary hepatomata in the rat and normal liver; they did find that the ratio of ^{32}P incorporation into phosphatidylcholine and phosphatidylethanolamine was increased in the tumours. Gas chromatography also revealed a reversal in the normal ratio of stearic to oleic acids in the tumour phosphatides. This increase in proportion of oleic acid was also noted by Sueyoshi and Miura (1939), in comparing sarcomata and benign myomata of the rabbit uterus, and by Veerkamp (1960) in Brown–Pearce, benzpyrene induced and Ehrlich ascites tumours. The interpretation of these analytical data in terms of membrane structure and function is made very difficult by the fact that the different cellular membranes may vary in quantity during malignant change, as for example the loss of much endoplasmic reticulum in liver cells of rats fed on carcinogenic azo-dyes, observed by Porter and Bruni (1959).

An analytical study of the phosphatides and a methylating enzyme system in some experimental rat and mouse tumours and normal tissues was made by Figard and Greenberg (1962). They showed that the enzyme system which methylates phosphatidylaminoethanol to phosphatidylcholine (lecithin) was very much reduced in all of the mouse tumours studied and that the Morris hepatoma which had the highest demonstrable enzyme activity, only possessed 20% of that of normal liver. However, in spite of reduced enzymatic activity, no marked abnormalities in phosphatide content were observed. The total phosphatides were less than in normal liver, as also observed in the Novikoff hepatoma by Novikoff (1957) and Weber and Cantero (1957), but this was due mainly to a diminution in total lipid content, as distinct from a diminution in the proportion of phosphatides, although when there was a change in proportions, the cephalins tended to increase and the lecithins to decrease. The pattern of fatty acid content of the tumour lipids was not considered to be significantly different from lipids of normal liver and erythrocytes.

Siperstein and his associates have demonstrated abnormal control of cholesterol synthesis in a number of liver tumours. Siperstein and Fagan (1966) showed that in liver cells, the major site of the feed-back system for the inhibition of cholesterol synthesis by excess dietary cholesterol is β-hydroxy-β-methylglutaryl reductase, which is responsible for the conversion of

β-hydroxy-β-methylglutarate to mevalonate. In contrast to normal liver cells, cells of the mouse hepatoma BW7756, the Morris rat hepatoma 5123–t.c., and one well-differentiated human hepatoma completely lacked the cholesterol negative feed-back control (Siperstein and Fagan 1964). This data may provide support for the various enzyme-deletion hypotheses of carcinogenesis. From the data quoted it can be seen that it is impossible to generalize about the lipids of whole tumours, because, although some of the conflicting statements reflect recent improvements in chromatographic and other techniques, genuine differences exist between hepatomas where there is a decrease in total phospholipids, and skin tumours, where there is an increase. At the present time no comment at all can be made on the lipid composition of tumour cell membranes on the basis of analytical data derived from whole tumours, and such comments that have been made are, to say the least, premature.

The painstaking work of Sylvén and his colleagues has revealed that viable tumour cells leak enzymes into their interstitial fluids more than their normal counterparts. This work will be discussed in more detail later, but for the moment the interest in these observations lies in the suggestion that enzyme release may indicate some change in the permeability properties of the tumour cell membrane. De Gier and Van Deenen (1961) have shown that in the case of different species erythrocytes, increased permeability to glycol could be directly correlated with increased proportions of lecithin in the phosphatides of their ghosts. It is obviously a far cry from the permeability of erythrocytes to glycol, to the leakage of enzymes from tumour cells with permeability in vivo. From the cited analytical data, however, there seems to be no justification at present for relating permeability changes in malignant cells to the lipid composition of their membranes.

6.1.2. Glycoproteins

It is a common clinico-pathological observation that the plasma levels of glycoproteins are significantly elevated in patients with cancer and many other diseases (Winzler 1965). Turumi and Dawes (1958) reported that the serum sialic acid level is raised in mice bearing transplanted mammary carcinomata, but less in mice with spontaneous tumours of the same type. Although the liver is quantitatively the major source of plasma glycoprotein, it is not the only one as demonstrated by Bekesi et al. (cited by Winzler and Bekesi 1966). The specific relationship of glycoproteins to cancer is the subject of a recent short review by Winzler and Bekesi (1966), in which many illustrative examples are given of the difficulties encountered in determining whether abnormal glycoproteins originate in cancer cells per se, or whether they are a non-specific result of tissue damage.

The presence of glycoproteins in ascites fluid in the presence of tumour cells has been observed by Hashizume (1957), Marcante (1963) and Miller (1964). Molnar and his associates (Molnar et al. 1965a,b) have demonstrated the liberation of newly synthesized amino sugar-containing compounds from Ehrlich ascites cell *in vivo* and *in vitro* within 20 min of exposure to ^{14}C-glucosamine. This material in some ways resembles the glycopeptides reported to be released from ascites tumour cell peripheries following incubation with trypsin (Langley and Ambrose 1964), and, in view of the ability of tumour cells to 'leak' enzymes (Sylvén 1958; Wu 1959; Sylvén and Bois 1960; Holmberg 1961), it is possible that some of these glycopeptides are released from the tumour cell peripheries by autolysis. Great caution is needed in interpreting the data with a view to determining the site of origin of material released following the treatment of cells with trypsin, owing to cell death and liberated intracellular contents.

The sialic acid content of some human tumours of the breast, colon and stomach was higher than in adjacent normal tissue (Barker et al. 1959); and Kawasaki (1958) has also reported that the glycoproteins extracted from human carcinoma of the stomach contained more sialic acids than those extracted from normal gastric mucosa.

Although glycoproteins are present in solid tissues of human and animal origin, no convincing qualitative differences between normal and malignant tissues have yet been demonstrated (Sylvén 1965).

It has been suggested (Chandler and Neuhaus 1964; Sarcione 1964; Winzler 1965) that the raised plasma glycoprotein level observed in patients with cancer is due to the increased synthesis of glycoprotein in the liver, as a result of 'information' provided by the tumour. As the biosynthesis of glycoproteins is regulated by the proteinaceous part of the molecules, as distinct from their oligosaccharide units, it seems possible that humoral factors act directly or indirectly on the liver, producing increased amounts of messenger RNA which in turn produces more protein.

With the exception of sialic acids, which will be discussed under the separate heading of surface charge, the overall impression is gained that the characterization of glycoprotein in the tumour cells periphery has hardly begun, due mainly to lack of suitable sensitive methods for their assay. Winzler and Bekesi (1966) consider that the most promising approach will lie in quantitative immunological techniques.

6.2 *Surface charge*

Attempts at comparing the surface charge of malignant cells of solid tumours with their normal counterparts were made by Ambrose et al. (1956) and Lowick et al. (1961), who demonstrated that malignant cells from stilboestrol-induced kidney tumours in the hamster and a butter-yellow hepatoma in the rat, had higher electrophoretic mobilities than their normal analogues. Ruhenstroth–Bauer (1965) has summarized much of his associates' and his own earlier work on the electrophoretic mobilities of malignant and non-malignant cells in the bone-marrow and peripheral blood, which shows that in myeloid and lymphatic leukaemia the leukaemic cells have a higher mobility than normal. However, they also note changes in 'haemocytopherograms' in acute inflammatory and osteolytic diseases among others. Owing to the well-known difficulties in obtaining 'normal' counterparts of malignant cells, the experiments reported by Forrester (1965) are very useful in this context, since they provide data on the electrophoretic mobilities of 'normal' and polyoma-transformed hamster kidney fibroblasts. The immediate observation was that although the mean mobilities of the transformed cells were not significantly different from the uninfected cells, the spread of mobilities was obviously much greater. The transformed cells cloned into two types with distinct colonial morphology when cultured on glass, which almost matches an electrophoretic separation of the clones into one having a mean mobility indistinguishable from normal, and the other which has a mean mobility some 25% higher than normal. The fact that following incubation with neuraminidase the mobility of both clones was reduced to the same value, was taken as evidence that the higher mobility of one was due to an increase of sialic acid moieties at its electrokinetic surface. Support for this suggestion came from the earlier work of Defendi and Gasic (1963) showing that polyoma-induced transformation of hamster embryo cells, was accompanied by the presence of a thick pericellular coat of acid mucopolysaccharide demonstrable by Mowry's modification of Hale's method, and not demonstrable following incubation of the transformed cells with neuraminidase.

The postulated correlation of malignancy with increased cell surface change density has drawn attention to the question of similar changes in relation to the growth process. Ben-Or et al. (1960) studied the electrophoretic mobilities of isolated cells from regenerating rat liver and found them to be higher than their normal counterparts. Heard et al. (1961) compared the mobilities of fibroblasts from embryonic and adult mice and found those of the embryonic cells to be higher. The observations of both groups suggested that raised electrophoretic mobility is possibly related to the growth process in general rather than malignancy per se. Eisenberg et al. (1962) published more detailed data on the relation of the electrokinetic properties of isolated rat liver cells during regeneration and postnatal growth. Their results show a rapid increase following partial hepatectomy, and that the mobility of cells from the livers of newborn animals was some 40% higher than those from adult organs. Fuhrmann (1965) does not regard increased electrophoretic mobility as a non-specific expression of cell proliferation, on the evidence that whereas the mobilities of both proliferating rat liver cells and malignant ascites liver cells are high, only the mobilities of the malignant cells are reduced by incubation with neuraminidase. These observations and the suggestion that sialic acid-mediated increase in cell-surface charge density is in some way specific to the malignant cell do not in themselves provide as clear cut answers to the problem of proliferation, as are required. Doljanski and Eisenberg (1965) have also demonstrated that neuraminidase is almost without effect on the electophoretic mobilities of cells isolated from normal and regenerating livers of the rat, mouse, hamster and guinea pig, but it seems doubtful that too much can be inferred in general terms from comparisons with liver cells which need isolation preparatory to measurement.

Chaudhuri and Lieberman (1965) have shown that the rise in electrophoretic mobility of the rat liver cell after partial hepatectomy is in fact due to an increase in surface neuraminate. Both neuraminidase and 30% ethanol markedly reduced the electrophoretic mobility of liver cells from partially hepatectomized animals, but had little effect on the mobility of cells from shan-operated animals; following enzyme and ethanol treatment, similar amounts of sialic acid were released from both types of liver cell. Owing to the possibility that separation artefacts are different in cells from normal and regenerating livers, the results do not demonstrate unambiguously the absence of sialic acid at the electrokinetic surface of normal cells. However, experiments do show that sialic acid is present in similar regions of the separated regenerate cells, and that under these conditions sialic acid is not only to be associated with the malignant cell (see figs. 6.1 a,b).

The whole question of the optimal technique for isolating cells from solid normal and malignant tissues is unsolved at the present time. If it is argued that, in general, the electrophoretic mobilities of malignant cells is higher than their normal counterparts, and the somewhat limited experimental evidence would support this contention in my opinion, then Vassar's (1963) important observations on the mobilities of cells isolated from normal and malignant tissues cast serious doubts on present techniques. In a series of 34 human tumours, including 13 gastrointestinal carcinomata with corresponding normal epithelium, Vassar noted that when measurements of electrophoretic mobility were made on mechanically isolated cells, normal and malignant epithelium were not significantly different. He also noted that incubation with neuraminidase produced much less reduction in mobility in carcinoma cells than in those derived from mesenchymal tumours. In the case of the lack of difference between carcinomata and normal epithelium, the possibility of artefact due to separation technique will next be examined.

In chapter 4 a case was presented for regarding cell separation as a spatially different phenomenon from cell adhesion, and it was postulated that when cells separate from substrata in general, they may leave peripheral material behind and/or separate with material from the substrata attached to their peripheries. As yet unpublished work by Mayhew and myself on the effects of treatment of cells from suspension cultures with a variety of enzymes, suggests that sialic acids in the cell periphery may protect other more deeply located anionic groups from enzyme-mediated cleavage from the cell periphery, in much the same way as demonstrated by Gottschalk (1960) for steric hindrance of tryptic digestion of salivary gland mucoprotein.

The observed increases in mobility of cells in low ionic strength media generally support the suggestion that the peripheral zones of cells can be regarded as a polyanionic 'sponge' (Seaman and Heard 1960), and it seems distinctly possible that the relative proportions of the different negatively charged groups (carboxyl, phosphate etc.) could be different at different spatial planes within the cell periphery. If this is the case, then the mere act of separation would, as indicated in fig. 6.1, alter the arrangement of anionic groups by effectively burying some and revealing others, from the viewpoint of electrokinetics. The end result might be cells which have the same electrophoretic mobility, but which show different electrokinetic response to incubation with neuraminidase, in spite of having similar amounts of sialic acid moieties liberated by neuraminidase treatment, as determined by chemical assay.

In the context of this section it is worthy of note that the work of Mayhew and O'Grady (1965) and Mayhew (1966) on parasynchronous suspension cultures of cells, where the cells can be examined without separation trauma, shows quite clearly that the electrophoretic mobility varies with the stage in the mitotic cycle, being highest during the mitotic peak phase. Treatment of cells at any phase of the cycle with neuraminidase reduces their mobility to a common level, as also in the case of rapidly and slowly growing cells. Using similar cells which were a 'permanent' strain developed from a human

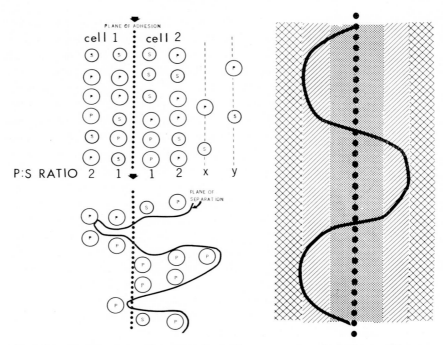

Fig. 6.1(a). Very diagrammatic 'explanation' of how separation of cells from solid tissues could lead to artifact. A: The plane of adhesion between two adherent cells is shown, together with the location of ionized sialic acid moieties S and other acidic groups, P (note P does not necessarily indicate specific chemical groups such as phosphate). In this diagram it is assumed that only the single 'row' of ionogenic groups immediately adjacent to the electrokinetic surface is reflected in it, and this may consist of what is conventionally regarded as cell and/or material conventionally considered to be intercellular material. The ratio of P to S groups is shown to vary at different levels. If the plane of separation does not coincide with the plane of adhesion then the electrokinetic surface of the separated cell will be chemically different from that at the plane of adhesion. Only cell I is shown for the sake of simplicity, but it will be appreciated from comparing the upper and lower diagrams that the two separated cells now have chemically different electrokinetic surfaces. Although the charge density and thus electrophoretic mobility may be the same at the two planes, neuraminidase will produce a greater drop in charge density in the plane of adhesion than at the plane of separation. This difference need not be reflected in chemical assay of liberated elements following enzyme treatment.

(b). This diagram represents, schematically, the effect of separating cells symmetrically along a plane (_____) which is spatially different from the plane of adhesion (●●●). If the differently shaded areas represent planes within the peripheral zones of two adjacent cells which are chemically and/or electrokinetically different from the adhesion interface, then separation can result in cells with different surface properties. Note that the symmetry of separation about the plane of adhesion would tend to produce a homogenous population of separated cells, in contrast to the heterogenous group produced by the asymmetrical separation depicted in fig. 6.1(a).

osteogenic sarcoma, it was also shown that measurement of electrophoretic mobility at various temperatures revealed higher values than calculated, at temperatures up to 37 °C, and these were interpreted as being due to changes in macromolecular conformation at the cell periphery (L. Weiss, 1966). Regardless of precise interpretation, it does seem that at least with some cells of the same status as far as malignancy is concerned, electrophoretic mobility is related to other cellular processes, including stage in the mitotic cycle, over and above the effects due to malignancy, contrary to the views of Fuhrmann (1965), Doljanski and Eisenberg (1965), Simon-Reuss et al. (1964) and others.

6.3 Calcium

Beebe (1904) and Clowes and Frisbie (1905) made the observation that the calcium content of a number of malignant tumours was somewhat less than in normal tissues. Carruthers and Suntzeff (1944) noted that in murine epithelium treated with methylcholanthrene, the calcium concentration fell soon after application of the carcinogen during the phase of benign hyperplasia. A second fall of tissue calcium occurred when the lesions became frankly malignant. Greenstein (1947) noted that as calcium is a diffusible tissue constituent, alteration in its local concentration may be brought about by toxic effects unrelated to the primary carcinogenic event. He also makes the general point that in this type of experiment, it would be of obvious interest to use non-carcinogenic analogues in the control series. Brunschwig et al. (1946a) found that human gastric carcinomata contained less calcium than the adjacent uninvolved mucosa, but that in a benign papilloma located between two discrete carcinomata, the calcium level was the same as in the malignant lesions. How much this similarity was due to diffusion processes is not clear. Brunschwig and his associates (1946b) also noted that, in the case of human colonic carcinomata, there was a reduction in calcium content compared to the adjacent normal mucosa. In contrast to the gastric papilloma, they noted that colonic papillomata in the region of the carcinomata contained more calcium than the malignant tissues, but less than the normal mucosa. In my own opinion, it would be reassuring to repeat and extend these observations on the calcium content of tumours, to a much wider range of fresh biopsy specimens, making use of the very sensitive and rapid technique of atomic absorption spectroscopy.

It is quite impossible to comment on the calcium content of the tumour

cell in general because of the dearth of data. In addition, analyses of whole
tumours do not permit localization of the proposed low calcium concentration to intercellular material, the cell periphery or cell interior. The often
made statement that the tumour cell periphery does not bind calcium cannot
be accepted uncritically since, in one of the few systematic studies made on
this topic, Bangham and Pethica (1960) have shown that the calcium concentration required to produce charge reversal in mouse cells is about the same
for Ehrlich ascites tumour cells as for isolated liver cells, indicating equal
calcium-binding capacity; lymphocytes and erythrocytes require more calcium, indicating less calcium-binding capacity than the tumour cells.

Lansing (1942, 1947) has tried to correlate the calcium content of cells
with their age; increased calcium, according to him, is a characteristic of
older cells, while the low calcium content of tumour cells reflects 'youth', as
distinct from malignancy.

The relationship of calcium to cell separation will be discussed in the
relevant section later.

6.4 Surface ultrastructure

6.4.1. Membranes and junctions

In tissues, four main types of cell junction may be generally recognized under
the electron microscope in fixed material:

(a) The so-called tight junction or zonula occludens (Farquhar and Palade
1963), where trilaminar structures are visualized as separated by about 100
to 200 Å.

(b) The so-called loose junction where the separation is uneven and greater
than 200 Å.

(c) The areas of gross cytoplasmic continuity seen between germinal cells by
Fawcett (1961).

(d) Special, highly organized regions, the desmosomes. These regions are the
subject of a most elegant study, and comprehensive survey of the literature
by Kelly (1966). This author's studies on the skin of late embryonic, larval
and immediate postmetamorphic newts, *Taricha torosa*, reveal no continuity
of tonofilaments between adjacent cells at desmosomes. The tonofilaments
are in fact closed filamentous loops, coursing towards or beyond attachment
sites, but invariably returning into the main filament tracts of their parent
cell. Kelly considers that the filamentous framework contributes to cellular

tensile strength, but not to cellular adhesion, which is partially dependent on 'extracellular' material which is arranged 'as pillars or partitions which are continuous with or layered upon the outer unit cell membrane leaflets and adjoined in a discontinuous dense midline of the desmosome'.

An interesting development in the nature of cell junctions came from studies on intercellular communications between *Drosiphilia epithelial* gland cells, with microelectrodes permitting conductivity measurements, and with microinjections of fluorescein. Loewenstein and Kanno (1964) demonstrated the free flow of ions and fluorescein at the tight junctions between the cells, at the site of hexagonal subunit structures (Wiener et al. 1964). Similar intercellular ionic communication has been noted between salivary gland and renal tubular cells of chironomus, sensory epithelial cells of elasmobranchs, and urinary bladder cells of the toad (Loewenstein et al. 1965). Penn (1966) has also described intercellular ionic communications in all directions, between mouse liver cells and their adherent neighbours. Hexagonal subunits, similar in appearance to those noted by Wiener et al. (1964), have also been observed by Benedetti and Emmelot (1965) in electron micrographs of negatively stained membranes isolated from rat liver cells, and by Robertson and Bodenheimer (1963) in the electrical synapses of Mauthner cells.

A recent exciting development has been reported by Loewenstein and Kanno (1966), who have compared ionic communication between normal rat liver cells and four types of hepatic tumour. They found that whereas low junctional resistance, i.e. ionic communication, could be demonstrated between the normal cells, no communication could be detected between the tumour cells within the limits of sensitivity of their techniques. In addition, these authors noted that the effective electrical resistance of the tumour cells was some 20 to 100 times higher than in normal cells, and that the cancer cells behaved as though they were normal cells with their communicating channels cut off (see also Penn and Loewenstein 1966; Nakas et al. 1966). If these interesting observations reflect a general rule, then it might well be that such behaviour as lack of contact inhibition to movement and growth (Dulbecco 1963; Berwald and Sachs 1963) in tumour cells is connected in some way with this lack of communication. The truth of this generality will doubtless be established by the use of this objective technique. The high resistivity of the tumour cell membranes seems to argue against the presence of polar pores in their membranes. It will be of great interest to watch the emergence of this field, linking specialized areas of membrane substructure with electrical coupling of adjacent cells.

In a computer search kindly carried out by the National Library of Medicine (Washington), for papers on electron microscopy on human solid tumours only, written in English, French or German, and published in the years 1964 and 1965, 169 citations were retrieved. Although no attempt will be made to review the vast literature, some definite points can be made about the peripheries of tumour cells examined in the fixed state at the useful levels of resolution of the electron microscope.

In a short general summary of the field Mercer (1963) notes that some of the published data are obviously concerned with dead or degenerate cells, and that the changes reported are typical of cell death and degeneration as distinct from neoplastic changes per se. In many tumours a range of cyto-differentiation is observed, and the patterns recorded in these seem to relate to differentiation rather than malignancy, as suggested by the data of Mercer (1961) and Birbeck and Mercer (1961).

In electron micrographs of tumours, where cellular proliferation is more marked than in normal tissues, considerably more variation of junctional substructure is seen. Although loose junctions have been noted between adjacent tumour cells, with simplification of structure, similar changes have been seen in regenerating rat liver following partial hepatectomy (Lane and Becker 1966). The labile nature of desmosomes has been described by Overton (1962), who noticed their disappearance in enzyme-dissociated embryonic chick cells, and their subsequent regeneration on culture. Luft (1964) has demonstrated a stainable material between membrane units, which probably corresponds to material removable by enzymes and chelating agents. The dynamic nature of other material involved in certain cell contact reactions has been studied by L. Weiss and Kapes (1966).

Attempts to relate the appearance of junctions with calcium, particularly in relation to the postulated calcium deficiency in malignant cells, were made by Coman (1954). Following perfusion of whole livers with EDTA by Anderson's (1953) technique, Coman noted that the cells became widely separated, whereas the cells of normal livers were tightly opposed. This was taken to indicate the existence of calcium bridges between normal liver cells. However, Coman also reported disappearance of trilaminar structures and other changes due to post-mortem degeneration. Easty and Mutolo (1960) failed to observe separation of liver cells followed perfusion of the adult rat liver with EDTA; however, this investigation has been criticized by Leeson and Kalant (1961) on the grounds that Easty et al. did not adequately perfuse their tissues. Coman's original observation was confirmed by Leeson and Kalant (1961), who perfused livers with EDTA, followed by osmium fixation. The separation observed by these authors was not accompanied by gross cell degeneration. The rather obvious experiment to determine whether the cells of malignant tumours of equal vascularity to the liver also separate following EDTA perfusion, has not yet been reported to my knowledge.

6.4.2. Contours

Cell surface contours may be examined face on, by two basic electron microscopic techniques. The first is by direct metal shadowing of membrane fragments on a grid, as done by Hillier and Hoffman (1953), who demonstrated a cobblestone texture of the surface of erythrocyte ghosts which was not destroyed by lipid solvents. A second technique involves shadowing of a replica, in which, for example, chromium is deposited on cells, and then carbon is deposited on the metal replica. Coman and Anderson (1955) studied erythrocytes prepared by the second technique, and encouragingly, their electron micrographs resembled those of Hillier and Hoffman. More recently Glaeser et al. (1966) have reported a variant of earlier techniques in which erythrocytes fixed in buffered OsO_4 solution were washed, sprayed onto mica and freeze-dried. The cell preparations were then covered with a carbon film from which organic matter was removed by flotation in NaOH solution, and the carbon replicas were examined directly. The individual 'cobblestones' observed by these workers were some 400 Å in diameter, which is more than twice that reported by Hillier and Hoffman. In addition, Glaeser and his colleagues noted the presence of long filamentous structures about 200 Å in diameter, which had high electron scattering centres. It was suggested that these filaments may not be artefactual, but may represent the lipoglycoprotein 'elinin', described by Dandliker et al. (1951). As discussed in chapter 1, 'elinin' itself may well be an artefact; this suggestion is therefore not too attractive. However, the general question of filamentous structures in this region of the cell is of some importance in relation to contact phenomena, since these may be the points of initial attachment, and their movement may be Brownian, in contrast to movements of the whole cell.

The earliest attempt to examine surface contours of malignant cells, and to compare them with their normal counterparts, was made by Coman and Anderson (1955). Using the techniques described earlier, these workers compared the surfaces of $V \times 2$ epidermoid cancer cells of the rabbit, with its normal squamous epithelial cells obtained from depilated skin. They noted that whereas the normal cells revealed a uniform ultrastructure consisting of particles having diameters over the range of 30 to 60 Å, the substructure of the malignant cells was much more heterogeneous, being built up of particles ranging in size from 30 to 300 Å. Using the same preparative technique as Coman and Anderson, the surface ultrastructure of normal and leukaemic lymphocytes of the rat were compared by Nowell and Berwick (1958). They demonstrated the presence of a particulate substructure consisting of unevenly distributed units some 100 to 300 Å in diameter, but failed to observe a difference between the normal and malignant cells. Berwick (1959) attempted to clarify the issue by examining surface contours of trypsin-treated rabbit cells from normal epidermis, $V \times 2$ carcinoma and the Shope papilloma which in some ways can be regarded as intermediate between the normal and malignant $V \times 2$ cells. Apart from gross changes involving the loss of 'prickles' by the tumour cells, Berwick confirmed the previous observations of Coman and Anderson regarding differences between the normal and $V \times 2$ malignant cells. The papilloma cells resembled the normal cells, in that their surfaces were homogenously particulate.

Catalano et al. (1960) made a rather interesting series of observations on the two sublines, M_{ss} and M_{As}, of the MCIM mouse sarcoma. Following subcutaneous inoculation of the ascitic subline M_{AA}, a solid tumour M_{As1} is produced which resembles M_{ss} tumours very closely in gross morphology, but has different biological behaviour in that it breaks up more readily into single cells and metastasizes more readily. A comparison of the surface contours of M_{ss} and M_{As1} cells was made to determine whether these behavioural differences would be reflected in ultrastructural changes. The electron micrographs revealed no differences between the two cell types; the surfaces of both of them were irregularly particulate, with 100 to 300 Å diameter granules. An attempt to compare surface contours without separation artefact was made by Easty and Mercer (1960), who studied metal-shadowed replicas of cultured normal cells from the renal cortex of hamsters with transplanted tumour cells from the same region; the cells were cultured on coverslips and fixed without removal. Apart from slight overlapping of the contiguous edges of the malignant cells, no fine structural differences were observed, and Easty and Mercer considered that the range of ultrastructural detail visualized by this technique reflected activity of individual cells rather than normalcy or malignancy.

In view of contrary evidence it seems unlikely that specific differences have been demonstrated between the surface contours of normal and malignant cells in general. It also seems possible that the ultrastructural differences observed by Coman and Anderson are due to artefacts induced by separation of cells from tissues, as distinct from pre-existing differences.

The conventional electron micrographic studies up to now, also do not, in my opinion, demonstrate changes in trilaminar structures specific to malignancy, but probably indicate heterogeneity, degeneration, regeneration etc., which can also be observed in non-malignant cells. A systematic study of the 'extramembranous' material lying between the trilaminar structures, by means of special, electron microscopic, staining techniques, appears to be a reasonable direction for future work.

6.5 *Changes associated with viruses*

It has been known that viruses can produce leukaemia since 1908, when Ellerman and Bang transmitted the disease to fowl with cell-free tumour extracts. Much of the present interest in viral-induced leukaemias stems from Gross's (1951) demonstration of cell-free transmission of a mouse leukaemia. Since then, leukaemia viruses have been described in animals by Graffi (1957), Friend (1957), Moloney (1960), Rauscher (1962) and others.

Evidence in favour of the viral aetiology of human leukaemia is indirect and has been briefly reviewed by Grace (1964b). Thus, virus-like particles have been seen in electron micrographs of leukaemic tissues and serum (Dmochowski 1963; Burger et al. 1964; and Almeida et al. 1963) and in cultures of myeloblasts from a patient with acute myeloblastic leukaemia (Iwakata and Grace 1964). Antisera prepared against pellets of virus-like particles centrifuged from plasma, reacted against leukaemic cells in the bone marrow and blood of leukaemic patients, but not of normal controls, and against myeloblasts maintained *in vitro* (Fink and Malmgren, cited by Grace 1964b). The immunofluorescent antibodies used by these workers (Fink et al. 1964) also adsorbed to cells from the Burkitt lymphoma (Burkitt and O'Conor 1961) which had been established in culture by Epstein and Barr (1964). Inoculation of animals with cells from human leukaemia has been somewhat inconclusive, but of three suckling monkeys surviving an injection of a suspension of Burkitt lymphoma cells, two developed tumours of their long bones after two years, which contained cells resembling those injected originally (Epstein et al. 1964). It will be appreciated that these interesting observations do not establish a causal relationship between viruses and human cancer; however as Grace (1965), among others has noted, if the same technical limitations had been imposed on studies of the chicken and mouse as on human material, it is doubtful that oncogenic viruses could yet have been isolated.

In addition to leukaemia, viruses can cause a wide variety of tumours in experimental animals, and some of the work done has been reviewed by Oberling and Guérin (1954), Furth and Metcalf (1958), Stanley (1958) Grace et al. (1960) and Old and Boyse (1966). Although the oncogenic nature of viruses can be shown by injecting them into animals frequently during foetal life or the neo-natal period, and tumours appear often after a latent period of one half of the animals life-span, this cannot be done with human viruses suspected of oncogenic properties. Some of the difficulties in establishing the viral aetiology of human tumours have been discussed by Grace (1964a) and include the activation of latent virus infections in experimental animals following the injection of human tumour extracts and the non-susceptibility of animals to human viruses. In addition to these difficulties, there is always the possibility that viruses which cause tumours in one species will be ineffective in others, as perhaps illustrated by human adenovirus 12 which produces malignant tumours when injected into newborn hamsters, but which has not been related to human cancer. SV40 virus from monkey tissues, which also produces tumours in hamsters, produced no increased incidence of cancer over a four year period in children given poliovirus vaccine containing it. On the other hand, the subcutaneous tumours observed by Bearcroft and Jamieson (1958) in a rhesus monkey colony in Yaba, Nigeria, and subsequently shown to be due to a pox virus (Andrewes et al. 1959) produced a tumour at the site of an accidental needle puncture in a laboratory technician (Grace and Mirand 1963).

Although the mechanisms of viral carcinogenesis in animal cells are not known at present, it seems reasonable to obtain working hypotheses from the many studies of the bacteriophage model. These suggest that complexes of cells and oncogenic viruses can exist in two main states (Dulbecco 1965), namely: (1) dependent and (2) independent complexes.

Dependent virus/cell interactions are those in which replication of viral nucleic acid is synchronous with replication of the host nucleic acid, and results in an undamaged, changed host cell. In contrast, independent interactions are those in which viral nucleic acid replicates non-synchronously with that of the host, and usually results in host cell death in one extreme, or in a steady-state relationship in the other. In the non-cytocidal, independent type of interaction; all host cells in a population contain virus, whereas in a carrier-state it is possible to derive non-infected clones from the population.

In dependent states, the viral genome can either persist as a complete unit or alternatively only a fragment of viral DNA survives and replicates as an integral part of the host cell DNA. Thus, either virus can be recovered from the host, as in the lysogenic state, in which it may be present as provirus; or, alternatively, the virus may disappear as such, but presence of a persisting part of its genomic function may be demonstrated as new, replicated antigen, by immunofluorescent or other techniques (Dulbecco 1965).

Until very recently, attempts to demonstrate an analogy between the bacteriophage model, and animal cells infected with oncogenic viruses have been unsuccessful. Dulbecco notes that many attempts to demonstrate the presence of provirus in converted cells, including use of all the methods used to induce virus-release in lysogenic bacterial cells, have been unsuccessful. Attempts were also made to demonstrate resistance of the converted cells to 'super-infection' with fresh polyoma virus, which might be analogous to the immunity of lysogenic bacteria carrying prophage. Although at first sight immunity of this type is suggested by *in vitro* experiments, in which 'converter' mouse embryo cells show an enhanced resistance to infection with new polyoma virus, (Vogt and Dulbecco 1960); *in vivo* experiments reveal no immunity in cells of mouse tumours (Hellström et al. 1960). Dulbecco (1961) considers that in the first case, the high resistance *in vitro* is due to selection attributable to the continued presence of polyoma virus in the cultures. However, apparently inexplicable immunity to super-infection with polyoma virus is seen in hamster cells converted both *in vivo* and *in vitro*. At the time of his review, Dulbecco concluded that the 'presence in the converted cultures of a viral DNA either in a vegetative or proviral state is thus undemonstrated, and probably unlikely'. The point should be made that in addition to nucleic acids, viruses also contain proteins and lipids, and Dulbecco (1961) notes that in the case of cells transformed by RNA-containing viruses, a vegetative viral genome may be present which continuously produces viral protein. Vogt and Rubin (1961) showed that following infection with the Rous virus, a protein which was antigenically similar to that of the Rous virus was found initially at the periphery of the infected cells.

Another case which tended to argue against the analogy between animal and bacterial cells in respect to 'provirus' and prophage, is that of SV40 virus induced tumours of the hamster, where spontaneous replication of infective virus occurs in only a minute fraction of a population carrying the viral genome.

Gerber and Kirschstein (1962) demonstrated the release of small amounts of virus from SV40 tumour cells following exposure to special methods of induction, by the resulting infection of other sensitive cells. Sabin and Koch (1963), by the use of similar techniques have essentially confirmed release of virus particles from the SV40 tumour after X-irradiation, and were of the opinion that their combined experimental data was insufficient to determine whether the information for synthesis of at least part of the viral antigen, was carried in the viral genome or not.

Against this background, some of the changes in the properties of the cell periphery produced by viruses can be noted and discussed.

Vogt and Dulbecco (1962) have compared the behaviour of hamster cells in culture before and after infection with polyoma virus, the non-infected cells alter the direction of their (amoeboid) movement on meeting each other and rarely crawl over each other, which is to say they exhibit 'contact inhibition' which was discussed in chapter 3. On the other hand, cells which have undergone the malignant change associated with infection do not change direction on meeting their fellows, and thus appear to have lost contact inhibition. In addition to this observation, Vogt and Dulbecco are under the impression that the uninfected cells adhere more firmly to their culture vessels than their converted counterparts. It is of considerable interest that at the same time as their behavioural patterns change, the neoplastic cells absorb less heterologous antiserum per cell than those which are uninfected. Thus, it would appear that a structural (immunological) change in the cell periphery, associated with the onset of malignancy, as evidenced by animal inoculations, can be associated temporarily with changes in contact inhibition and cell–substratum adhesion, although it should be emphasized that a causal relationship between any of these changes has certainly not been established.

Morgan et al. (1962) have studied the peripheries of cells in the chick embryo chorioallantoic membrane, after infection with influenza (RNA) virus, which differentiates in this region of the cell. Electron micrographs of cells treated before fixation with ferritin-conjugated antibodies to the virus, reveal viral antigen in the periphery of the host cell. These observations essentially confirmed those made by Hotchin et al. (1958), who made electron micrographic studies of haemadsorption. The electron micrographic evidence suggests that the peripheries of the infected cells become modified to include viral antigen and that in being extruded from the host the viral particles themselves become 'coated' with this 'host/viral' membrane.

New 'surface' antigens have been described in lymphoma cells induced by Maloney virus (Klein and Klein 1964, Haughton 1965) and in leukaemic cells induced by Graffi virus (Pasternak 1965). New antigens have also been observed in hamster cells following their malignant conversion by papovavirus SV40 *in vivo* and *in vitro*. Evidence of the specificity of these antigens is provided by tests involving the rejection of transplants (Koch and Sabin

1963; Defendi 1963); by complement-fixation tests (Habel et al. 1965) and by immunofluorescent techniques (Pope and Rowe 1964). The latter tests point to the localization of new antigen in the nucleus; however, as new antigen cannot be demonstrated in hamsters immunized with live SV40 virus and then proven resistant to SV40 tumour cells, antigens other than this are thought to be involved in graft rejection and these may well be present at the tumour cell periphery. Tevethia et al. (1965) have shown that hamster cells which have undergone malignant conversion both *in vitro* and *in vivo*, following exposure to the SV40 virus, possess new antigens at their peripheries, as demonstrated by immunofluoresence. Antibodies prepared against this peripheral antigen do not cross-react with normal cells of hamster and other species or with other tumour cells. The work quoted here is not intended to represent the vast amount of literature on this topic, but merely to indicate some of the more recent unequivocal work, demonstrating change in the (immuno-) chemical composition of the cell periphery following non-lethal viral infection.

A notable attempt has been made by Marcus (1962a) to follow the changes occurring in the peripheries of HeLa cells after infection with Myxovirus (Newcastle disease virus NDV) by means of an elegant haemadsorption test. The HeLa cells are first exposed to virus at $0\,°C$, and then brought to $37\,°C$, to permit viral penetration (Marcus 1959). At zero time the infected cells are seeded in petri dishes in non-virucidal growth medium (Marcus and Puck 1958). At given times after this, the growth medium is removed and replaced by an erythrocyte suspension at $4\,°C$. This temperature minimizes the enzymatic destruction of receptor sites on the HeLa cells, which in turn would lead to 'elution' of adsorbed erythrocytes. After washing the cultures with cold saline buffered to p H 6, apparently all of the erythrocytes not adsorbed to the HeLa cells are removed, and in these circumstances the adsorption of a single erythrocyte to a HeLa cell is significant. Using this very carefully defined technique on HeLa cells infected with an average of one virus particle, Marcus showed that changes occurred in their peripheries after some $4\frac{1}{2}$ hours, as manifest by the adsorption of one erythrocyte per cell. The number of erythrocytes adsorbed increases exponentially to reach a maximum of 30 (chicken) erythrocytes per cell 12 hours after the infective event. After 25 hours cytopathic effects occur and reduce the numbers of adsorbed cells observed. The points of attachment of the individual erythrocytes are thought to indicate areas of the cell periphery which are modified to release new virus, as suggested by the fact that the 'doubling' time of adsorption is equivalent to the rate of liberation of plaque-forming viral particles (Marcus

1962b). Two interesting findings reported by Marcus (1962a) are that in bipolar cells, their two ends are consistently the first sites of change associated with haemadsorption; and that cells tending to a crescent shape, where the nucleus is on the concave side, the spread of change around the cell periphery in the region of the cell–substratum interface always proceeds along the convex edge of the cell. After haemagglutination, positive cells were treated with a specific antiserum to NDV; they reverted to a haemagglutinitin negative state after being washed free of excess antibody. However, when neutralized cells were re-incubated, they began to show haemagglutination again after one and a half hours, which was complete over the whole cell periphery after three hours, and which was indistinguishable from un-neutralized cells. As destruction or dissociation of antibody/viral antigen complexes is unlikely under the conditions of neutralization used, Marcus reasonably concludes that there is *de novo* synthesis of viral antigen at the cell periphery following neutralization. This may indicate that once a steady-state is reached in the amount of viral antigen at the cell periphery, the feed-back control requires that these antigenic sites be functionally accessible. If they are not, then 'repression' to synthesis is reduced, and more antigen is put into the cell periphery to keep up with the requirements of virus extrusion. It would be of interest therefore to follow the development haemagglutination progressively, in the same cell. Marcus (1962) noted that this is possible, but had not been done.

Chick fibroblasts infected *in vitro* with Rous sarcoma virus (RSV) show cytopathic changes which are not lethal and, following division, the daughter cells remain infected. The cytological changes following infection have been observed *in vivo* by Manaker and Groupe (1956), among others. The observation by Vogt and Rubin (1962) that, following infection with RSV chick fibroblasts form rounded up piles of cells in cultures, led them to study changes produced at the peripheries of these cells. Viral antigens have been observed by use of the fluorescent antibody technique in the peripheral regions of chicken cells which had undergone malignant conversion following infection with RSV, *in vivo* by Malmgren et al. (1960) and Mellors and Munroe (1960) and *in vitro* by Noyes (1960) and Vogt and Rubin (1961). Vogt and Rubin (1962) have described in some detail, the antigenic changes occurring at the peripheries of chick embryo cells *in vitro*, following infection with an average of one focus-forming unit of RSV per cell, and note that shedding of virus by the cells occurred after the third day, whereas bound-peripheral viral antigen appeared in this region after 24 hours. The viral antigen could be removed from the cell surface, as judged by immunofluorescent techniques, after incubation for 2 min in 0.05% trypsin. By means of electron-microscopic and fluorescent studies carried out on the same chick cells cultured adherent to formvar membranes, they also showed that 4 days after infection with RSV, the areas containing virus particles coincided with those stained with fluorescent antibody, and, as a result of this and other data, conclude that the RSV associated with the infected cell is located in the cell periphery. This conclusion agrees with the findings of Gaylord (1955) and others, and has been shown to occur in the case of other avian tumour viruses (Benedetti and Bernhard 1958; Nishiumi et al. 1961; Dmochowski et al. 1961). Vogt and Rubin note that, at times coincident with antigenic changes in the chick cells and viral shedding, the fibroblasts themselves contract to a rounded form, and that there is a disappearance of the filopodia with which the fibroblasts normally make contact with their fellows in culture. They suggest that these changes in various peripheral properties of fibroblasts may be correlated with apparent loss of contact inhibition (Abercrombie and Ambrose 1958), and thereby relate structural changes in RSV-infected cells with their contact behaviour. Analyses of cell contact make it clear that many factors must be considered before correlating structural change with social behaviour of cells, and for the moment the data of Vogt and Rubin cannot be interpreted as indicating a straightforward causal relationship between structure and behaviour.

Hamster cells which have undergone a morphological transformation *in vitro*, following exposure to polyoma virus, tend to overlap each other when cultured on glass surfaces, but this apparent modification of contact inhibition is not invariably associated with malignant conversion, as judged by their ability to produce tumours when injected into adult hamsters (Defendi et al. 1963). Associated with this virus-induced conversion, Defendi and Gasic (1963) have demonstrated the appearance of thick pericellular 'coats' of acid mucopolysaccharide as determined by Mowry's (1958) modification of Hale's method; the 'coats' are removable following incubation with neuraminidase, indicating that they contain sialic acid. This data is in agreement with those of Forrester et al. (1962) which demonstrate that similar polyoma-converted hamster cell clones have shown an increase in electrophoretic mobility that is reduced following incubation with neuraminidase. Defendi and Gasic (1963) point out that this finding is comparable to that of Erichsen et al. (1961), that an increase in acid mucopolysaccharide production and secretion follows the infection *in vitro* of chick embryo fibroblasts by Rous sarcoma virus, although there is no evidence that these mucopolysaccharides are present at the cell surface. Defendi and Gasic note that the changes observed by them persisted in cells maintained *in vitro* for periods as long as one and a half years at the time of their paper. It is of interest that marked increase in hyaluronate production has also been observed in cultures of transformed foetal rat fibroblasts exposed intermittently to cobaltous chloride by Daniel et al. (1961). It is very unlikely that this change was due to an accidental viral infection, as it was confined only to those cultures treated over approximately eight months with the cobalt salt. Weiss (1962) examined these cells of Daniel and her colleagues by means of mechanochemical detachment tests, with and without the addition of potent hyaluronidases, and noticed no facilitation of their detachment from glass substrata, and concluded that in this case the hyaluronate could not be regarded as a 'bound' structural component of the cell periphery, but should be more properly considered as an 'unbound' excretion. As on the one hand viral contamination can cause changes, and on the other, 'contamination' with trace metals can produce similar changes; great caution is required in attributing their cause in any but the most rigidly controlled experiments. Hukill and Vidone (1965) are among many others to study the histochemical reactions of mucus and other polysaccharides in tumours. They note that in a series of cases of carcinoma of the bladder, small amounts of sialomucin are usually found around the malignant cells in the intercellular regions, but that there is apparently no correlation between the presence, absence or amount of staining reaction and the clinical course of the disease. It is conceivable that many different agents, not all of them carcinogenic, can cause changes in observable peripheral mucosubstances, and that to suggest a causal relationship between observed change, malignancy and or differences in contact inhibition is premature.

References

Abercrombie, M., and Ambrose, E. J. (1958). Exptl. Cell Res. 15, 332
Almeida, J. D., Hasselback, R. C., and Ham, A. W. (1963). Science 142, 1487
Ambrose, E. J., James, A. M., and Lowick, J. H. B. (1956). Nature 177, 576
Anderson, N. G. (1953). Science 117, 627
Andrewes, C. H., Allison, A. C., Armstrong, J. A., Bearcroft, G., Niven, J. S. F., and Pereira, H. G. (1959). Acta, Unio Intern. Contra Cancrum 15, 1760
Bangham, A. D., and Pethica, B. A. (1960). Proc. Roy. Phys. Soc. (Edinburgh) 28, 43
Barker, S. A., Stacey, M., and Tipper, D. J. (1959). Nature 184, 68
Bearcroft, W. G. C., and Jamieson, M. F. (1958). Nature 182, 195
Beebe, S. P. (1904). Am. J. Physiol. 12, 167
Benedetti, E. L., and Bernhard, W. (1958). J. Ultrastructure Res. 1, 309
Benedetti, E. L. and Emmelot, P. (1965). J. Cell Biol. 26, 299
Ben-Or, S., Eisenberg, S., and Doljanski, F. (1960). Nature 188, 1200

References 285

Berwald, Y., and Sachs, L. (1963). Nature **200**, 82
Berwick, K. (1959). Cancer Res. **19**, 853
Birbeck, M. S. C., and Mercer, E. H. (1961). Nature **189**, 558
Brunschwig, A., Dunham, L. J., and Nichols, S. (1946a). Cancer Res. **6**, 230
Brunschwig, A., Dunham, L. J., and Nichols, S. (1946b). Cancer Res. **6**, 233
Bullock, W. E., and Cramer, W. (1914). Proc. Roy. Soc. B **87**, 236
Burger, C. L., Hanis, W. W., Anderson, N. G., Bartlett, T. W., and Kniseley, R. M. (1964). Proc. Soc. Exptl. Biol. Med. **115**, 151
Burkitt, D., and O'Conor, G. T. (1961). Cancer **14**, 258
Carruthers, C., and Davis, B. (1961). Cancer Res. **21**, 82
Carruthers, C., and Heining, A. (1964). Cancer Res. **24**, 485
Carruthers, C., and Suntzeff, V. (1944). Science **19**, 245
Catalano, P., Nowell, P., Berwick, L., and Klein, G. (1960). Exptl. Cell Res. **20**, 633
Chandler, A. M., and Neuhaus, O. W. (1964). Am J. Physiol. **206**, 169
Chaudhuri, S., and Lieberman, I. (1965). Biophys. Biochem. Res. Comm. **20**, 303
Clowes, G. H. A., and Frisbie, W. S. (1905). Am. J. Physiol. **14**, 173
Coman, D. R. (1954). Cancer Res. **14**, 519
Coman, D. R., and Anderson, T. F. (1955). Cancer Res. **15**, 541
Dandliker, W. B., Moskowitz, M., Zimm, B., and Calvin, M. (1951). J. Amer. Chem. Soc. **72**, 5587
Daniel, M. R., Dingle, J. T., and Lucy, J. A. (1961). Exptl. Cell Res. **24**, 88
Defendi, V. (1963). Proc. Soc. Exptl. Biol. Med. **113**, 12
Defendi, V., and Gasic, G. (1963). J. Cell. Comp. Physiol. **62**, 23
Defendi, V., Lehman, J. M., and Kraemer, P. (1963). Virology **19**, 592
De Gier, J. and Van Deenen, L. L. M. (1961). Biochim. Biophys. Acta **49**, 286
Dmochowski, L. (1963). Texas Rep. Biol. Med. **21**, 113
Dmochowski, L., Grey, C. E., Burmester, B. R., and Walter, W. G. (1961). Texas Rep. Biol. Med. **19**, 545
Doljanski, F., and Eisenberg, S. (1965). In, E. J. Ambrose, ed., Cell electrophoresis, Churchill Ltd., London
Dulbecco, R. (1961). Cancer Res. **21**, 975
Dulbecco, R. (1963). Science **142**, 932
Dulbecco, R. (1965). Amer. J. Med. **38**, 669
Easty, G. C., and Mercer, E. H. (1960). Cancer Res. **20**, 1608
Easty, G. C., and Mutolo, V. (1960). Exptl. Cell Res. **21**, 374
Eisenberg, S., Ben-Or, S., and Doljanski, F. (1962). Exptl. Cell. Res **26**, 451
Ellermann, V., and Bang, O. (1908). Zentr. Bakteriol. **46**, 595
Epstein, M. A., and Barr, Y. M. (1964). Lancet **1**, 252
Epstein, M. A., Woodall, J. P., and Thomson, A. D. (1964). Lancet **2**, 288
Erichsen, S., Eng, J., and Morgan, H. R. (1961). J. Exptl. Med. **114**, 435
Farquhar, M. G., and Palade, G. E. (1963). J. Cell Biol. **17**, 375
Fawcett, D. W. (1961). Exptl. Cell Res. Suppl. **8**, 174
Figard, P. H., and Greenberg, D. M. (1962). Cancer Res. **22**, 361
Fink, M. A., Malmgren, R. A., Rauscher, F. J., Orr, H. C., and Karon, M. (1964). J. Natl. Cancer Inst. **33**, 581
Forrester, J. A. (1965). In, E. J. Ambrose, ed., Cell electrophoresis. Churchill Ltd., London, p. 115

Forrester, J. A., Ambrose, E. J., and MacPherson, I. A. (1962). Nature **196**, 1068
Friend, C. (1957). J. Exptl. Med. **105**, 307
Fuhrmann, G. F. (1965). In, E. J. Ambrose, ed., Cell electrophoresis. Churchill Ltd., London, p. 92
Furth, J., and Metcalf, D. (1958). J. Chron. Dis. **8**, 88
Gaylord, W. H. (1955). Cancer Res. **15**, 80
Gerber, P., and Kirschstein, R. L. (1962). Virology **18**, 582
Glaeser, R. M., Hayes, T., Mel, H., Tobias, C. (1966). Exptl. Cell Res. **42**, 467
Gottschalk, A. (1960). Nature **186**, 949
Grace, J. T. (1964a). Bull. N.Y. Acad. Med., 2nd Series, **40**, 495
Grace, J. T. (1964b). Proc. 5th Natl. Cancer Conf. p. 637
Grace, J. T. (1965). Cancer Res. **25**, 1477
Grace, J. T., and Mirand, E. A. (1963). Ann. N. Y. Acad. Sci. **108**, 1123
Grace, J. T., Mirand, E. A., and Mount, D. T. (1960). A. M. A. Arch. Internal Med. **105**, 482
Graffi, A. (1957). Ann. N. Y. Acad. Sci. **68**, 540
Greenstein, J. P. (1947). The chemistry of cancer. Academic Press, New York, p. 55, 184, 246
Gross, L. (1951). Proc. Soc. Exptl. Biol. Med. **76**, 27
Habel, K., Jensen, F., Pagano, J. S., and Koprowski, H. (1965). Proc. Soc. Exptl. Biol. Biol. Med. **118**, 4
Hashizume, K. (1957). Tohoku J. Exptl. Med. **65**, 195
Haughton, G. (1965). Science **147**, 506
Haven, F. L., and Bloor, W. R. (1956). Advan. Cancer Res. **4**, 237
Haven, F. L., Bloor, W. R., and Randall, C. (1951). Cancer Res. **11**, 619
Heard, D. H., Seaman, G. V. F., and Simon-Reuss, I. (1961). Nature **190**, 1009
Hellström, I., Hellström, K. E., Sjögren, H. O., and Klein, G. (1960). Exptl. Cell Res. **21**, 255
Hillier, J., and Hoffman, J. F. (1953). J. Cell. Comp. Physiol. **42**, 203
Holmberg, B. (1961). Cancer Res. **21**, 1386
Hotchin, J. E., Cohen, S. M., Ruska, H., and Ruska, C. (1958). Virology **6**, 689
Hukill, P. B., and Vidone, R. A. (1965). Lab. Invest. **14**, 1624
Iwakata, S., and Grace, J. T. (1964). N. Y. J. Med. **64**, 2279
Kawasaki, H. (1958). Tohoku J. Exptl. Med. **68**, 119
Kelly, D. E. (1966). J. Cell Biol. **28**, 51
Klein, E., and Klein, G. (1964). J. Natl. Cancer Inst. **32**, 547
Koch, M. A., and Sabin, A. B. (1963). Proc. Soc. Exptl. Biol. Med. **113**, 4
Kögl, F., Smak, C., Veerkamp, J. H., and Van Deenen, L. L. M. (1960). Z. Krebsforsch. **63**, 558
Lane, B. P. and Becker, F. F. (1966). Amer. J. Path. **48**, 183
Lang, A. (1939–40). Z. Krebsforsch. **49**, 20
Langley, O. K., and Ambrose, E. J. (1964). Nature **204**, 53
Lansing, A. I. (1942). Biol. Bull. **82**, 385
Lansing, A. I. (1947). Science **106**, 187
Leeson, T. S., and Kalant, H. (1961). J. Biophys. Biochem. Cytol. **10**, 95
Lewis, W. C. M. (1927). J. Cancer Res. **11**, 16
Loewenstein, W. R., and Kanno, Y. (1964). J. Cell Biol. **22**, 565
Loewenstein, W. R., and Kanno, Y. (1966). Nature **209**, 1248
Loewenstein, W. R., Socolar, S. J., Higashino, S., Kanno, Y., and Davidson, N. (1965). Science **149**, 295

Lowick, J. H. B., Purdom, L., James, A. M., and Ambrose, E. J. (1961). J. Roy. Microscop. Soc. **80**, 47

Luft, J. H. (1964). J. Cell Biol. **23**, 54A

Malmgren, R. A., Fink, M. A., and Mills, W. (1960). J. Natl. Cancer Inst. **24**, 995

Manaker, R. A., and Groupé, V. (1956). Virology **2**, 838

Marcante, M. L. (1963). Clin. Chim. Acta **8**, 799

Marcus, P. I. (1959). Virology **9**, 546

Marcus, P. I. (1962a). Symp. Quant. Biol. **27**, 351

Marcus, P. I. (1962b). Bacteriol. Proc., p. 131

Marcus, P. I., and Puck, T. T. (1958). Virology **6**, 405

Mayhew, E. (1966). J. Gen. Physiol. **49**, 717

Mayhew, E., and O'Grady, E. A. (1965). Nature **207**, 86

Mellors, R. C., and Munroe, J. S. (1960). J. Exptl. Med. **112**, 963

Mercer, E. H. (1961). Proc. Roy. Soc. Med. **54**, 1057

Mercer, E. H. (1963). In, R. W. Raven, ed., Cancer progress volume. Butterworth, London, p. 66

Mider, G. B., Tesluk, H., and Morton, J. J. (1948). Acta Unio. Internat. contra Cancrum **6**, 409

Miller, E. E. (1964). Growth **28**, 167

Molnar, J., Lutes, R. A., and Winzler, R. J. (1965a). Cancer Res. **25**, 1438

Molnar, J., Teegarden, D. W., and Winzler, R. J. (1965b). Cancer Res. **25**, 1860

Moloney, J. B. (1960). J. Natl. Cancer Inst. **24**, 933

Morgan, C., Rifkind, R. A., and Rose, H. M. (1962). Symp. Quant. Biol. **27**, 57

Mowry, R. W. (1958). Lab. Invest. **7**, 566

Nakas, M., Higashino, S., and Loewenstein, W. R. (1966). Science **151**, 89

Nishiumi, Y., Okano, H., and Imai, T. (1961). Proc. Soc. Exptl. Biol. Med. **107**, 88

Novikoff, A. B. (1957). Cancer Res. **17**, 1010

Nowell, P. C., and Berwick, L. (1958). Cancer Res. **18**, 1067

Noyes, W. F. (1960). Virology **12**, 488

Oberling, C., and Guérin, M. (1954). Advan. Cancer Res. **2**, 253

Old, L. J., and Boyse, E. A. (1966). Med. Clin. N. Am. **50**, 901

Overton, J. (1962). Develop. Biol. **4**, 532

Pasternak, G. (1965). J. Natl. Cancer Inst. **34**, 71

Penn, R. D. (1966). J. Cell Biol. **29**, 171

Penn, R. D., and Loewenstein, W. R. (1966). Science **151**, 88

Pope, J. H., and Rowe, W. P. (1964). J. Exptl. Med. **120**, 121

Porter, K. R., and Bruni, C. (1959). Cancer Res. **19**, 997

Rauscher, F. J. (1962). J. Natl. Cancer Inst. **29**, 515

Robertson, J. D., and Bodenheimer, T. S. (1963). J. Cell Biol. **19**, 159

Ruhenstroth-Bauer, G. (1965). In, E. J. Ambrose, ed., Cell electrophoresis. Churchill Ltd., London, p. 66

Sabin, A. B., and Koch, M. A. (1963). Proc. Natl. Acad. Sci. (Wash.) **50**, 407

Sarcione, E. J. (1964). J. Biol. Chem. **239**, 1686

Seaman, G. V. F., and Heard, D. H. (1960). J. Gen. Physiol. **44**, 241

Simon-Reuss, I., Cook, G. M. W., Seaman, G. V. F., and Heard, D. H. (1964). Cancer Res. **24**, 2038

Siperstein, M. D., and Fagan, V. M. (1964). Cancer Res. **24**, 1108

Siperstein, M. D., and Fagan, V. M. (1966). J. Biol. Chem. **241**, 602

Stanley, W. M. (1958). Ann. N. Y. Acad. Sci. **71**, 1100

Sueyoshi, Y., and Miura, K. J. (1939). J. Biochem. (Japan) **29**, 481

Sylvén, B. (1958). Acta Unio. Intern. contra cancrum **14**, 61

Sylvén, B. (1965). In, R. W. Jeanloz and E. A. Balazs, eds., The amino sugars. Academic Press, New York and London, Vol. II. A, Ch. 25, p. 195

Sylvén, B., and Bois, I. (1960). Cancer Res. **20**, 831

Tevethia, S. S., Katz, M., and Rapp, F. (1965). Proc. Soc. Exptl. Biol. Med. **119**, 896

Turumi, K-I., and Dawes, M. L. (1958). Cancer Res. **18**, 575

Uramoto, M. (1932). J. Biochem. (Japan) **16**, 69

Vassar, P. S. (1963). Lab. Invest. **12**, 1072

Veerkamp, J. H. (1960) Thesis Utrecht. Cited by Veerkamp, Mulder and Van Deenen (1961)

Veerkamp, J. H., Mulder, I., and Van Deenen, L. L. M. (1961). Z. Krebsforsch. **64**, 137

Vogt, M., and Dulbecco, R. (1960). Proc. Natl. Acad. Sci. **46**, 365

Vogt, M., and Dulbecco, R. (1962). Symp. Quant. Biol. **27**, 367

Vogt, P. K., and Rubin, H. (1961). Virology **13**, 528

Vogt, P. K., and Rubin, H. (1962). Symp. Quant. Biol. **27**, 395

Wallach, D. F. H., Soderberg, J., and Bricker, L. (1960). Cancer Res. **20**, 397

Weber, G., and Cantero, A. (1957). Exptl. Cell Res. **13**, 125

Weiss, L. (1962). Exptl. Cell Res. **30**, 509

Weiss, L. (1966). J. Natl. Cancer Inst. **36**, 837

Weiss. L., and Kapes, D. L. (1966). Exptl. Cell Res. **41**, 601

Wiener, J., Spiro, D., and Loewenstein, W. R. (1964). J. Cell Biol. **22**, 587

Winzler, R. J. (1965). In, The amino sugars. Vol. IIA, Academic Press, New York, p. 337

Winzler, R. J., and Bekesi, J. G. (1966). In, Busch, ed., Methods in cancer research. Academic Press, New York

Wu, R. (1959). Cancer Res. **19**, 1217

Yasuda, M., and Bloor, M. R. (1932). J. Clin. Invest. **11**, 677

CHAPTER 7

Separation of malignant cells from the primary tumour

7.1 General considerations

In this discussion it will be assumed that metastases arise from cells disseminated from primary tumours, as distinct from liberated oncogenic viruses. Although with this qualification, it may be stated that unless malignant cells separate from the primary tumour, metastasis will not occur; the converse, that the release of cells always gives rise to metastases, is not true. Possibly the most realistic way of looking at cell separation is as a rate-regulating process for metastasis. Many experiments have been made in the past, relating tumour takes in experimental animals to the number of malignant cells injected into them, and examples of this work are found in the papers of Furth and Kahn (1937), Hewitt (1953) and Fisher and Fisher (1960). Fig. 7.1, which is based on Hewitt's studies on the injections of very carefully controlled numbers of viable sarcoma 37 cells into the subcutaneous tissues of inbred mice, shows that over the dose range studied, the more cells delivered to a site the greater the proportion of takes.

The effect of cell viability on tumour takes is shown indirectly in data quoted by McDonald (1961) (fig. 7.2), in which advantage is taken of the deleterious effects of allowing cell suspensions to incubate at room temperature (22 °C). It is of interest that in the case of murine sarcoma 37, Hewitt (1953) has shown that the presence of a large number of dead cells in small inocula of viable cells may slightly enhance the development of tumours. However, from the aspect of metastasis the main interest will be in those processes causing the liberation of viable cells from tumours.

Before specific mechanisms of cell separation processes within a primary tumour are discussed, it should be noted that tumours consist of heterogenous cell populations, and that at any one time only a small percentage of their constituent cells need be involved in any process. Thus, Caspersson and Santesson (1942) described two main types of malignant cells in sections of

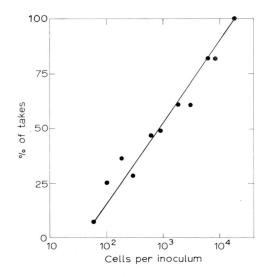

Fig. 7.1.   Relationship between number of takes and average subcutaneous inoculum of viable tumour cells. Based on data given by Hewitt (1953).

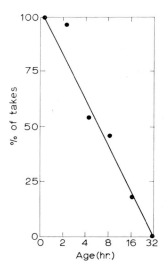

Fig. 7.2.   Percentage of takes in Sprague–Dawley rats after subcutaneous injections of 25,000 Walker 256 cells, 'aged' at room temperature for the times indicated. Based on data given by McDonald (1961).

human carcinomas. The A-type of cell which was found near to blood vessels, was small and spherical, had a high nuclear/cytoplasmic ratio, but its cytoplasm contained a high concentration of RNA. On the other hand, the B-type cell which was characteristically found away from blood vessels and therefore found to be more frequently closer to necrotic areas, was larger than the A-type, and contained a greater proportion of cytoplasm in which the concentration of RNA was lower. In addition to these two malignant cell types, intermediate forms were also noted. Craigie (1954) described cells of similar appearance to the A- and B- types in rodent ascites tumours, which he called α- and β-types, and, in addition, described a 'paramorph', which is a contracted form of the α-type; the morphology of the three cell types is not fixed. Roberts and Trevan (1957) studied these morphological changes *in vitro*, and demonstrated that the $\alpha \rightarrow \beta$ change could be induced by raising the environmental CO_2 to 40 mm Hg partial pressure, and that the $\beta \rightarrow \alpha$ change could be rapidly brought about by reduction in CO_2 partial pressure. Later work by Taylor (1962) on embryonic chick cells *in vitro*, showed that raising the environmental pH caused cellular contraction, and that reduction in pH caused cellular contraction, and that reduction in pH caused cell spreading. These rapidly reversible changes did not occur when [HCO_3] and [CO_2] were varied without changing the pH. Taylor's work thus supports the suggestion made by Roberts and Trevan, that the change is due to a pH-shift. Many *in vitro* studies have shown that rounded cells are more easily detached from a variety of substrata, than their spread counterparts, as would be expected from considerations of areas of true contact between cell and substratum (L. Weiss 1960). It is of considerable interest that the rounded A-type cells, which might be expected to separate most easily from primary tumours, are found where the vascular supply is best, and from where transport to other sites might well begin.

In addition to the overt morphological changes such as central necrosis in relation to vascularization, which occur in tumours as they increase in size, irreversible changes termed 'tumour progression' by Foulds (1951) also take place. These changes are reflections of variation within the constituent cell populations which may be recognizable in terms of morphology and change in contact reactions *in vitro* (Roberts and Trevan 1960; Trevan and Roberts 1960; Roberts 1963), and may be attributable to recognizable genetic change (Klein 1961; Hauschka 1961) imposed by selective pressure from the environment.

In the cancer patient receiving chemotherapy, the emergence of resistant cells may occur. The work of Harris and his associates and others (Harris

1963) has shown correlation between resistance and karyotype and, as will
be discussed later, karyotype may also be reflected in changes in the cell
periphery, which modify the immunological response of cells.

The problem of which cells in a heterogeneous population separate to
ultimately form metastasis is of very considerable importance in experimental
design and interpretation. If the distribution of some cellular parameter is
plotted as in fig. 7.3, then metastasizing cells can either be liberated from a
part of the population, or, alternatively, from the population as a whole.
The liberated cells can then be regarded as passing through a 'black box'
which represents the subsequent stages before the emergence of a metastasis,
upon the constituent cells of which, the distribution of the selected cellular

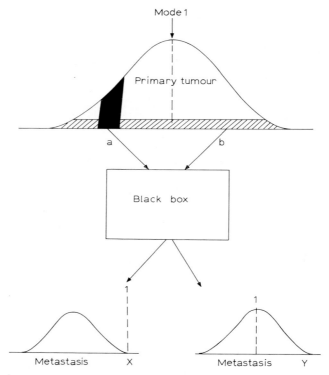

Fig. 7.3. Cells selected from part (a) or all (b) of the heterogeneous population of the
primary tumour give rise to metastases X and Y. Examination of the modes of any cell
parameter in X and Y will only enable discrimination to be made between cases a and b,
if mode 1 remains constant in the primary tumour, and if the intermediate steps ('black
box') are not selective.

parameter can be studied. If the mode of the parameter has shifted from the primary to the secondary tumour, then providing the black box is not selective; this could be taken as evidence that metastasis thas occurred from only parts of the primary tumour cell population as a whole. On the other hand, if the black box is selective, then absence of modal change does not necessarily imply release of cells representative of the primary tumour cell population as a whole.

Some illustrative examples of the difficulties come from studies on the chromosomal patterns of tumour cell populations. Yamada et al. (1966) record the diversity of karyotype seen in a series of human solid primary tumours and solid metastases, and the authors note that the rather meagre data suggest that metastatic cells have a similar karyotype to that of the parent tumour. However, when differences are present, these are variations of the chromosomal constitution existing in the primary tumour. Thus Rabotti's (1959) observation that, in a number of human metastatic lesions, the chromosome number was higher than in the primary foci, can be explained in terms of shift within a pre-existing population. Zeidman (1965) has suggested that only particular cell mutants from the primary tumour can be retained in organs to give rise to metastases. From the previous discussion, this interesting suggestion will be very difficult to prove or disprove. Greene (1965) does not regard the retention of tumour cells as being due to genetic factors, since in experimental animals, even though most cells were not retained by the lung on first passage, retention occured on recirculation. Leighton (1964, 1965) has also discussed the concept that in tumour cell populations containing more than one stem cell line, a 'metastatic stock' may be regulated by some sort of 'interclonal equilibrium' with other parts of the population.

The situation is obviously very complex as evidenced by Sandberg and Yamada's (1966) detailed studies on the cells from the effusions of one patient with pseudomyxoma peritonei, over a period of one month. During this period of time, the modal number of chromosomes varied considerably, and even within groups of cells with the same chromosome number, there was much diversity of karyotype. The authors note the ultimate emergence of two distinct marker chromosomes in over 90% of cells examined, compared with about 40% a month earlier. The variability in karyotype and karyotypic selection going on not only in the primary tumour but also in metastases, makes it quite impossible to determine at the moment, whether metastases arise from the cell population of the primary tumour as a whole, or just from part of it; nonetheless, both possibilities must be borne in mind.

From these few quoted examples, it will be apparent that, ideally, experiments designed to study the separation of daughter cells from primary tumours should take cognizance not only of numbers of cells liberated under given conditions, but also their viability, type and *in situ* position. Few experiments on *in vivo* systems satisfy these criteria.

7.2 Cell detachment from tumours

Credit for focussing attention on quantitative aspects of cell detachment from tumours must be given to Coman who, in 1944, measured the force required to separate pairs of cells, under direct observation, *in vitro*. One of a pair of cells was anchored with a fixed microneedle, while the other was separated from it by distraction with another microneedle; the force required was estimated by the curvature produced in the moving needle which had previously been calibrated with known weights. It was observed that pairs of malignant cells from both the lip and cervix uteri were separated at curvatures corresponding to 0.47 and 0.18 mg respectively, compared with cells from either benign papillomata of the skin (1.25 mg) or normal epithelial cells, from the lip (1.42 mg) or cervix (1.11 mg). This type of test measures cell separation, which is possibly distinct from cell adhesion, as discussed in chapter 4; however cell separation is the relevant parameter in this connection. Although the forces measured are peak forces involving an artefactual frictional component and, as discussed in chapter 4, their value is expected to be rate-dependent, it is not expected that the rates of cell distraction described by Coman were markedly different with the different cell pairs studied. Whatever the explanation, in the case of the tissues described, Coman made a most valuable contribution in observing that some malignant cells separate more easily than comparable non-malignant cells. A rather more acceptable experiment from the viewpoint of physical reproducibility was described by McCutcheon et al. (1948) who compared the separation of cells from human adenocarcinomata with their normal counterparts. Similar pieces of tissue suspended in physiological saline, were subjected to standardized agitation in a mechanical shaker, and cell counts were performed on both the fluid and tissue fragments. In 20 out of 21 experiments, more cells were liberated from the carcinomata, than from the corresponding normal tissues. Tjernberg and Zajicek (1965) noted that when various human tumours were aspirated with a syringe, many more free cells were present in aspirates from carcinomas than from benign epithelial tumours. Thus Coman's original observation was substantiated. It is surprising that more confirmatory work has not been done on many other tissues, since these observations form the basis of many current views on the metastasis of tumours.

In vivo the factors determining cell separation are the distractive forces of either the cells themselves or applied to them on the one hand, and the rupture strength of the cell/cell system on the other. As there is no evidence to suggest that the locomotive energy of malignant cells, or the distractive energy exerted through their attached processes, is different from their normal counterparts, the ensuing discussion will be confined to applied distractive forces, and factors reducing the rupture strength of cell/cell systems.

7.3 Applied distractive forces

The role of normal body movements in the dissemination of tumour cells is discussed by Cole (1961), who mentions respiratory movements of the lung, peristalsis, muscle contractions, and the various degrees of shaking associated with body movements. Although Cole considers these factors to be comparatively minor, he quotes the poor five years survival rates on lung tumours which may reflect the fact that the respiratory cycle occurs about twenty times per minute; that the survival rate in patients with oesophageal and gastric cancer is lower than in other portions of the gastro-intestinal tract where peristalsis is less marked. It appears that the situation is much too complex to make any useful positive correlations between these types of body movement and the dissemination of malignant cells, although, particularly in the case of skeletal muscle movements, it would not be surprising if they played a role.

Manipulation of tumors can play a definite part in tumour dissemination, and has long been suspected. Thus, in 1885, Gerster expressed the view that one of the advantages of amputation of tumour-bearing limb is to reduce handling and dissemination. Direct support showing the possible role of operative manipulation comes from many studies of the numbers of cancer cells present in the peripheral circulation during operation. Roberts and his associates (1960) give examples of cell counts on blood samples obtained at two-minute intervals from the inferior vena cava during cervical dilation and uterine curvettage on patients with cervical and endometrial cancer, which show the rapid appearance of malignant cells in the blood following operative manipulation. Many other illustrative examples from clinical practice, which also emphasize the role of manipulation, are quoted in Cole et al. (1961) text. Many animal experiments on the effects of tumour massage on metastases are also discussed by Cole et al., including Tyzzer's (1913) report describing how massage of subcutaneous tumours in mice leads to a much higher incidence of pulmonary metastases than in controls.

The various experimental data on the incidence of cells in the blood following massage of tumours also tend to support Coman's hypothesis that tumour cells are more easily detached than their normal counterparts, since normal cells have not been recorded after similar manipulative procedures on normal organs.

7.4 Non-mechanical factors affecting cell separation

It will be appreciated from the discussion in chapter 4 that the factors governing initial contacts between single cells are probably not the same as those affecting cell separation. An analysis of cell contact can in principle be approached from a knowledge of true cell surface properties, whereas in analyses of cell separation, the whole cell peripheral zone must be considered. The initial question posed is whether or not the peripheral regions of malignant cells differ structurally in any way from their normal counterparts, which would facilitate their separation from primary tumours. From what has been said previously, at the moment, no differences have been indisputably characterized between the peripheries of malignant cells in general, and normal cells in general.

7.4.1. Calcium and cell separation

The first indication that calcium played a part in cell separation came in 1894, when Ringer and Sainsbury showed that small amounts of calcium salts would prevent the disintegrative action of distilled water on the fresh water *Oligochaete tubifex*. In 1900, Herbst demonstrated that blastomeres of *Echinus microtuberculatus* could be dispersed in calcium-free sea water. The isolated cells continued to divide, but remained free, and naturally enough further embryonic development stopped. Galtsoff (1925) showed that dissociated sponge cells would not reaggregate in the absence of divalent cations. Since as noted in chapter 3, some reaggregation phenomena occur as a result of active amoeboid movement, which in turn depends upon cells making contact with a substratum, it is of interest that Pantin (1926) observed that marine limax amoebae are unable to move in calcium-free media. Further details of the function of calcium in invertebrates are reviewed by Robertson (1941).

On the basis of earlier work, Coman (1944) suggested that the decreased mutual adhesion between neoplastic cells might be related to a decreased calcium content. Zeidman (1947) observed that calcium removal facilitated the separation of cells by the technique of quantitative micromanipulation, and De Long et al. (1950) and Coman (1953) proposed, in general way, that much of metastasis could be accounted for in terms of low calcium content of tumours.

Although as noted earlier, it seeems unwise to generalize about the low concentrations of calcium observed in tumours, there is considerable evidence that removal of calcium facilitates the separation of cells from each other and various non-cellular substrata.

It has been known for some time that cells carry a net negative charge at their surfaces, and it is not surprising that the role of calcium should have been visualized as a 'bridge' linking the acidic groups of two adhering cells. Other roles of calcium have been postulated in terms of its effect on the electrical double-layer which effectively reduces the potential energy barrier to cell contact (L. Weiss 1960) and its part in stabilizing coacervates of mucosubstances (Robertson 1941; Pantin 1926; Rinaldini 1958). The experimental evidence from a number of different systems indicates that this type of reaction of calcium is considerably more complex than the simple non-specific reaction of a divalent cation with any acidic group. In addition the role of calcium should be considered carefully from the viewpoint of whether cell adhesion or cell separation has been measured or discussed.

Some rough index of the strength of binding of calcium to carboxyl groups of different acids for example, comes from the solubility in water of different calcium salts. Thus about 37g calcium acetate dissolves in 100 ml of water at 20 °C, whereas only 0.000067 g of calcium oxalate is soluble under the same conditions, indicating that the binding between the calcium ion and the carboxyl groups is much stronger in the case of oxalate than acetate. The effect of the proximity of a hydroxyl group to the carboxyl is reflected in comparison of the solubility of calcium propionate (49g/100ml) to calcium lactate (3.1g/100ml), or of calcium succinate (0.19g/100ml) to calcium malate (0.32g/100ml) or calcium tartrate (0.0032g/100ml).

$COO \cdot Ca$	$COO \cdot Ca$	$COO \cdot Ca$
$\mid$	$\mid$	$\mid$
CH_2	CH_2	$CH \cdot OH$
$\mid$	$\mid$	$\mid$
CH_2	$CH \cdot OH$	$CH \cdot OH$
$\mid$	$\mid$	$\mid$
$COO \cdot Ca$	$COO \cdot Ca$	$COO \cdot Ca$
Calcium succinate	Calcium malate	Calcium tartrate

In addition to regarding the periphery of the isolated cell as a polyanion, the polysaccharides of connective tissues also carry negatively charged groups and are discussed as polyelectrolytes by Schubert (1964) in a useful review. The intercellular polysaccharides carry at least one and sometimes more than two acidic groups on each disaccharide unit. Schubert points out that in tissues most of the polysaccharides occur as sodium salts because sodium is by far the most common ion in the extracellular space; however cations are exchanged to an extent determined by their concentration and valency, but the exchange is never complete. Thus 50% of the sodium and potassium ions, and about 70% of the calcium ions associated with chondroitin sulphate appear to be firmly bound. A discussion by Katchalsky (1964) of some of the physical aspects of the interactions of divalent counter ions with polyelectrolytes is relevant here. Katchalsky observes that for inorganic univalent counter ions around a polyelectrolyte, it can be assumed that they act as non-specific point charges, and that differences between expected and theoretical results could usually be attributed to hydration radii, although in the case of polarizable ions and organic counter ions, Van der Waals' interactions may occur. However, the behaviour of different divalent ions with polyelectrolytes may be markedly different, indicating some sort of ionic specificity. For sytems such as these, the product of osmotic coefficient ρ_p, and the ideal value of osmotic pressure, should be the observed osmotic pressure. The lower the value of ρ_p the greater the fraction of immobilized counter ions which do not contribute to osmotic pressure. Alexandrowicz (1959, 1960) found by experiment that ρ_p is only affected by ionic concentrations to a minor degree, is decreased considerably with ionization, and, over a wide range, is inversely proportional to the number of charged groups per polymer. Katchalsky has taken, as evidence of ionic specificity, the osmotic coefficients for the interactions of a number of different ionic species with alginic acid. In the case of the univalent ions Na^+, K^+ and NH_4^+ the values for ρ_p are 0.41, 0.35 and 0.27 respectively, indicating that there is little specificity and that in all three cases about 35% of the counter ions are free to contribute to osmotic pressure. On the other hand the values of ρ_p for Mg^{++} and Ca^{++} are 0.15 and 0.01 respectively, indicating a marked difference, i.e. specificity, between these divalent cations and that in the case of calcium, 99% are bound to the polyelectrolyte, presumably with the formation of neutral ion pairs. Importantly in the present context, there may be a mixture of complex formation with parts of a polymer, and a rather less well defined and weaker attraction of divalent ions to non-specific regions. Carr (1953) demonstrated that in the case of bovine serum albumin, only 8% of its carboxyl groups form true complexes with calcium ions, while the remainder form weaker electrostatic combinations.

Curtis (1962) noted that although Rappaport et al. (1960) considered that negatively charged glass promotes cell adhesion by binding calcium ions, which form a bridge between the glass and cells; erythrocytes do not stick together in the presence of calcium ions, in spite of the fact that their charge density is probably as high as other cells, which do. The appreciation of specificity in the combination of calcium with acidic groups possibly provides an explanation for these apparent contradictions. The fact that the net negative charge on many different mammalian cells is not reversed by concentrations of calcium exceeding 0.1 M (Bangham and Pethica 1960) may also be taken as evidence of specificity. Although it is not at all clear what part the charge at the cell surface plays in determining cellular interactions, if the ionogenic groups present showed no specificity, then they might well be neutralized by the ions of the interstitial fluids, which might be physiologically inconvenient.

Studies of the effect of treatment of murine sarcoma 37 cells with EDTA disodium revealed that they became more easily deformable when measured on the microelastimeter (L. Weiss and Clement 1966; L. Weiss 1967). Normal deformability could be fully restored to the cells by incubating them in Hanks' balanced saline containing calcium ions with or without magnesium ions. On the other hand, deformability properties could only be partially restored by Hanks' solution containing magnesium, but no calcium ions, providing another example of difference in the specificity of calcium and magnesium ions. Cells treated with calcium EDTA showed no change. These results were taken to indicate that calcium ions help to maintain the mechanical properties of the peripheries of these particular tumour cells. Cells subjected to any of these treatments showed no significant change in electrophoretic mobility, which implies that not more than 5 to 10% of the chelated calcium, which was measured by atomic adsorption spectrometry, could have been removed from 'superficial' charged groups reflected at the hydrodynamic slip-plane. As the deformability changes probably indicate changes in the peripheral zones of cells, as distinct from their interiors (Wolpert 1960) it would appear that of the calcium bound in the periphery of sarcoma 37 cells, most is not bound to true surface groups but to groups deeper than about 10 Å from the slip-plane. From the analytical viewpoint, it is unfortunate that in cell biology, the relative physiological importance of various chemical interactions cannot be assessed by numbers alone. Thus, on purely quantitative reasoning, it might be suggested that the main function of calcium was to increase the cohesive strength of the cell periphery, thereby hindering cell separation by rupture, and that the calcium 'bridges' might be visualized running tangentially, deep within the peripheral region (fig. 7.4a). In contrast, radially directed calcium bridging between adjacent cells (fig. 7.4b), with or without the agency of interposed macromolecules, might well be considered to play a quantitatively minor role in these particular cells, which tend not to be mutually adherent, since calcium ions could not bridge the minimum gap of 20 Å $(10+10)$ between two opposed, susceptible, 'deep' anionic groups. It might thus be argued that they do not adhere because they

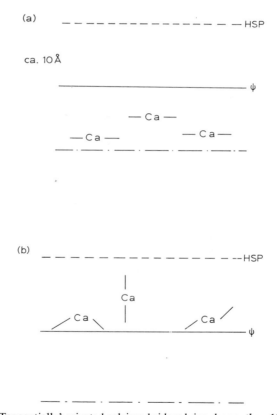

Fig. 7.4.   (a) 'Tangentially' oriented calcium bridges lying deeper than 10 Å from hydro-dynamic slip-plane (HSP) and not bound to anionic groups in plane of surface charges (Ψ). Removal of these Ca ions would not result in detectable change in cellular electrophoretic mobility.   (b) 'Radially' oriented calcium bridges at plane of surface charges. Removal of these Ca ions would result in change in cellular electrophoretic mobility.

cannot form radially oriented calcium 'bridges'. However, it must be remembered that ascites tumour cells do adhere, apparently strongly, to the peritoneum, and if calcium bridges are involved in this process, association with acidic groups at the cell surface must be involved. It is quite clear that information is required on the binding of calcium ions to negatively charged groups at the true surface of cells, where radial bridging could occur. The arguments developed here do not permit conclusions to be drawn at present on the relative importance of radial or tangential calcium bridges, in either cell adhesion or separation, or to decide whether the often suggested calcium deficiencies of tumours are responsible for deficient cell binding or adhesion on the one hand, or ease of separation or low cohesive strengths on the other.

7.4.2. Charge and separation

Klein and Klein (1956) isolated a number of strains of the murine MCIM sarcoma, M_{ss}, M_{tlf} M_{as} and M_{aa} in which there appears to be a progression of capacities of the cells to separate from each other. M_{ss}, when injected subcutaneously, tends to metastasize slowly to form in the lungs, at least, discrete secondary lesions, the cells of which infiltrate poorly. When the solid tumour is implanted intraperitoneally, it does not produce free ascitic forms. The M_{ss} tumour could therefore be regarded as one characterized by low separative ability of its constituent cells. M_{tlf} is a solid tumour in subcutaneous sites, which, when injected into the peritoneal cavity, gives rise to both free ascites cells and solid tumours, and may therefore be looked upon as possessing greater separative potential than M_{ss}. M_{as} is a solid tumour passaged subcutaneously, which metastasizes and infiltrates readily, and produces mainly free ascites on first injection in the peritoneal cavity. Thus the cells of the M_{as} strain would appear to separate from each other more readily than either the M_{ss} or the M_{tlf} varieties. The last strain is designated M_{aa}, and is routinely passaged as an intraperitoneal ascites tumour. Although the M_{aa} strain of cells have great propensity to separate from each other in the peritoneal cavity, they do in fact tend to stick in a monolayer to the peritoneal mucosa and presumably will form solid tumours if injected subcutaneously. I find it difficult to generalize about these strains of tumour cells in terms of their abilities to separate and adhere on the one hand, and their ability to metastasize on the other. The metastasis of cells from primary tumours in the peritoneal cavity and subcutaneous tissues cannot be considered exclusively in terms of the malignant cells, but must also depend on the nature of the environment and its effects on parts of metastatic process additional to cell separation. Bearing this difficulty in mind, it is nonetheless of considerable interest that Purdom et al. (1958) have demonstrated a progressive increase in electrophoretic mobility in the various strains of MCIM tumours, viz. M_{ss}, M_{tlf} M_{as} M_{aa}, and Ambrose (e.g. Abercrombie and Ambrose 1962) has repeatedly suggested that the increased charge density of these cells is directly related to their purported loss of adhesiveness by virtue of the increased electrostatic repulsion between them, and that metastasis or invasiveness can therefore be directly related to low cell adhesiveness and high surface charge-density. In making these correlations, it has been overlooked that the most 'invasive' cells in the body are macrophages, lymphocytes and granulocytes, all of which have low electrophoretic mobilities (Ruhenstroth–Bauer 1965; L. Weiss et al. 1966). The 'first-order' correlation between change and invasiveness on metastasis is therefore, in my opinion, quite untenable. In the quoted paper, Ambrose further suggests that the reason for the progressive increase in charge density is a reduced capacity to bind cations, notably calcium. Until the calcium binding capacity of this series of MCIM tumours is determined experimentally, it is difficult to take this explanation seriously. Cook et al. (1963) have also examined physicochemical differences between ascitic and solid forms of sarcoma 37, derived from a common pool of ascites cells, and injected subcutaneously and intraperitoneally in inbred strains of mice. An important point of difference between this work and that of Purdom et al., is that studies were not made on selected strains of tumours, but on populations undergoing site-induced modulation as suggested by Lasnitzki (1953), and confirmed on the evidence that bimodal distribution of electrokinetic parameters, commensurate with the numbers of cells present, was not demonstrated as would have been expected, had selection from pre-existing populations occurred (Cook et al. 1963). Under these conditions, the mean mobilities of cells mechanically isolated from solid tumours was -0.92 ± 0.08 μ $sec^{-1} \cdot volt^{-1} \cdot cm$, compared with -1.16 ± 0.12 for ascitic cells; the difference being significant at the 0.1% level. On treatment of both types of cell with neuraminidase there was a significant reduction in the mobilities of the ascites cells to -0.77 ± 0.10 μ $sec^{-1} \cdot volt \cdot^{-1} cm$, whereas there was no significant change in the mobilities of the cells derived from the solid tumour. The amounts of sialic acid released by neuraminidase treatment was the same in both groups of cells; implying that in the case of the ascites cells at least some–probably most of the sialic acid was bound with its ionized carboxyl groups in the electrokinetic shear plane, while in the cells from the solid tumour the sialic acid was either in a non-ionized state, or had its ionized groups deep to the plane where they could influence electrophoretic mobility. The main evidence suggesting that unionized sialic acid is present in the cell periphery has been the unwarranted assumption that the activity of neuraminidase is confined to this region, and that the excess of amounts of sialic liberated by neuraminidase as determined by assay, over the amounts calculated from electrophoretic data, was due to non-ionization or location. Simon-Reuss et al. (1964) expressed doubts on the postulated non-entry of neuraminidase into cells, and recently Nordling and Mayhew (1966) have demonstrated that in fact neuraminidase does enter cells, as do so many other macromolecules. The question then arises of whether the lower electrophoretic mobility of cells from solid sarcoma 37 tumours, compared to ascitic forms, is due to the deep location of neuraminidase 'sensitive' acidic groups with respect to the shear plane.

As suggested in the preceeding chapter, the act of isolation of cells from solid tumours may well leave charged groups of one cell stuck to, or buried in the periphery of its previously adjacent fellows in such a way that it is not detectable by measurements of electrophoretic mobility. Until this problem of separation technique is resolved, I am not prepared to accept the type of first order correlation between surface charge density and cell separation advanced by Ambrose.

7.4.3. Enzymes and separation

In chapter 4, in the general discussion of cell separation, quantitative data was presented which showed that cell separation could be facilitated by enzymes acting in the cell periphery/connective tissue region. The question to be considered now is the special relationships of enzymes to tumours.

It will be recalled that following the development of the lysosome concept (De Duve 1959), Dingle (1962) postulated that degradative changes in connective tissues could be due to release of lysosomal hydrolases, and that L. Weiss (1965) showed that sublethal release of these enzymes was associated with facilitated detachment of cells from artificial glass substrata. It would thus appear that if a case can be made out for preferential sublethal autolysis of the complex composed of the peripheries of malignant cells and/or their adjacent connective tissue, then this process could reasonably be regarded as contributing to their release from primary tumours.

Normal plasma contains a considerable variety of peptidases (Grassmann and Heyde 1930; Stern et al. 1951; Goldbarg and Rutenburg 1958; and many others). The level of these enzymes is known to increase in many types of inflammatory and traumatic states, in addition to cancer (Fleisher and Butt 1953), and their source of origin has been the subject of much discussion (Zamecnik et al. 1945; Fruton et al. 1948; and Smith et al. 1950). Ottoson and Sylvén (1960) showed that normal mouse plasma contained at least two groups of proteinases which showed optimal activity at pH 2 to 5 against urea-denatured haemoglobin. Assays of acid proteinases were made on the plasma of mice carrying the Ehrlich–Landschutz ascites tumour, at different times. It was noted that following an initial fall in enzyme level to barely detectable amounts, there was a gradual increase in activity up to twice normal amounts. The suggestion, that the origin of the raised enzyme level was the tumour cells themselves, was corroborated by assays made on cell-free ascitic fluid (Sylvén et al. 1959) obtained from mice carrying the same ascites tumour as those on which the plasma levels were determined. The plasma and ascitic fluid enzyme levels corresponded to each other, in that after an initial fall, the ascitic level rose to about three times that of normal plasma just before the animals died. It was concluded that in the case of these ascites cells, the most likely source of the increased dipeptidase and acid proteinase activity was the tumor cells themselves.

A note of caution must be sounded in assessing some of the results of enzyme assays of plasma, particularly in mouse tumours. Notkins (1965) has reviewed much of the evidence showing that infection with the lactic dehydrogenase virus can result in increased plasma levels of lactic dehydrogenase, isocitric dehydrogenase, malic dehydrogenase, phosphohexose isomerase and glutathione reductase. However, acid phosphatase, leucine amino-peptidase and α-glycerophosphate dehydrogenase were unaffected by the LDH viruses. Notkins mentions preliminary studies suggesting that the raised plasma levels of enzymes are due to a failure of the reticulo-endothelial system to 'clear' them, due to the direct action of virus on the reticulo-endothelial system.

It has been known for many years that tumours of many types may be associated with lysis of connective tissue elements including collagen, in addition to muscle and bone. Sylvén (1945) and Sylvén and Malmgren (1957) have surveyed much of the literature relating to connective tissue destruction and have described in detail the initial denaturation of collagen fibres characterized by loss of birefringence, followed by the formation of an apparently amorphous gel which is then digested. Sylvén and his associates have over the last few years produced much data on the release and localization of enzymes in tumours, particarly with reference to the invasiveness of solid tumours, and the destruction of normal surrounding tissues by them. By an ingenious system of examination of punch biopsies and specific staining reactions, Sylvén and Malmgren (1957) demonstrated dipeptidases and cathepsins at the advancing edge of infiltrative tumours. This was considered to be, at least in part, an active process as distinct from a passive leakage following cell death, since the enzymes were not demonstrable in the metabolically less active central regions of the same tumours, which are populated by the dormant cells of Caspersson's B-type. The suggestion that the younger tumour cells contain more proteolytic and peptidase activity than mature cells has been supported by von Bens (1959).

It is also of interest that quantitative histochemical reactions for susceptible —SH groups in cells of solid tumours left Sylvén and Malmgren with the impression that the younger, peripheral, Caspersson type A cells contain a higher concentration of thiol groups than the centrally located B-types. If this impression is reflected in the peripheral regions of type A cells, these would presumably be more susceptible to detachment following release of enzymes, and it is generally accepted that the peripheral cells of solid tumours are more likely to metastasize than their more centrally located counterparts.

Malmgren and Sylvén (1959) made similar observations on the location and assay of arginase, and later Malmgren and Sylvén (1960) made a study of the histological distribution of glutathione (GSSG) reductase activity in solid and ascitic tumours and normal tissues of the mouse. They observed that the distribution of GSSG reductase in solid tumours parallels that of the catheptic activities, and is some 4–6 times higher at their peripheries than centres. They calculated that the activity in the A-type cells was about twice that of normal liver cells, and that cells of the L strain had activities similar to those of normal fibroblasts. Holmberg (1961, 1962) has compared the *in vitro* release of catheptic, GSSG reductase and lactic dehydrogenase activities of L strain fibroblasts with ascites tumor cells, on the basis that the non-tumourogenic L strain might form a standard of normality with which to compare the tumour cells. Although this comparison may be invalid, the results are suggestive, in that whereas the catheptic, GSSG reductase and lactic dehydrogenase activity of the medium containing tumour cells increased two to three times during two hour's incubation, no measurable change was detected in the medium containing L cells.

The need for accurate quantitation of enzymes present in the interstitial fluid around the cells comprising solid tumours, has emphasized the lack of knowledge of the composition of normal interstitial fluids, as distinct from oedema fluids (Gamble 1954; Weisberg 1953). A small number of techniques have been developed to sample interstitial fluid. Maurer (1938) inserted fine glass capillary tubes into frogs' muscles parallel to the fibres, and this sampling technique has more recently been utilized by Creese et al. (1962). Vozel and Zajicek (1962) analysed the fluid obtained by centrifugation of material aspirated during needle-biopsies of tumours. Both of these techniques are 'blind' procedures, and the latter is also potentially traumatic to the tumour cells. In connection with sampling procedures note should be made of Gullino and Grantham's (1961) technique of sampling the blood going to, and leaving experimental tumours, by implanting them into the ovarian regions of animals, which are exteriorized and surrounded by a waxed container; the blood supply being derived from only one artery and vein, the ovarian vessels.

Recent attempts at determining the nature of the interstitial fluid in solid tumours have largely revolved around the techniques of Sylvén and Gullino. Sylvén's technique, as described by Sylvén and Bois (1960), consists of sampling free interstitial fluid in glass capillaries 0.1 to 0.6 mm in diameter, from the oedematous periphery of tumours. These authors point out that the blunt dissection required to make 'pouches' from which tissue fluids are collected may result in trauma, and that precise localization of the origin of the fluid is not possible. Gullino et al. (1964) consider that much of the interstitial fluid collected by Sylvén and Bois is probably derived from disrupted cells; however, having seen a demonstration of this technique by Dr. Sylvén, I do not regard this criticism too seriously. The technique devised by Gullino and described by Gullino et al. (1964) consists essentially of embedding a chamber made from 2 mm lengths of plastic tube, with their ends sealed with millipore filters, into actively growing exteriorized tumours growing in the ovarian bed, as described above. The tumours tended to completely envelope the chamber, from which cell-free fluid could be withdrawn through a sealed-in polyethylene tube. Each sample could be compared with the blood flowing in and out of the tumour through its pedicle, with lymph and peritoneal fluid, and with fluid obtained by implanting chambers into normal tissues. This technique is always open to the criticism that if non-tumour cells grow over the membranes nearest the tumour and on the outside of the chamber, then an additional permeability barrier is interposed; also, it may be criticized because necrotic areas may drain into the chambers whereas with Sylvén's technique it is possible to discriminate between the periphery of a tumour and its centre. Although, as recognized by their inventors, neither of these techniques is ideal, much useful information relating to the internal microenvironment of tumours has been gained through their use.

Sylvén and Bois (1960) compared the enzyme content of solid unicentric tumour-transplants in mice, with normal mouse plasma and peritoneal fluid. They observed that the cell-free fluid collected by them contained about 5% more protein than the peritoneal fluid. In addition, the catheptic activity of the fluid was three to four times as high as corresponding plasma, and the arginase and GSSH reductase activities were increased from five to twenty times. It was suggested that the enzymes originated from tumour cells, and that the leakage was due to the increased permeability of the cells themselves. Burgess and Sylvén (1962) studied the activity of lactic dehydrogenase in a variety of mouse tumours, and plasma and peritoneal fluid from normal and tumour-bearing mice. The enzyme activities in the tumour fluids, particularly at the centres of young tumours, were considerably higher than in normal plasma or peritoneal fluid. Later work (Burgess and Sylvén 1963) showed that the introduction of tumours into animals can produce large changes in lactic dehydrogenase activity, which varies with tumour type, and that this increase could not be entirely attributed to breakdown of tumour cells or erythrocytes.

An additional technique for the histochemical localization of enzyme activities has recently been reviewed by Daoust (1965), and consists of incubating films of substrate in contact with tissue sections. When unstained areas of the film are compared with the conventionally stained tissue section, the site of enzyme activity is revealed. The method has so far been used to localize ribonucleases, deoxysibonucleases, proteases, amylase and hyaluronidase. By use of this technique Daoust and Amano (1963) demonstrated that in contrast to other enzymes in thirty-two different type of human and experimental tumours the neoplastic cells themselves showed little demonstrable RNASe and DNASe activity, which was confined to connective tissue stroma and necrotic neoplastic regions.

The various evidence discussed shows that in association with the actively growing parts of tumours, from which metastasizing cells are commonly thought to arise, there is a high concentration of enzymes which would be capable of facilitating the separation of cells from the tumour periphery by sublethal degradation of either the cell peripheries and/or associated restraining-connective tissue. Whether the pH in this region is optimal for such enzymatic activity, particularly for those enzymes requiring very acid conditions, such as the cathepsins, is open to conjecture and will be partly determined by surface, as distinct from bulkphase pH (see chapter 2). However, it is of interest that Eden et al. (1955) have recorded pH values of around 6.55 by placing glass electrodes in rat tumours, following intraperitoneal injections of glucose, as compared to values of *p*H 7.3 in normal muscle.

The release of enzymes from tumour cells may well be dependent in some way on an immunological reaction between antibodies developing in the patient and his tumor cells, as suggested by experiments on *in vitro* systems (L. Weiss 1965).

7.5 *Metabolic and related processes and separation*

In chapter 4, it was noted that factors tending to create or emphasize heterogeneity produce structural weakness. It was argued that in the case of cell separation, the increased heterogeneity due to the increased flux of materials across cell peripheries in metabolic and pinocytotic processes would favour structural or cohesive weakness, reflected in the facilitation of cell separation. Experimental evidence from *in vitro* systems was thought to substantiate this hypothesis.

The questions to be posed in the present context are firstly, whether metabolic and pinocytotic processes are in fact different in malignant cells and their normal counterparts, and whether any correlation exists between these processes and metastatic phenomena. It will be appreciated that direct and unambiguous correlations of this type are almost entirely precluded by the complexity of the metastatic process *in vivo*.

7.5.1. *Engulfment*

An excellent detailed review of macrophages has been given by Jacoby (1965) from 1883, when Metchnikoff demonstrated the presence of macrophages throughout metazoa, which were characterized by their amoeboid nature and ability to phagocytose. The general topic of phagocytosis has also been reviewed by Woodin (1962) and will not be treated in detail here.

Pinocytosis, 'the drinking by cells', was described *in vitro* by Lewis (1931, 1937) in macrophages and sarcoma cells. On the basis of his well-known studies on amoebae, Holter (1959) in a review concludes that there is no clear cut division between phagocytosis and pinocytosis. Although many *in vivo* studies have indicated that normal tissue cells will phagocytose particles, Jacoby observes that macrophages do so at a higher rate and to a greater extent. *In vitro*, pinocytosis is often a marked feature of malignant cells and those of the reticulo-endothelial system; however, it is also seen in 'normal' cells, particularly following the addition of serum to cells grown previously in protein-free media (L. Weiss 1964). Although it seems impossible to establish any absolute quantitative correlation between heterogeneity-producing engulfment and cellular invasiveness, it is of interest that some reticulo-endothelial and tumour cells which are infiltrative *in vivo*, exhibit marked phagocytosis and pinocytosis. It must be remembered that, at most, such structure-weakening processes will play a subsidiary role in cell separation, as evidenced by the fact that there are well-recognized sessile cells in the reticulo-endothelial system, such as the Kupffer cells of the liver.

7.5.2. *Growth and metabolism*

In vitro experiments on fibroblasts (chapter 4) revealed that over the range of 20 to 37 °C, the higher the temperature, and hence metabolic rate, among other things, the more easily were cells detached from glass substrata. When facilitation of cell detachment was compared in this fibroblast/glass system with the amount of chick embryo extract added to the medium, a suggestive correlation was obtained between growth rate and cell detachment. Leighton (1965) has noted a similar effect in Walker carcinosarcomata cultured *in ovo* at 90° and 100°F on chick chorioallantois. At the lower temperature, conventional histological examination revealed a tumour consisting of adherent spindle-shaped cells, whereas at the higher temperature the tumours consisted of polyhedral cells which were separate from one another. Trevan and Roberts (1960) observed that the formation of stable sheets among murine ascites epithelioma cells *in vitro* may be prevented or even reversed by renewing their culture fluid; an observation which also suggests a correlation between metabolic activity and cell separation.

It may be remarked here that cells can usually be separated mechanically from the rapidly growing organs of chick and mouse embryos with far greater ease than from their adult counterparts. This may, of course, reflect chemical differences in the cell peripheries and/or the adjacent intercellular matrices, in addition to any of the postulated structural effects.

It is difficult to correlate growth rate of tumours *in vivo* with cell separation and/or metastasis, partly because of the difficulties inherent in assessing growth rate, partly because it is not known whether interest should be focused on growth parameters of whole tumours or localized regions of them, and partly because in different tumours the intermediate steps between cell separation and the establishment of metastases may well be different. The growth rate of human tumours has been discussed recently by Steel and Lamerton (1966), who have critically examined much of the older literature. These authors emphasize, as others have done previously, that the sparsity of data is due to two main limitations. Firstly, repeated measurements of volume are only possible on superficial, palpable tumours, or on those which can be clearly delineated on radiographic examination, such as primary or secondary growths in the lung or bones. Secondly, it is not usually justifiable to withhold treatment while making repeated observations. Steel and Lamerton also conclude that measurements of tumour volume are preferable to those of tumour diameter, and that doubling time is only rigidly applicable to tumours exhibiting exponential growth. Simple examination of many tumours reveals a diversity of necrobiotic processes, and this, together with the recognition of immunoselection, implies that exponential growth is unlikely.

Wallace (1961) has reviewed a good deal of evidence showing that the numbers of cells required for tumour transplantation in mice vary considerably with tumour type, and will affect the incidence of metastases in cases where the numbers of released cells are around critical levels.

Evidence linking growth rate indirectly with cell separation comes from the studies of Romsdahl et al. (1960), on the incidence of circulating malignant cells in 42 patients with melanomata. When the growth rate was 10% or less per week, 8% of the samples of peripheral blood contained tumour cells; when the increase was 10 to 20% per week, 25% of the samples were positive; and at rates of size increase in excess of 20% per week, some 66% of of the specimens contained neoplastic cells. In addition, the incidence of circulating cancer cells increases as the cancer becomes more advanced (Engell 1955; Scheinin and Koivuniemi 1963) when degenerative changes occur, which would also favour separation of viable cells by means of enzyme release from their dead or dying fellows. Obviously, however, the more widespread the disease the more foci there are from which release of cells can occur.

Although many experimental studies (Lucké and Schlumberger 1949; Tyzzer 1913; Wood 1919; and Zeidman et al. 1950) have indicated that the number of metastases varies with the length of time their primary tumours have been growing, not many studies appear to have been made on growth rate. Although Zeidman and his associates failed to detect a relationship between tumour size and number of metastases, they only used a small group of animals in their experiments. Later, more extensive work by Wood et al. (1954) with the T241 sarcoma in C57 mice, revealed a highly significant statistical correlation between the number of pulmonary metastases developing and 'the size attained by the primary tumour in a given time interval'.

Taylor and Nathanson (1942) made an attempt to index growth rate with a growth coefficient which could be applied to palpable tumours, and which was calculated very approximately from the average size and duration of the primary lesion. Although, as realized by Taylor and Nathanson, their growth coefficient is an extremely crude parameter, it is of interest that Glücksmann (1948) has examined the clinical data of Taylor and Nathanson, and of Paterson et al. (1946), and has obtained a significant correlation between the growth coefficients of a number of palpable human epithelio-mata and their metastatic spread to regional lymph nodes. These data are of great interest in that, owing to similarities of tumour type, transport and subsequent processes, they do in fact suggest that growth rate plays a part in metastasis, possibly through facilitating the separation of cells from the primary tumour, although they clearly do not establish a causal relationship between cell separation and growth rate.

An observation probably relating to cell separation and metastasis is seen in some skin cancers where even a very superficial invasion of the dermis by malignant melonama is often associated with widespread metastases, in contrast to squamous-cell carcinoma showing the same histological degree of invasion. Allen (1954) has attempted to correlate this finding with the lack of cohesiveness of the constituent cells of the melanocarcinomata, as visualized in histological sections, where they are often seen as separate entities. In contrast, the cells of the usually more slowly growing squamous-cell carcinomata are seen as adherent by light microscopy.

It must emphasized that growth rate is not thought to be the only factor affecting cell separation, and that no estimate can be given of its quantitative importance, or even if growth rate is to be correlated with heterogeneity, or enzyme release, for example. The complexity of metastasis in regard to growth rate is illustrated by the fact that giant fibroadenoma of the breast often grows very rapidly but does not metastasize; schirrous carcinoma of the breast grows slowly but often metastasizes, and slow-growing carcino-mata of the prostate, kidney and thyroid often produce metastases (Willis 1952, 1953).

References

Abercrombie, M., and Ambrose, E. J. (1962). Cancer Res. **22**, 525
Alexandrowicz, Z. (1959). J. Polymer. Sci. **40**, 113
Alexandrowicz, Z. (1960). J. Polymer. Sci. **43**, 337
Allen, A. C. (1954). In, The skin, C. V. Mosby Company, St. Louis, p. 882
Bangham, A. D., and Pethica, B. A. (1960). Proc. Roy. Phys. Soc. (Edinburgh) **28**, 43

Benz, G. von (1959). Oncologia 12, 128

Burgess, E. A., and Sylvén, B. (1962). Cancer Res. 22, 581

Burgess, E. A., and Sylvén, B. (1963). Cancer Res. 23, 714

Carr, C. W. (1953). Arch. Biochem. 43, 147

Caspersson, T., and Santesson, L. (1942). Acta Radiol. Suppl. 46

Cole, W. H., McDonald, G. O., Roberts, S. S., and Southwick, H. W. (1961). Dissemination of cancer. Appleton-Century-Crofts, Inc., New York

Coman, D. R. (1944). Cancer Res. 4, 625

Coman, D. R. (1953). Cancer Res. 13, 397

Cook, G. M. W., Seaman, G. V. F., and Weiss, L. (1963). Cancer Res. 23, 1813

Craigie, J. (1954). Advan. Cancer Res. 2, 197

Creese, R., D'Silva, J. L., and Shaw, D. M. (1962). J. Physiol. 162, 44

Curtis, A. S. G. (1962). Biol. Rev. 37, 82

Daoust, R. (1965). Intern. Rev. Cytol. 18, 191

Daoust, R., and Amano, H. (1963). Cancer Res. 23, 131

Duve, C. De (1959). In, T. Hayashi, ed., Subcellular particles. Ronald Press, New York, p. 128

Dingle, J. T. (1962). Proc. Roy. Soc. Med. 55, 109

Eden, M., Haines, B., and Kahler, H. (1955). J. Natl. Cancer Inst. 16, 541

Engell, H. C. (1955). Acta Chir. Scand. Suppl. 201

Fisher, E. R., and Fisher, B. (1960). Cancer 12, 926

Fleisher, G. A., and Butt, H. R. (1953). J. Clin. Invest. 32, 674

Foulds, L. (1951). Ann. Roy. Cell. Surg. (Eng.) 9, 93

Fruton, J. S., Smith, V. A., and Driscoll, P. E. (1948). J. Biol. Chem. 173, 457

Furth, J., and Kahn, M. C. (1937). Am. J. Cancer 31, 276

Galtsoff, P. S. (1925). J. Exptl. Zool. 42, 183

Gamble, J. L. (1954). Chemical anatomy, physiology and pathology of extracellular fluid, a lecture syllabus. Harvard University Press, Cambridge, Massachusetts

Gerster, H. G. (1885). New York J. Med. 41, 233

Glücksmann, A. (1948). Brit. J. Radiol. 21, 559

Goldbarg, J. A., and Rutenburg, A. M. (1958). Cancer 11, 283

Grassmann, W., and Heyde, W. (1930). Z. Physiol. Chem. 188, 69

Greene, H. S. M. (1965). Acta Cytol. 9, 138

Gullino, P. M., and Grantham, F. H. (1961). J. Natl. Cancer Inst. 27, 679

Gullino, P. M., Clark, S. H., and Grantham, F. H. (1964). Cancer Res. 24, 780

Harris, M. (1963). Cell culture and somatic variation. Academic Press, New York and London

Hauschka, T. S. (1961). Cancer Res. 21, 957

Herbst, C. (1900). Roux' Arch. Entwicklungsmech. Organ. 9, 424

Hewitt, H. B. (1953). Brit. J. Cancer 7, 367

Holmberg, B. (1961). Cancer Res. 21, 1386

Holmberg, B. (1962). Acta Unio Intern. Contra Cancrum 18, 237

Holter, H. (1959). Intern. Rev. Cytol. 8, 481

Jacoby, F. (1965). In, E. M. Wilmer, ed., Cells and tissues in culture. Academic Press, London and New York, Vol. 2, p. 1

Katchalsky, A. (1964). Biophys. J. (Suppl.) 4, 9

Klein, G. (1961). In, R. J. C. Harris, ed., Biological approaches to cancer chemotherapy, Academic Press, New York, p. 201

Klein, G., and Klein, E. (1956). Ann. N. Y. Acad. Sci. **63**, 640

Lasnitski, I. (1953). Brit. J. Cancer **7**, 233

Leighton, J. (1964). Progr. Exptl. Tumor Res. Karger, Basel, **4**, 98

Leighton, J. (1965). Acta Cytol. **9**, 138

Lewis, W. H. (1931). Johns Hopkins Hosp. Bull. **49**, 17

Lewis, W. H. (1937). Amer. J. Cancer **29**, 666

Long, H. P. De, Coman, D. R., and Zeidman, I. (1950). Cancer **3**, 718.

Lucké, B., and Schlumberger, H. (1949). J. Exptl. Med. **89**, 269

Malmgren, H., and Sylvén, B. (1959). Cancer Res. **19**, 525

Malmgren, H., and Sylvén, B. (1960). Cancer Res. **20**, 204

Maurer, F. W. (1938). Am. J. Physiol. **124**, 546

Mc Cutcheon, M., Coman, D. R., and Fontaine, B. M. (1948). Cancer **1**, 460

Mc Donald, G. O. (1961). In, W. H. Cole, G. O. Mc Donald, S. S. Roberts, and H. W. Southwick, Dissemination of cancer, Appleton-Century-Crofts, Inc., New York, p. 349

Nordling, S. and Mayhew, E. (1966). Exptl. Cell Res. **44**, 552

Notkins, A. L. (1965). Bacteriol. Rev. **29**, 143

Ottoson, R., and Sylvén, B. (1960). Arch. Biochem. Biophys. **87**, 41

Pantin, C. F. A. (1926). Brit. J. Exptl. Biol. **3**, 275

Paterson, R., Tod, M. C., and Russell, M. (1946). The results of radium and X-ray therapy in malignant disease. Livingstone, Edinburgh

Purdom, L., Ambrose, E. J., and Klein, G. (1958). Nature **181**, 1586

Rabotti, G. (1959). Nature **183**, 1276

Rappaport, C., Poole, J. P., and Rappaport, H. P. (1960). Exptl. Cell Res. **20**, 465

Rinaldini, L. M. (1958). Intern. Rev. Cytol. **7**, 587

Ringer, S., and Sainsbury, H. (1894). J. Physiol. **16**, 1

Roberts, D. C. (1963). Brit. J. Cancer **27**, 142

Roberts, D. C., and Trevan, D. J. (1957). Ann. Rept. Imp. Cancer Res. Fund **54**, 18

Roberts, D. C., and Trevan, D. J. (1960). Brit. J. Cancer **14**, 716

Roberts, S., Long, L., Jonasson, O., McGrath, R., McGrew, E., and Cole, W. H. (1960). Surg. Gynecol. and Obstet. **111**, 3

Robertson, J. D. (1941). Biol. Rev. **16**, 106

Romsdahl, M. M., Potter, J. F., Malmgren, R. A., Chu, E. W., Brindley, C. O., and Smith, R. R. (1960). Surg. Gynecol. Obstet. **111**, 675

Ruhenstroth-Bauer, G. (1965). In, E. J. Ambrose, ed., Cell electrophoresis. Churchill, London, p. 66

Sandberg, A. A., and Yamada, K. (1966). Cancer. **19**, 1869

Scheinin, T. M., and Koivuniemi, A. P. (1963). Cancer **16**, 639

Schubert, M. (1964). Biophys. J. (Suppl.) **4**, 119

Simon-Reuss, I., Cook, G. M. W., Seaman, G. V. F., and Heard, D. H. (1964). Cancer Res. **24**, 2038

Smith, E. L., Cartwright, G. W., Tyler, F. H., and Wintrobe, M. M. (1950). J. Biol. Chem. **185**, 59

Steel, G. G., and Lamerton, L. F. (1966). Brit. J. Cancer **20**, 74

Stern, K., Birmingham, M. K., Cullen, A., and Richter, R. (1951). J. Clin. Invest. **30**, 84

Sylvén, B. (1945). Acta Radiol. Suppl. **59**

Sylvén, B., and Bois, I. (1960). Cancer Res. 20, 831

Sylvén, B., and Malmgren, H. (1957). Acta Radiol. Suppl. **154**

Sylvén, B., Ottoson, R., and Révész, L. (1959). Brit. J. Cancer **13**, 551

Taylor, A. C. (1962). J. Cell Biol. **15**, 201

Taylor, G. W., and Nathanson, I. T. (1942). Lymph node metastases. Oxford University Press

Tjernberg, B., and Zajicek, J. (1965). Acta Cytol. **9**, 197

Trevan, D. J., and Roberts, D. C. (1960). Brit. J. Cancer **14**, 724

Tyzzer, E. E. (1913). J. Med. Res. **28**, 309

Vozel, J. M., and Zajicek, J. (1962). Experientia **18**, 149

Wallace, A. C. (1961). Canad. Cancer Conf. **4**, 139. Academic Press, New York and London

Weisberg, H. F. (1953). 'Water, electrolyte and acid-base balance. The Williams and Wilkins Company, Baltimore

Weiss, L. (1960). Intern. Rev. Cytol. **9**, 187

Weiss, L. (1964). Exptl. Cell Res. **33**, 277

Weiss, L. (1965). Exptl. Cell Res. **37**, 540

Weiss, L. (1967). J. Cell Biol. **33**, 341

Weiss, L., and Clement, K. (1966). Ann. Med. Exptl. Biol. Fenniae **44**, 155

Weiss, L., Mayhew, E., and Ulrich, K. (1966). Lab. Invest. **15**, 1304

Willis, R. A. (1952). The spread of tumours in the human body, 2nd ed. Butterworth, London

Willis, R. A. (1953). Pathology of tumours, 2nd ed. Butterworth, London

Wolpert, L. (1960). Proc. Roy. Phys. Soc. (Edinburgh) **28**, 107

Wood, F. C. (1919). J. Am. Med. Assoc. **73**, 764

Wood, J. S., Holyoke, E. D., Clason, W. P. C., Sommers, S. C., and Warren, S. (1954). Cancer **7**, 437

Woodin, A. M. (1962). Biochem. Soc. Symp. **22**, 126

Yamada, K., Takagi, N., and Sandberg, A. A. (1966). Cancer **19**, 1879

Zamecnik, P. C., Stephenson, M. L., and Cope, O. (1945). J. Biol. Chem. **158**, 135

Zeidman, I. (1947). Cancer Res. **7**, 386

Zeidman, I. (1965). Acta Cytol. **9**, 136

Zeidman, I., McCutcheon, M., and Coman, D. R. (1950). Cancer Res. **10**, 357

CHAPTER 8

Movements and transport of malignant cells

Malignant cells from the primary tumour, can infiltrate adjacent normal tissues and following entry into blood or lymphatic vessels, be carried to distant sites.

8.1 Malignant infiltration

Malignant infiltration can occur without separation of malignant cells from their parent lesion; they may be pushed through the tissues by the pressure of the growing primary tumour, and this *vis a tergo* is well recognized and described in standard pathological texts such as that of Willis (1952). On mechanical principles, it would be expected that such spread would follow the paths of least resistance along natural anatomical tissue planes, and Young (1959) has illustrated this point with jelly models viewed with polarized light. This method of extension of a primary tumour may occur at multiple points of its periphery by tongue-like extensions whose continuity with the primary tumour may only be revealed by serial sections. The appearance of extensions of these may lead to the false impression in single sections, of malignant foci which are separate from the primary lesion. Willis states that this type of direct spread due to *vis a tergo*, is the 'initial and fundamental mode of spread of most neoplasms'. *In vitro*, considerable motility is often observed at the edges of sheets of cells or tissue explants, and from the experimental evidence of Gustafson and his colleagues quoted in chapter 3, it is clear that by virtue of adherent filopodial extensions, cells can pull tissue masses behind them. Schneider (1958) and Wolff and Schneider (1957) have shown that individual cells can invade normal embryonic tissues under cultured conditions where pressure effects of the type implied by the term *vis a tergo* are clearly inapplicable. Therefore, while the importance of this latter type of contiguous spread cannot be denied, and is often apparently encountered in clinical practice, it cannot be considered as the only form of malignant infiltrative mechanism.

Virchow (1863), Grohe (1865) and Carmalt (1872) observed actively moving cells in smears of freshly excised tumours. Although Virchow is usually given credit for first observing active crawling movements in malignant cells, it is not clear from his original description whether he was actually observing histiocytes or malignant cells. Since that time, well authenticated examples of the active movement of neoplastic cells have come from studies of tissue cultures by many workers including Carrel and Burrows (1911), Hanes and Lambert (1912), Russell and Bland (1933), Ludford (1934), Lewis (1936), Cox and Cranage (1937) and Coman (1942). The suggestion that invasion of normal by malignant tissues might depend on the active amoeboid movements of neoplastic cells was apparently made first by Waldeyer in 1872 and later by Vierth (1895). Lambert (1916) measured the velocity of crawling malignant cells *in vitro*, and calculated that by amoeboid movement alone, malignant cells could migrate from the breast to the axillary lymph nodes in about four weeks. More recently Enterline and Coman (1950) measured the migration rates of malignant cells in culture and observed rates as high as 4 to 5 μ per min; they also observed that under similar cultural conditions isolated normal epithelial cells can move at the same rates as their malignant counterparts.

It is difficult to judge when the development of secondary tumours adjacent to a primary neoplasm is due to cells which have actively migrated from the parent tumour, or due to cells which have invaded local blood or lymphatic vessels and have been carried to the site of secondary growth. Single malignant cells may be seen infiltrating normal tissues, for example, in gastric carcinomata and melanocarcinomata, and Allen (1954), among others, presents many well-documented examples of isolated, pigmented malignant cells invading the dermis in cases of malignant melanoma. However, Allen also notes that just deep to the epithelium, there are many thin-walled lymphatic and venous channels which are not apparent in standard histological preparations unless they are opened up, and that the malignant cells presumably gain easy access to these. Thus, the appearance of satellite nodules cannot be taken as evidence that the neoplastic cells initiating them actively migrated through the tissues from the primary site.

The important point would appear to be not whether normal and malignant cells can move, but whether they are free to move. Freedom of movement is more complicated than simple separation of cells from their parent tissue or tumour, but also concerns their subsequent interactions with the tissues which they are invading, and this in turn does not permit clear-cut discrimination between all malignant cells on the one hand, and all normal cells on the other.

The role of connective tissues in relation to invasiveness has been reviewed by Vasiliev (1958), who quotes many Russian papers which have not been translated into English. Vasiliev first considers invasive growth by non-malignant tissues, and quotes Fischer's (1906) experiments in which subcutaneous injections of scarlet red into rabbits' ears produced inflammatory lesions morphologically similar to squamous carcinomata, which invaded the underlying connective tissues, and which subsequently regressed. Other examples of non-malignant invasion described by Vasiliev include inflammatory epithelial proliferations in lungs, kidneys, salivary glands, mammary glands and skin, in a variety of laboratory animals. A common pattern seen is the formation of a bed of connective tissue which precedes the epithelial invasion. Whether the connective tissue stimulates the invasion, or whether the epithelial tissue stimulates the connective tissue, or whether indeed there is such a simple first order relationship at all, is uncertain.

Other examples of non-malignant invasion are to be found in the invasion of endometrium by trophoblast. Placentation has been reviewed in detail by Amoroso (1952) and Böving (1959) and a useful technique for studying this phenomenon in organ-culture, where environmental factors can be analyzed, has been described by Glenister (1961a). This worker (Glenister 1961b) has shown that the initial phase of attachment of the blastocyst to isolated cultured endometrial strips is not dependent on underlying myometrium, as once supposed, but appears to be due to a direct surface interaction between the developing embryo and the endometrium. Glenister notes that as he uses embryo extract and serum in his culture media, it is not possible to rule out hormonal or other influences; and indeed Lajos et al. (1958) have shown that the connective tissues in cultured human placental explants proliferate in sera from non-pregnant subjects, whereas the epithelial elements proliferate in the presence of sera from women in early pregnancy. Epithelial polarity or the location of endometrial glands appear not to affect the attachment or invasion sites. Trophoblastic invasion is most marked where the endometrium is devitalized, thus in contrast to the inflammatory invasions discussed by Vasiliev, and fibroblast proliferation is not an essential prerequisite to invasion. Glenister notes that the parts of the trophoblast actively invading are not syncytial, which contrasts with Böving's (1959) concept that malignant invasion is cellular, whereas trophoblastic invasion is syncytial in nature. It is of interest that the differentiation of the trophoblast is in some way influenced by underlying mesenchyme, and that in culture, syncytium is only produced in trophoblastic specimens containing mesoderm (Glenister 1962). Thus, invasiveness may well be correlated with contact reaction between the invading cells and the tissues being invaded. Glenister (1961b) speculates that in its early invasive phase, the trophoblast consists of primitive pleomorphic cells, which eventually differentiate into non-invasive, absorptive cyto- and syncytio-trophoblast following interaction with underlying mesenchyme. If this mesenchymal restraint is lost, there may be reversion to the more primitive, invasive tissues which may represent chorionepitheliomata. It may be noted that both normal and malignant trophoblastic cells invade blood vessels, and that both may metastasize to other organs (Douglas et al. 1959).

In 1934 Purr suggested that catheptic lysis of stroma was involved in tumour spread. The role of lytic activities of enzymes in invasion-connective tissues, as it relates to the important work of Sylvén and his colleagues, has been discussed in chapter 7. A similar suggestion was advanced by Gersh and Catchpole (1949), who observed destruction of PAS-positive ground substance of connective tissue by rapidly growing tumours, which they attributed to the action of collagenolytic enzymes. Burstone (1956) has also commented on the proteolytic activity of human neoplasms in this context. At various times attempts have been made to correlate invasiveness with the amount of hyaluronidase present in the tumours. These attempts have been unsuccessful, as have attempts to promote invasion by injection of hyaluronidase (see Vasiliev for a review of this work). In the cases where hyaluronidase has been demonstrated, it would appear to originate in contaminating bacteria (Kiriluk et al. 1950; Reggianini 1953).

An interesting development has been Mottet's (1961) demonstration that fibroblastic aminopeptidases can apparently play a part in invasion, at least in the case of Hep-3 tumour cells. The implication of many of the observations and hypotheses on the mode of action of various enzymes and diffusion-promoting factors in invasion, is that stromal dissolution promotes spread. Mottet (1963) devised a test of the hypothesis that the tensile strength of the stroma was a restraining factor in invasion, by studying the spread of Hep-3 carcinoma on normal chick chorioallantoic membranes, and on membranes in which the tensile strength was decreased by previous treatment with the lathyritogenic agent β-amino-propionitrile. Mottet noticed no difference in spread as assessed by weight and cross-sectional diameter of the tumours. Although in his system, Mottet could not detect a difference, the validity of this system to invasion of tissues in depth by tumours, is questionable. In my opinion, invasion of a tumour by simple expansion due to growth is expected to be promoted by stromal lysis. On the other hand, stromal lysis might well be expected to hinder spread due to active cell movements, by destroying the substrata over which tumour cells crawl.

The movement of separated cells away from the primary tumour through connective tissues may well involve contact inhibition, as described in chapter 3, in connection with morphogenetic movements of cells. *In vitro*, fibroblasts growing on, and crawling over glass, interfere with each other's movements on contact and when fibroblasts from embryonic chick heart or neonatal mouse skeletal muscle come into contact with each other they form stable adhesions, even between cells from the two different species. (Abercrombie and Heaysman 1954a). Qualitative work by Abercrombie and Heaysman (1954b) and by Abercrombie and Ambrose (1958) failed to reveal contact inhibition *in vitro*, between murine sarcoma cells and these fibroblasts. Little change in surface activity could be seen when sarcoma cells met each other. A detailed quantitative study of the *in vitro* contact interactions between chick and mouse fibroblasts as described above, and murine Crocker and sarcoma 37 cells, was made by Abercrombie et al. (1957). According to population density, and cell overlap measurements which were amenable to statistical analysis, Abercrombie and his colleagues could detect no evidence of contact inhibition of the tumour cells by the fibroblasts; it also appeared that the movements of the tumour cells were actually stimulated by contact with fibroblasts. It should be noted that not all of the tumour cells showed loss of contact inhibition, reflecting the heterogeneity of the population. It was also observed that although the fibroblasts did not obstruct the movements of tumour cells, the tumour cells significantly inhibited the movements of the fibroblasts. Although an explanation cannot be given for this paradoxical situation, Abercrombie et al. raise the possibility that the tumour cells may exert a deleterious effect on the 'normal' tissues, as observed by Ludford and Barlow (1944), which is possibly concerned with lactic acid produced by the tumour cells (Carrel and Ebeling 1928; Fischer et al. 1929) diffusing out. It is a common observation in cell culture that acidity of the medium tends to favour cell adhesion to glass, as determined by cell spreading. It is therefore conceivable that, under suitable conditions, by increasing the areas of fibroblast surfaces attached to glass, the movements of these cells can be inhibited. Contact inhibition in relation to tumour cell invasiveness is critically discussed by Abercrombie (1961), who points out that it is not all-or-none phenomena and is influenced by cultural conditions. In addition, the migration of cells out from rat liver, explanted at various times following partial hepatectomy, changes considerably, suggesting that contact inhibition can also change during regenerative processes (Abercrombie and Harkness 1951). Curtis (1961) has also demonstrated a possible link between metabolic processes and contact inhibition, with his observation that inhibition is partially lost in fibroblasts when the amount of chick embryo extract in their culture fluid is increased beyond a certain level. Although invasiveness may be related to loss of contact inhibition, on the additional evidence that macrophages which are also 'invasive' are not inhibited by fibroblasts (Oldfield 1963), Abercrombie concludes that contact inhibition is not the whole story, and certainly histological studies of tumours *in vivo* confirm this view.

Stoker (1964) has shown that hamster cells which had undergone polyoma virus-induced transformation, exhibit inhibition of movement and possibly division, when grown on glass *in vitro*, close to 'normal' fibroblasts. However, the transformed cells do not show such contact inhibition amongst themselves. Stoker therefore advanced the hypothesis that transformation by polyoma virus does not affect the ability of these cells to respond to signals, but that the event affects the production of such regulatory information.

An important reservation on Abercrombie's work on contact inhibition is that the experiments were carried out on 'two-dimensional' cell stysems. The invasiveness of a wide variety of tumour cells in three dimensions has been elegantly demonstrated *in vitro* in embryonic chick organs, by Wolff and Schneider (1957) and by Schneider (1958). Unpublished experiments of my own made in Wolff's laboratory in 1961 showed that in contrast to malignant cells, adjacent cultured fragments of embryonic heart, mesonephros and liver do not infiltrate into one another, within the limits of cell identification possible in conventionally stained sections. As high-resolution cinemicroscopy has not been done on these three-dimensional systems, it cannot be stated with certainty that invasiveness is correlated with loss of contact inhibition, even at the level of light microscope. In this culture system it may be that invasiveness is in some way related to the preferential growth of the malignant cells; as in older cultures, the tumours tend to overgrow the embryonic explants.

Another qualification about the correlation of contact inhibition and invasiveness is concerned with the question of whether embryonic fibroblasts are to be regarded as 'normal', when compared with tumour cells. This objection is only partially met by experiments with oncogenic viruses in which the social behaviour of cells, before and after malignant conversion, is compared. Temin and Rubin (1958), among others, have shown that fibroblasts which previously exhibited contact inhibition, as evidenced by the formation of stable cell sheets on glass, lose inhibition following conversion by the Rous virus, as evidenced by their ability to pile up on top of each other. In all of these types of experiments the question of the normalcy of the 'control' cells presents a difficult problem.

Pulvertaft et al. (1959) studied the behaviour of cultured human thyroid cells on glass. 'Transformation' was a clear-cut event, marked by changes in cell morphology, growth rate, virus suspectibility and loss of ability to synthesize organic iodine-containing compounds, including monoidotyrosine, triiodotyrosine and thyroxine. In the present context it is of interest that in early cultures of 'untransformed' cells, disc-like aggregates were seen, which are often taken as evidence of the correlation between malignancy and loss of contact inhibition. On the other hand, 'transformed' thyroid cells growing on glass were not observed by us, to form three-dimensional aggregates. Other evidence suggesting that loss of contact inhibition in cells cultured on glass may not be related to malignancy per se, comes from Sanford's (1966) extensive experiments. It may also be mentioned here that loss of contact inhibition to growth also does not appear to be directly related to malignancy, but, according to Eagle and Levine (1947), is to be related to karyotype. Thus in my opinion, while contact inhibition, as described by Abercrombie, is a definite part of cellular social behaviour, loss of contact inhibition cannot be considered to invariably correlate with malignancy, any more than exhibition of contact inhibition invariably indicates normalcy.

A significant approach to the problem of studying the three-dimensional social relationships between malignant cells and fibroblasts has been provided by Leighton and Kline (1954) and by Leighton et al. (1959) using the sponge-matrix tissue culture technique. In this technique, normal human tissues from adults and embryos are grown in plasma-clot on cellulose sponge. When fibroblastic growth is established in the sponge-matrix, a small inoculum of malignant cells (HeLa, Eagle's KB and Osgood's J-96 strains) growing in 'Gelfoam' is placed on the sponge, and the tumour cells migrate into it. The degree of invasion varied with the amount of fibroblastic growth in the host culture, and was directed by the orientation of the connective tissue cells. Invasion was minimal when the fibroblasts were lying parallel to the surface of the tumour implant, and maximal when they were at right angles to the margin of the implant. It is surprising that this system which offers the potentialities for varying cell combinations (Leighton and Kalla 1958) and environmental conditions (Leighton et al. 1956) has not been more widely used.

The interactions of connective tissues with malignant cells is not an over-worked field in spite of its obvious potential importance. Although Vasiliev (1958) concluded that proliferation of connective tissues favours the growth of tumour transplants and their spread and metastasis, this is not borne out by the experiments of Molomut et al. (1955) and Hewitt (1956). Furthermore, although Vasiliev relates a reported tumour-inhibitory effect of cortisone to its suppression of inflammatory response and fibroblastic reactions, many have found an enhancement of tumour growth in cortisone-treated animals. It appears unwise at present to draw any conclusions from the mass of con-flicting evidence on malignant cell/connective tissue interactions.

8.2 *Entry of malignant cells into vessels*

Malignant cells may enter the blood stream by becoming passively detached from tumours after they have invaded veins, or by active invasion of the tumour capillary bed after detachment. Entry of cells into the blood stream may also occur via lymphatics.

Direct invasion of veins by tumours has been well-known since Billroth's (1855) description of malignant cells in the veins draining a teratoma of the testis. Willis (1952) gives a very full review of the literature pertaining to venous invasion. It has only been appreciated fairly recently, (see Willis 1952; Dukes 1944) that venous invasion is a common occurrence, which is often only apparent in standard histopathological preparations after staining the vessel walls for elastic tissue (Sunderland 1949; Friedell and Parsons 1962). The various clinical aspects of venous invasion are well summarized by Griffiths and Salsbury (1965), who conclude that there is a relationship between venous invasion and visceral metastasis, which is complicated by the fact that vascular dissemination is often limited by the occurrence of thrombosis in invaded vessels. In addition, venous occlusion has been de-monstrated by radiographic techniques and is thought to be more common than actual invasion of veins. These authors also note that detachment of tumour cells from the invading lesion will be facilitated by higher rates of blood flow.

The entry of malignant cells into blood vessels will depend to some extent on the vascularization of the tumours. Ribbert (1904) considered that many tumours had poor blood supply at their centres; this progressive central vascular insufficiency is related to poor nutrition and central necrosis.

Much of the earlier literature on the vascularization of tumours is reviewed by Goldacre and Sylvén (1962) who confirmed and extended earlier observations when they studied the distribution of systemic lissamine green in various solid mouse tumours. It was shown that only a narrow shell ranging from 0.1 to to 2 mm in thickness was coloured by the injected dye, while the remainder of the tumour was uncoloured, due either to lack or blockage of blood vessels. Viable malignant cells were demonstrated in regions where the dye had not penetrated. Thus, unless metastasis is accomplished solely by cells of the peripheral zone of tumours, cells from the interior of the tumour mass must migrate to its periphery for haematogenous spread to occur. It may be that in the untreated tumours, metastasis only occurs from peripheral cells; however, during radiotherapy the comparatively well-oxygenated cells near the blood supply are approximately three times more radiosensitive (Thomlinson 1960) than those in hypoxic regions of the tumour. Thus following a course of radiotherapy, metastasis may involve the centrifugal migration of cells from hypoxic regions of tumours. It is surprising that such migrations, which might well involve contact inhibition, have not been systematically studied.

Tumour cells may also enter the lymphatic channels which drain into blood vessels. Some of the earlier work indicating that malignant cells enter lymphatic channels has been reviewed by Watne et al. (1960a), who also observed them in the thoracic duct lymph of about a quarter of 30 patients with advanced malignant disease. Although these authors found no correlation between pulmonary metastases and tumour cells in the lymph, they nonetheless conjectured that passage of malignant emboli via the thoracic duct into the blood is an important mode of dissemination. Tjernberg and Zajicek (1965) cannulated the lymph vessels leaving nodes which were the sites of metastases in rabbits bearing the $V \times 2$ carcinoma, and observed that increased numbers of tumour cells were released following massage.

Leaf (1900) suggested from injection studies that lymphatic vessels communicate directly with veins, and Pressman and Simon (1961) have demonstrated direct communications between lymph nodes and veins. Bron et al. (1963) also demonstrated the connection between lymph vessels and veins in man, by fluoroscopic observation of movements of contrast oil passing directly from lymph nodes into veins. The demonstration of lymphatic portal vein communications in animals (Griffiths and Salsbury 1963) and man (Perez-Tamayo et al. 1963), also suggests that tumour cells may enter the bloodstream via lymphatics other than the thoracic duct.

Cells may also apparently move from the blood into lymphatics, and Sjövall (1936) and Gowans (1959) showed that lymphocytes are continuously recirculating between blood and lymph. Yoffey and Courtice (1956) have also reviewed the evidence showing that erythrocytes leave capillaries, traverse tissue spaces and enter the lymph. Fisher and Fisher (1966) have studied the movements of ^{51}Cr-labelled Walker tumour cells in the rat, and conclude that there is free interchange between cells in the blood and lymph via the interstitial space.

The diversity of the potential pathways of circulating malignant cells may well account for some of the many bizarre metastatic patterns recorded in the literature.

8.3 *Tumour cells in the peripheral blood*

Following the post-mortem detection of tumour cells in peripheral blood by Ashworth in 1869, few studies were made in this field, apart from those of Pool and Dunlop (1934), until the systematic studies of Engell in 1955. Since that time, very many papers have been published on this topic, which have been critically reviewed by Griffiths and Salsbury (1965) and in Acta Cytologica, volume 9 (parts 1 and 2, 1965). One of the main points of these criticisms is that many of the estimates of the incidence of malignant cells in the peripheral blood were unreliable, because of the technical difficulties associated with tumour cell isolation, and the difficulties associated with recognition of some normal and tumour cells in isolated blood fractions. Spriggs (1960) among others, considered that tumour cells were 'overdiagnosed' in many of the early series and Christopherson (1965) draws attention to the enormous discrepancy in, for example, identification of malignant cells in 1.5% of blood samples from 144 patients with cancer (Raker et al. 1960), and Mello's (1963) positive results in 96.5% of his cases. Raker et al. noted that some 42% of their cases had circulating megakaryocytes which could be mistaken for malignant cells, and Christopherson comments that in his experience, the poorer the quality of the specimen, the higher the yield of abnormal cells. Among those cells which may be mistakenly identified as malignant cells, particularly in poor preparations or by inexperienced observers, are megakaryocytes, plasma cells, endothelial cells and aggregates of degenerate monocytes. This is illustrated by the finding of Moore et al. (1962) that there was a similar incidence of apparently malignant cells in subjects with and without cancer. Bearing in mind the difficulties of identification and isolation, I think it encouraging that more recent results show a good measure of agreement as exemplified by the similar positive results obtained in samples of peripheral blood obtained from the antecubital veins of patients with carcinoma by Moore and Sandberg (1960 – 8.2%) Spriggs (1962 – 4%), Sellwood et al. (1964 – 6.5%), West et al. (1964 – 6.4%) and Griffiths and Salsbury (1965 – 8.5%).

The data collected by Cole et al. (1961) and by Griffiths and Salsbury (1965) suggest that the 'resting' level of tumour cells in the blood of patients with cancer is somewhat less than 10 cells per ml. However, bearing in mind that there are about 65 to 75 ml blood per kg body weight, it will be appreciated that a considerable number of malignant cells is likely to be circulating at any given time.

In view of the limitations in technique described earlier, it does not appear profitable to discuss further numerical data except in a general way. Watne et al. (1960b) reported a worse survival rate among patients with cancer and circulating tumour cells, than in those with no detectable tumour cells in the peripheral blood, and these conclusions appear generally acceptable. On the other hand, the mere presence of tumour cells in the blood does not necessarily presage the development of metastases, since most of the circulating cells are thought to die in the blood stream, as postulated in many papers including those of Levin and Sittenfield (1910), Weil (1913), Takahashi (1915), Iwasaki (1915), Warren and Gates (1936), Saphir (1947), Walther (1948), Watanabe (1954), Baserga and Saffiotto (1955) and Wood et al. (1961).

It has been stressed that mere identification of tumour cells in the blood is of little prognostic significance, unless it is also determined whether or not they are viable (Watne et al. 1960b and Moore 1960), however, due to technical difficulties associated with the small numbers and proportions of malignant cells present in the blood, it has to date not been possible to make extensive viability determinations on specimens from patients. In this context, a viable cell would be one which has reproductive capacity; and this would presumably be determined either by their ability to form tumours in suitable experimental animals or to reproduce in culture as attempted by Moore et al. (1959) and McDonald and Cole (1961).

The best type of evidence of the viability of circulating tumour cells is that blood from animals with tumours produces neoplasms when injected into normal animals (Blummenthal 1929; Jonasson 1959); however, it must be borne in mind that a number of animal tumours have viral origins and that the occurrence of tumours in a 'host' animal may in fact indicate an oncogenic viraemia in the 'donor'. Other evidence of viability of circulating tumour cells is provided by the experiments of Baserga et al. (1960), in which circulating cells previously exposed to tritiated thymidine were shown to have incorporated it into DNA which was present in the subsequent developing metastases.

A promising approach to the bioassay of circulating tumour cells has been described by Baker and Wood (1967) in which heart blood was removed from rabbits at intervals of 3 minutes to 21 days after they had received intravenous injections of ascitic V2 carcinoma cells. The heart blood was then injected intravenously into a further group of rabbits which were later examined for developing lung tumours. It was shown that the ability of these recipients to develop lung tumours was not simply dependent on the absolute number of tumour cells in the heart blood injected to them.

8.4   The attachment of tumour cells to vascular endothelium

If tumour cells in the blood are to multiply, it would appear that they must attach themselves to vascular endothelium, and their rapid disappearance from the peripheral blood (Selecki 1959) corresponds to their retention in organs (Ambrus et al. 1956). It is not known why tumour cells do not survive well in the peripheral blood or indeed whether this is a peculiarity of tumour cells or normal tissue cells not especially adapted for life in an unattached state. It may be that the answer is to be found in the microenvironmental requirements of unadapted cells, which are damaged by dilution of this part of their peripheral zone or microenvironment. This may be analogous to the loneliness phenomenon which is well-known in cell culture, where, in order to grow single cells or very small numbers of them, some form of constraint over environmental exchange is required, which may be atttained by growing cells in capillary tubes or in microdrops.

Weiss and Woodbridge (1966) have made an attempt to formulate some of the physical factors involved when cells being carried in the bloodstream make contact with the vascular endothelium. Cells in fluid undergoing streamline flow will tend to move from the faster flow lines to the slower, which will in turn tend to bring the endothelial and malignant cells together. However, this force will fall off to zero when the hydrodynamic slip-plane near the vessel wall is reached. Under conditions of turbulent flow, vortices which develop may effectively hurl cells at the vessel wall with enough kinetic energy to overcome the potential energy barrier (see chapter 4) between them and the vascular endothelium. The magnitude of the repulsive barrier (V_R) can be roughly estimated from the model of a sphere approaching a flat plate, in which, when only electrostatic repulsion and London–Van der Waals' attraction are considered:

$$V_R = 16Da\left(\frac{kT}{e}\cdot\gamma\right)^2 \exp\left(-KH\right) - \frac{Aa}{6H},$$

where

$$\gamma = \frac{\exp(y) - 1}{\exp(y) + 1} \quad \text{and} \quad y = \frac{e\psi}{2kT}.$$

If the cell and vascular endothelium are both considered to have a surface potential ψ of -15 mV, the value of dielectric constant, D, is taken to be that of serum 180 (Pollack et al. 1965), the value of the Debye–Hückel parameter, K, is that for a 0.145 M sodium chloride solution, and the value of A to be about 6×10^{-15} ergs (Wilkins et al. 1962). Then in the case of a malignant cell of radius $10\,\mu$, at $37\,°C$, the maximum value of V_R approximates to 2×10^{-10} ergs. Assuming that the malignant cell has a mass, m, of approximately 10^{-11} g, then, in order to have enough kinetic energy, $\frac{1}{2}\,mv^2$, to be able to overcome a potential energy barrier of 2×10^{-10} ergs, its velocity (V) must exceed about 6 cm per sec.

It was assumed that the surface potential on both the vascular endothelium and the malignant cells was about the same. However, Sawyer and Himmelfarb (1965) have suggested on the basis of their streaming potential measurements that the zeta-potential for large vessel walls is of the order of hundreds of millivolts. Zeta-potentials of this order indicate charge densities more than an order of magnitude higher than those normally found at the surface of any other type of mammalian tissue cell. Some doubt exists about the value calculated by Sawyer and Himmelfarb, since their measurements were made *in vivo*, for pulsatile, non-laminar flow of blood, which is a rheologically anomalous, chemically complex fluid; under these circumstances interpretation of streaming potential data is extremely difficult. In the case of two surfaces where one has a higher potential than the other, Bierman (1955) has shown that as the surfaces closely approach each other, there can be an attraction along the resulting potential energy gradient. If Bierman's equation is applied to the case of cell with a surface potential of -15 mV approaching vascular endothelium at -150 mV, then at distances of separation less than about 50 Å there will be attraction. Thus, Sawyer and Himmelfarb's estimate is of some importance in determining whether, at close approach, cells are attracted or repelled by vessel walls, and it would be of considerable interest to redetermine this value under experimental conditions leading to a more definite interpretation.

Even in the comparatively simple case of streamline flow, owing to the presence of velocity profiles across the stream of flowing blood, the velocity of transported cells cannot be estimated with certainty at distances of tens of Ångstrom from the vessel walls. Thus, although mean peak blood velocities in many different vessels are tabulated by McDonald (1960), there is no way of telling whether the velocities of malignant cells perpendicular to the vascular endothelium in fact exceed the computed critical velocity of about 6 cm per sec at the site of the potential energy barrier. In the dog, the peak blood velocity in arterioles and capillaries is given as 0.28 and 0.05 cm per sec respectively, which are too low to enable the calculated potential energy barrier to be overcome, even if these velocities were normal to the vessel walls. In the absence of more precise numerical values for the various symbols in the potential energy equations, it is difficult to assess the usefulness of this approach; at the moment it appears more valuable to consider other trapping mechanisms, since, as Sawyer and Harshaw (1964) also suggest, the electrostatic repulsion between vascular endothelial and cells prevents contact. Possibly if the charge on the cells or vessels walls were reduced by some physio-pathological mechanism, then contact could take place.

In 1903 Schmidt showed the attachment of malignant cells to vascular endothelium by the agency of thrombi; an association recognized and explored extensively by Wood (1958, 1964), by means of an ingenious visual technique, in which a 15 micron layer of vascularized tissue of the rabbit ear enclosed in a chamber between two transparent plates can be observed cinemicrographically. Tumour cells, usually the ascitic V2 carcinoma, can be injected into the central artery proximal to the chamber and their reactions with the vascular endothelium can be recorded under a variety of experimental conditions. These studies, and others by Wood et al. (1961) show that tumour cells lodge within capillaries and are quickly surrounded by a mesh of fibrin in which platelets and later leucocytes can be identified, and in which the tumour cells are capable of proliferation and subsequent invasion of the vascular endothelium. The films showed that most of the slowly infused malignant cells died, and that these dead cells which were less liable to stick to the endothelium than living ones, entered the venules, where they were surrounded by leucocytes to form thrombi, within which the tumour cells lysed inside 10 to 15 minutes. The mechanism of the intravascular destruction of tumour cells is not understood. Wood (1964) further notes that the minority of infused cells which are destined to penetrate the vascular endothelium have a tendency to stick to it in the form of loose aggregates of three or more cells. The initial adhesion of embolic carcinoma cells to the capillary endothelium observed by Wood, was independent of capillary diameter, and rate of blood-flow and therefore considered to indicate that the attachment of tumour cells is not simply due to the mechanical filtering ability of the capillaries.

It is known that even in the absence of severe dehydration, primary cancers, particularly of the lung and stomach but also other organs, are often associated with thrombosis, which is frequently located at sites some distance from the primary lesion (Lieberman et al. 1961). The question then arises of whether thrombotic phenomena are associated with the attachment of malignant cells to vascular endothelium. The factors influencing thrombus formation *in vivo* have been reviewed by Mustard et al. (1962), and apart from purely humoral factors, changes in vessel walls must also be considered. Not only can a variety of traumatic procedures make localized areas of endothelium the site of thrombotic lesions, which could act as traps for circulating malignant cells, but also changes in vessel direction can promote deposition of thrombotic material. It must be remembered that monocytes and polymorphonuclear leucocytes can effectively remove such deposits, and that in the larger vessels they may be covered over by endothelial proliferation. The involvement of tumour cells in thrombotic reactions was suggested by the observations of Lawrence et al. (1952) that fractions from the V2 carcinoma exhibited thromboplastic activity *in vivo* as evidenced by shortening of the prothrombin time. O'Meara (1958) showed that human tumours induced fibrin deposition by virtue of a heat-labile thromboplastin. O'Meara and Jackson (1958) attempted to relate invasiveness of normal tissues by carcinoma cells, to the deposition of fibrils of fibrin which is considered to form not only an ideal environment in which the tumour cells can proliferate, but also to interfere with the nutrition of normal cells in the region. A combination of both of these two effects is considered to promote invasiveness. Holyoke and Ichihashi (1966) have essentially confirmed part of O'Meara's findings with their demonstration that there was more thromboplastic activity in homogenates of C3H spontaneous mammary tumors than in normal breast tissue, which itself was not markedly different in activity from breast tissue from precancerous forced-bred females. Boggust et al. (1963) have fractionated the coagulative factor of human tumours into four groups by chromatography on DEAE cellulose, and showed that one of the fractions (B), which is also present in normal tissues, has little or no activity; of the other three fractions, one is thermolabile; none of the fractions will coagulate fibrinogen and therefore probably do not contain thrombin.

Using rabbit-ear preparations, Wood (1964) has described three types of thrombi during and following the injection of V2 carcinoma cells. Firstly there is an injury thrombus or haemostatic plug formed around the site of entry of the hypodermic needle, which is composed mainly of platelets. Secondly, as the tumour cells were slowly infused they aggregated and were rapidly trapped in a fibrin-like mesh. Thirdly, after the injection had ceased red cell thrombi were formed. Fibrin was involved in this process on the evidence of localization of ^{125}I-labelled fibrinogen in the thrombi, which was observed in radioautographs. One to four hours after the thrombi were formed, fibrinolytic agents were injected into the preparations through the same needle as the tumour cells. Injection of urokinase-activated plasminogen and urokinase acted rather more slowly than the previous fibrinolytic agent, but still completely broke up the tumour thrombi.

If cell adhesion to the vascular endothelium is an essential part of the metastatic process, and if thrombus formation or fibrin emeshment is a necessary pre requisite for this, it might be expected that anticoagulants and fibrinolytic agents should reduce the incidence of metastasis, by keeping cells in the peripheral circulation where presumably they will perish. Clifton and Agostino (1962, 1963) Wood et al. (1961), Retik et al. (1962) and Koike (1964) observed in experimental animals that the number of pulmonary metastases following the intravenous administration of tumour cells was reduced by heparin. Fisher and Fisher (1961) observed fewer metastases in livers of rats given heparin after intraportal injection of Walker carcinosarcoma cells. This effect of heparin is not due to any carcinostatic activities, since heparin has little or no effect on the growth of tumour tissues (Balazs and Holmberg 1949; Kreisler 1952; Lippman 1957; King et al. 1958). A similar decrease in pulmonary metastases following intravenous injections of tumour cells was produced by fibrinolysin (Clifton and Grossi 1956; Clifton and Agostino 1962, 1963; Grossi et al., 1960; Agostino et al. 1961; Wood 1964), and by adminstration of dicoumarol (Wood 1964). Conversely, when the fibrinolytic activity of the blood was reduced by induced hyperlipaemia, there was an increased number of pulmonary metastases after intravenous injection of Walker cells into rats (Clifton et al. 1961; Clifton and Agostino 1963) and V2 carcinoma cells into rabbits (Mikata et al. 1962). Various fibrinolytic agents inhibit the growth of HeLa cells *in vitro* (Thornes and Martin 1961), and Lisnell and Mellgren (1963) showed that dicoumarol is also cytotoxic, thus their antimetastatic activity cannot necessarily be correlated with their anticoagulant activity. Another possibility is that these various anticoagulants and fibrinolytic agents act by reducing the incidence of pulmonary lodgement and in effect direct cells to less suitable environments. In support of this hypothesis Boeryd (1965) has shown that, in mice treated with heparin, the number of pulmonary metastases was reduced following intravenous injection of a 20-methylcholanthrene-induced rhabdomyosarcoma, whereas the number of liver metastases was increased. In the same system, the plasminogen inhibitor epsilon-amino-*n*-caproic acid (EACA) increased the total volume of pulmonary metastases, suggesting that the heparin and EACA affect the passage of tumour cells through the lungs, but that in the liver a thrombotic trapping mechanism is not essential. Clinical investigations of the use of anticoagulants and fibrinolysins in the control of metastasis are few, presumably because of the dangers of haemorrhage. However, it is of interest that, in a report on the incidence and mortality of cancer in patients with thromboembolic disease, some of whom were receiving anticoagulant therapy, Michaels (1964) noted that the incidence of metastases was less in the group receiving anticoagulants. It is to be hoped that this line of adjuvant therapy, possibly in conjunction with chemotherapy (Agostino and Clifton 1963) will be systematically explored.

In addition to 'electrostatic' and thrombotic trapping of cells in blood vessels, mechanical trapping must be considered, in which large cancer cells are presumed to be filtered out of the blood by a capillary bed. In this connexion, it is often overlooked that cancer cells are very deformable, as evidenced by their ability to actively crawl through holes 1 to $2\,\mu$ diameter (Shelton and Rice 1958). The direct observations of Wood et al. (1961) show quite clearly that, in their rabbit ear preparations, the capillaries do not act as simple mechanical filters because the diameter of the capillaries did not affect the length of time the tumour cells remained adherent to the vascular endothelium. Griffiths and Salsbury (1963) made experiments which also mitigate against mechanical trapping, in which glass beads 4 to 44 μ in diameter were able to travel through the liver and lungs of rats within a few minutes, during which time at least some of them passed through capillary beds, as confirmed by direct observation. Although it is often stated that metastases are common in particular organs such as the lungs because they act as massive filtration beds for circulating tumour cells, it must be remembered that capillary beds or even whole organs can be by-passed by arteriovenous shunts or by venous anastomoses. A classic example of venous 'by-pass' is the vertebral venous system demonstrated by Batson (1940, 1957) which anatomically accounts for the presence of metastases of prostatic and other cancers in the bones and brain, in the absence of pulmonary foci. The passage of tumour cells through organs has been demonstrated in the case of the lungs by Zeidman and Buss (1952) and in the case of the liver and kidney by Zeidman et al. (1956). While these experiments provide elegant demonstration of the fact that *most* of the neoplastic cells entering these organs leave them, it is often overlooked that appreciable numbers are in fact retained. If only a minority of circulating cells are retained in an organ on each of repeated passages through it, then unless other controlling mechanisms are operative, enough cells could be trapped to give rise to metastases.

Cortisone has an interesting, but as yet inexplicable effect in promoting the adhesion of some malignant cells to vascular endothelium. Thus Wood et al. (1961) quote examples of how in animals treated with cortisone a few hours prior to the administration of tumour cells, the cells show increased adhesion to the vascular endothelium. Although it might be expected that factors promoting endothelial adhesion would favour metastasis formation and, in addition, cortisone may also reduce the immune response to tumours, it must also be remembered that cortisone and hydrocortisone also apparently possess direct anti-tumour activity. It is not surprising therefore that the reports of the effects of cortisone on metastasis are often contradictory, as noted by Gasic and Gasic (1957), in describing the enhancement of metastases by cortisone in animals bearing primary tumours by liberating tumour emboli into the circulation. Roberts et al. (1959) observed that surgical stress may cause a marked diminution in the numbers of circulating tumour cells. Wood et al. have made the interesting suggestion that stress-mediated steroid hormone release may promote endothelial attachment, thereby reducing the numbers of circulating malignant cells, and cause an increase in metastasis. They comment that postoperative stress may be the explanation for the well-known clinical observation that following an exploration of an inoperable tumour, some patients develop many metastases.

8.5 The penetration of vascular endothelium by tumour cells

Wood et al. (1961) have described the changes which occur at the light microscope level when adherent cells invade the vascular endothelium of capillaries, less commonly small arterioles, and probably venules. Within a period of a few minutes to several hours, there is a loss of definition of the endothelium, adjacent to the thrombus. Although the cause of the undoubted endothelial damage is obscure, it is known that various polypeptides are capable of initiating it. Holmberg (1964) has isolated a cytotoxic polypeptide from interstitial and ascitic fluids from humans, rats and mice. The pure compound contained the amino acids Cys, Glu, Gly, Arg, Val, Leu, Tyr and

Ala, and its cytotoxic activity depended on the presence of free SH groups. It would be of interest to determine if Holmberg's cytotoxic polypeptide in fact influences the penetration of tumour cells through vascular endothelium. According to Wood et al., leucocytes migrate to the site of endothelial damage and their migration through the vessel creates endothelial defects through which cancer cells pass.

The movement of particles across vessels is of obvious relevance to penetration by malignant cells. Chambers and Zweifach (1940) and Jancsó (1947) injected colloidal carbon into 'inflamed' blood vessels and noted that it accumulated at the site of inflammation. Chambers and Zweifach suggested that the carbon adhered to a cement between the endothelial cells, whereas Jancsó suggested that the endothelial cells phagocytosed the particles. Later work by Marchesi (1962) on the inflamed rat mesentery, demonstrated electronmicroscopically that injected carbon particles penetrate junctions between the endothelial cells. The basement membrane of the endothelium, and the periendothelial sheath of cells together with their basement membrane, constituted the main barrier to free movement of the carbon. The passage of colloidal mercuric sulphide from the blood stream across the walls of venules, along intercellular spaces, following the application of serotonin or histamine, has been described by Majno and Palade (1961). The work thus tends to confirm the suggestion made in 1876 by Arnold, that channels open up between the cells lining small blood vessels during inflammation. It should be emphasized that the existence of functional intercellular channels between endothelial cells in the absence of inflammation has been questioned in the light of electron microscopic evidence by Palade (1953, 1961) and Bennett et al. (1959). This would suggest that in the penetration of endothelium by cells in general and malignant cells in particular, the inflammatory response may be of considerable importance.

A definitive study at electron microscopic level, of the passage of leucocytes, excluding lymphocytes, and erythrocytes through the walls of inflamed venules in the rat mesentery is due to Marchesi and Florey (1960) and Marchesi (1961). In a beautiful series of electron micrographs, these workers showed cells extending pseudopods into the junctions between the endothelial cells; the pseudopods may continue into the peri-endothelial spaces, by which time they are very much extended, compared with the dimensions of the cells protruding them. No changes were recognized in the inflamed endothelium of the venules; no intercellular cement was identified, and no electron-dense material could be visualized on either the surfaces of the endothelial cells or the leucocytes, to account for their mutual adhesion prior to penetration. However, it should be noted that these workers did not use heavy metal-staining which might have demonstrated the presence of mucosubstances. It is to be asked, why leucocytes are required to precede malignant cells in penetrative processes. It is possible that part of the exposure of junctions is in some way connected with the activity of released enzymes from the leucocytes; the lysosomal hydrolases could be activated by the inflammatory response and provide the necessary enzymes, if weakening of intercellular matrix or facilitation of endothelial cells separation is required (Weissmann and Fell 1962; Fell and L. Weiss 1965; L. Weiss 1965). On the other hand, it is possible that this intimate relationship of leucocytes requires a very deformable cell; although no data are available, apart from the monocyte, these are remarkably easily deformed (L. Weiss et al. 1966).

Lymphocytes are not expected to play a role in the movement of malignant cells across the vascular endothelium, on the assumption that the neoplastic cells penetrate the junctional spaces, since the lymphocytes migrate across the vessel walls by entering the endothelial cells and traversing their cytoplasm. In demonstrating this transcellular movement of lymphocytes, Marchesi and Gowans (1964) also noted that at least in the post-capillary venules of rat lymph nodes, the lymphocytes do not pass through the intercellular junctions. The entry of lymphocytes into cells of the vascular endothelium may possibly be correlated with the monocytotic activity demonstrated by Palade (1953), Wissig (1958) and Marchesi (1965) among others.

The fate of the tumour cells lodged in different organs will be discussed in the next chapter.

References

Abercrombie, M. (1961). Canad. Cancer Conf. Academic Press, New York, **4**, 101
Abercrombie, M., and Ambrose, E. J. Exptl. Cell Res. **15**, 332
Abercrombie, M., and Harkness, R. D. (1951). Proc. Roy. Soc. **B138**, 544
Abercrombie, M., and Heaysman, J. E. M. (1954a). Exptl. Cell Res. **6**, 293
Abercrombie, M., and Heaysman, J. E. M. (1954b). Nature **174**, 697
Abercrombie, M., Heaysman, J. E. M., and Karthauser, H. M. (1957). Exptl. Cell Res. **13**, 276
Agostino, D., and Clifton, E. E. (1963). Ann. Surg. **157**, 400
Agostino, D., Grossi, C. E., and Clifton, E. E. (1961). Ann. Surg. **153**, 365
Allen, A. C. (1954). In, The skin, Civ. Mosby Company, St. Louis, p. 838 et seq
Ambrus, J. L., Ambrus, C. M., Byron, J. W., Goldberg, M. E., and Harrison, J. W. E. (1956). Ann. N. Y. Acad. Sci. **63**, 938
Amoroso, E. C. (1952). In, A. S. Parkes, ed., Marshall's physiology of reproduction. Longmans, Green and Co., London, Vol. 2, p. 127 et seq.

Arnold, J. (1876). Virchows Arch. Pathol. Anat. Physiol. **66**, 77

Ashworth, T. R. (1869). Australian Med. J. **14**, 146

Baker, R. R. and Wood, S. (1967). Surg. Gyn. Obstet. **124**, 742

Balazs, A., and Holmgren, H. J. (1949). Proc. Soc. Exptl. Biol. Med. **72**, 142

Baserga, R., Kisielski, W. E., and Halvorsen, K. (1960). Cancer Res. **20**, 910

Baserga, R., and Saffiotto, U. (1955). A. M. A. Arch. Pathol. **59**, 26

Batson, O. V. (1940). Ann. Surg. **112**, 138

Batson, O. V. (1957). Am. J. Roentgenol. **78**, 195

Bennett, H. S., Luft, J. H., and Hampton, J. C. (1959). Am. J. Physiol. **196**, 381

Bierman, A. J. (1955). J. Colloid Sci. **10**, 231

Billroth, S. (1855). Virchows Arch. Pathol. Anat. Physiol. **31**, 265

Blummenthal, F. (1929). Z. Krebsforsch. **29**, 549

Boeryd, B. (1965). Acta Pathol. Microbiol. Scand. **65**, 395

Boggust, W. A., O'Brien, D. J., O'Meara, R. A. Q., and Thornes, R. D. (1963). Irish J. Med. Sci. **447**, 131

Böving, B. G. (1959). Ann. N. Y. Acad. Sci. **80**, 21

Bron, K. M., Baum, S., and Abrams, H. L. (1963). Radiology **80**, 194

Burstone, M. S. (1956). J. Natl. Cancer Inst. **16**, 1149

Carmalt, W. H. (1872). Virchows Arch. Pathol. Anat. Physiol. **55**, 481

Carrel, A., and Burrows, M. T. (1911). J. Exptl. Med. **13**, 571

Carrel, A., and Ebeling, A. H. (1928). J. Exptl. Med. **48**, 105

Chambers, R., and Zweifach, B. W. (1940). J. Cell. Comp. Physiol. **15**, 255

Christopherson, W. M. (1965). Acta Cytol. **9**, 169

Clifton, E. E., and Agostino, D. (1962). Cancer **15**, 276

Clifton, E. E., and Agostino, D. (1963). Radiology **80**, 236

Clifton, E. E., and Grossi, C. E. (1956). Cancer **9**, 1147

Clifton, E. E., Agostino, D., and Minde, K. (1961). Cancer Res. **21**, 1062

Cole, W. H., McDonald, G. O., Roberts, S. S., and Southwick, H. W. (1961). Dissemination of cancer. Appleton-Century-Crofts, Inc., New York

Coman, D. R. (1942). Cancer Res. **2**, 618

Cox, L. B. and Cranage, M. L. (1937). J. Pathol. Bact. **45**, 477

Curtis, A. S. G. (1961). J. Natl. Cancer Inst. **26**, 253

Douglas, G. W., Thomas, L., Carr, M., Cullen, M. N., and Morris, R. (1959). Am. J. Obstet. Gynecol. **78**, 960

Dukes, C. (1944). Proc. Roy. Soc. Med. **37**, 131

Eagle, H. and Levine, E. M. (1967). In press

Engell, H. C. (1955). Acta Chir. Scand. Suppl. **201**

Enterline, H. T., and Coman, D. R. (1950). Cancer **3**, 1033

Fell, H. B., and Weiss, L. (1965). J. Exptl. Med. **121**, 551

Fischer, B. (1906). Munch. Med. Wochschr. **53**, 2041

Fischer, A., Laser, H., and Meyer, H. (1929). Z. Krebsforsch. **29**, 270

Fisher, B., and Fisher, E. R. (1961). Surgery **50**, 240

Fisher, B., and Fisher, E. R. (1966). Surg. Gyn. Obstet. **122**, 791

Friedell, G. H., and Parsons, L. (1962). Cancer **15**, 1269

Gasic, G., and Gasic, T. (1957). Brit. J. Cancer **9**, 88

Gersh, I., and Catchpole, H. R. (1949). Am. J. Anat. **85**, 457

Glenister, T. W. (1961a). Proc. Roy. Soc. **B154**, 428

Glenister, T. W. (1961b). J. Anat. **95**, 474

Glenister, T. W. (1962). J. Obstet. Gynecol. **69**, 809

Goldacre, R. J., and Sylvén, B. (1962). Brit. J. Cancer **16**, 306

Gowans, J. L. (1959). J. Physiol. **146**, 54.

Griffiths, J. D., and Salsbury, A. J. (1963). Brit. J. Cancer **17**, 546

Griffiths, J. D., and Salsbury, A. J. (1965). Circulating cancer cells. Thomas, Springfield, Illinois

Grohe, F. (1865). Virchows Arch. Pathol. Anat. Physiol. **32**, 445

Grossi, C. E., Agostino, D., and Clifton, E. E. (1960). Cancer Res. **20**, 605

Hanes, F. M., and Lambert, R. R. (1912). Virchows Arch. Pathol. Anat. Physiol. **209**, 12

Hewitt, H. B. (1956). Brit. J. Cancer **10**, 564

Holmberg, B. (1964). Z. Krebsforsch. **66**, 65

Holyoke, E. D., and Ichihashi, H. (1966). J. Natl. Cancer Inst. **36**, 1049

Iwasaki, T. (1915). J. Pathol. Bact. **20**, 85

Jancsó, M. (1947). Nature **160**, 227

Jonasson, O. (1959). Surg. Forum **9**, 577

King, D. W., Bensche, K. G., and Simbonis, S. (1958). Cancer Res. **18**, 382

Kiriluk, L. B., Kremen, A., and Glick, D. (1950). J. Natl. Cancer Inst. **10**, 993

Koike, A. (1964). Cancer **17**, 450

Kreisler, L. (1952). Science **115**, 145

Lajos, L., Molnár, L., and Görcs, J. (1958). Acta Morphol. Acad. Sci. Hung. **8**, 273

Lambert, R. A. (1916). J. Cancer Res. **1**, 169

Lawrence, E. A., Bowman, D. E., Moore, D. B., and Bernstein, G. I. (1952). Surg. Forum **3**, 694

Leaf, C. H. (1900). Lancet **1**, 606

Leighton, J., and Kalla, R. L. (1958). Ann. N. Y. Acad. Sci. **76**, 513

Leighton, J., Kalla, R. L., Kline, I., and Belkin, M. (1959). Cancer Res. **19**, 23

Leighton, J., and Kline, I. (1954). Texas Rept. Biol. Med. **12**, 868

Leighton, J., Kline, I., Belkin, M., and Tetenbaum, Z. (1956). J. Natl. Cancer Inst. **16**, 1353

Levin, I., and Sittenfield, M. J. (1910). Proc. Soc. Exptl. Biol. Med. **8**, 114

Lewis, W. H. (1936). Harvey Lectures **31**, 214

Lieberman, J. S., Borrero, J., Urdaneta, E., and Wright, I. S. (1961). J. Am. Med. Assoc. **177**, 542

Lippman, M. (1957). Cancer Res. **17**, 11

Lisnell, A., and Mellgren, J. (1963). Acta Pathol. Microbiol. Scand. **57**, 145

Ludford, R. J. (1934). Sci. Rept. Imperial Cancer Res. Fund **11**, 734

Ludford, R. J., and Barlow, H. (1944). Cancer Res. **4**, 694

Majno, G. and Palade, G. E. (1961). J. Biophys. Biochem. Cytol. **11**, 571

Marchesi, V. T. (1961). Quart. J. Exptl. Physiol. **46**, 115

Marchesi, V. T. (1962). Proc. Roy. Soc. B **156**, 550

Marchesi, V. T. (1965). Invest. Ophthalmol. **4**, 1111

Marchesi, V. T., and Florey, H. W. (1960). Quart. J. Exptl. Physiol. **45**, 343

Marchesi, V. T., and Gowans, J. L. (1964). Proc. Roy. Soc. B **159**, 283

McDonald, D. A. (1960). Blood flow in arteries. E. Arnold (Publishers) Ltd., London, p. 53

McDonald, G. O., and Cole, W. H. (1961). Am. J. Surg. **101**, 11

Mello, R. P. de (1963). Acta Cytol. **7**, 62

Michaels, M. (1964). Lancet **2**, 832

Mikata, A., Imai, H., and O'Neil, R. M. (1962). Exptl. Mol. Pathol. **1**, 37

Molomut, N., Spain, D., Kreisler, L. and Warshaw, L. (1955). Cancer Res. **15**, 181

Moore, G. E. (1960). Surg. Gynecol. Obstet. **110**, 360

Moore, G. E., Mount, D. T., and Wendt, A. (1959). Surg. Forum **9**, 572

Moore, G. E. and Sandberg, A. A. (1960). Acta, Unio Intern. Contra Cancrum **16**, 405

Moore, S., Townsend, D. E. R., Palmer, J. D., and Sigman, H. (1962). Can. J. Surg. **5**, 366

Mottet, N. K. (1961). Am. J. Pathol **39**, 17

Mottet, N. K. (1963). Lab. Invest. **12**, 809

Mustard, J. F., Murphy, E. A., Rowsell, H. C., and Downie, H. G. (1962). Am. J. Med. **33**, 621

Oldfield, F. E. (1963). Exptl. Cell Res. **30**, 125

O'Meara, R. A. Q. (1958). Irish J. Med. Sci. **394**, 474

O'Meara, R. A. Q. and Jackson, R. D. (1958). Irish J. Med. Sci. **391**, 327

Palade, G. E. (1953). J. Appl. Physics **24**, 1424

Palade, G. E. (1961). Circulation **24**, 368

Perez-Tamayo, R., Thornbury, J. R., and Atkinson, R. J. (1963). Am. J. Roentgenol. **90**, 1078

Pollack, W., Hager, H. J., Reckel, R., Toren, D. A., and Singher, H. O. (1965). Transfusion **5**, 158

Pool, E. H., and Dunlop, G. R. (1934). Am. J. Cancer **21**, 99

Pressman, J. J., and Simon, M. B. (1961). Surg. Gynecol. Obstet. **113**, 537

Pulvertaft, R. J. V., Davies, J. R., Weiss, L., and Wilkinson, J. H. (1959). J. Pathol. Bacteriol. **77**, 19

Purr, A. (1934). Biochem. J. **28**, 1907

Raker, J. W., Taft, P. D., and Edmonds, E. E. (1960). New Engl. J. Med. **263**, 993

Reggianini, O. (1953). Bull. Soc. Ital. Biol. Sper. **29**, 329

Retik, A. B., Arons, M. S., Ketcham, A. S. and Mantel, N. (1962). J. Surg. Res. **2**, 49

Ribbert, H. (1904). Deut. Med. Wochschr. **30**, 801

Roberts, S., Watne, A. L., McGrath, R. G., McGrew, E. A., and Cole, W. H. (1959). Surg. Forum **9**, 595

Russell, D. S., and Bland, J. O. W. (1933). J. Pathol. Bacteriol. **36**, 273

Sanford, K. K. (1966). Intern. Conf. Tissue Culture in Cancer Res. (Tokyo, Oct. 21–22)

Saphir, O. (1947). Am. J. Pathol. **23**, 245

Sawyer, P. N., and Harshaw, D. H. (1964). Surgery **54**, 846

Sawyer, P. N., and Himmelfarb, E. H. (1965). In, P. N. Sawyer, ed., Biological mechanisms in vascular homostasis and intravascular thrombosis. Appleton-Century-Crofts, New York, p. 69

Schmidt, M. B. (1903). Die Verbreitungswerke der Karzinome und die Beziehung generalisierter Sarkome zu den leukämischen Neubildungen. Fischer, Jena

Schneider, N. (1958). Arch. Anat. Micr. Morphol. Exptl. **47**, 573

Selecki, E. E. (1959). Australian J. Exptl. Biol. Sci. **37**, 489

Sellwood, R. A., Kuper, S. W. A., Burn, J. I., and Wallace, E. N. (1964). Brit. Med. J. **1**, 1683

Shelton, E., and Rice, M. E. (1958). J. Natl. Cancer Inst. **21**, 137

Sjövall, H. (1936). Acta Pathol. Microbiol. Scand. Suppl. **27**

Spriggs, A. I. (1960). Proc. Roy. Soc. Med. **53**, 169

Spriggs, A. I. (1962). Proc. lst Intern. Congr. Exfol. Cytol. p. 206

Stoker, M. (1964). Virology **24**, 165

Sunderland, D. A. (1949). Cancer **2**, 429

Takahashi, M. (1915). J. Pathol. Bacteriol. **20**, 1

Temin, H. M., and Rubin, H. (1958). Virology **6**, 669

Thomlinson, R. H. (1960). Brit. J. Cancer **14**, 555

Thornes, R. D., and Martin, W. T. (1961). Irish J. Med. Sci. **431**, 487

Tjernberg, B., and Zajicek, J. (1965). Acta Cytol. **9**, 197

Vasiliev, J. M. (1958). Brit. J. Cancer **12**, 524

Vierth, K. (1895). Beitr. Pathol. Anat. **18**, 515

Virchow, R. (1863). Virchows Arch. Pathol. Anat. Physiol. **28**, 237

Waldeyer (1872). Virchows Arch. Pathol. Anat. Physiol. **55**, 67

Walther, H. E. (1948). Krebsmetastasen. Benno Schwabe, Basel

Warren, S., and Gates, O. (1936). Am. J. Cancer **27**, 485

Watanabe, S. (1954). Cancer **7**, 215

Watne, A. L., Hatiboglu, I., and Moore, G. E. (1960a). Surg. Gynecol. Obstet. **110**, 339

Watne, A. L., Sandberg, A. A., and Moore, G. E. (1960b). Cancer Res. **3**, 160

Weil, R. (1913). J. Med. Res. **28**, 497

Weiss, L. (1965). Exptl. Cell Res. 37, 540

Weiss, L., and Woodbridge, R. F. (1966). Fed. Proc. **29**, 88

Weiss, L., Mayhew, E., and Ulrich, K. (1966). J. Clin. Invest. **15**, 1304

Weissmann, G., and Fell, H. B. (1962). J. Exptl. Med. **116**, 365

West, J. T., Malmgren, R. A., and Chu, E. W. (1964). Surg. Gynecol. Obstet. **119**, 83

Wilkins, D. J., Ottewill, R. H., and Bangham, A. D. (1962). J. Theoret. Biol. **2**, 176

Willis, R. A. (1952). The spread of tumours in the human body. Butterworth, London

Wissig, S. L. (1958). Anat. Record. **130**, 467

Wolff, E., and Schneider, N. (1957). Arch. Anat. Microscop. Morphol. Exptl. **46**, 173

Wood, S. (1958). Arch. Pathol. **66**, 550

Wood, S. (1964). Bull. Swiss Acad. Med. Sci. **20**, 92

Wood, S., Holyoke, E. D., and Yardley, J. H. (1961). Can. Cancer Conf. Academic Press, New York, **4**, 167

Yoffey, J. M., and Courtice, F. C. (1956). Lymphatics, lymph and lymphoid tissue. Harvard University Press, Cambridge, Massachusetts, p. 94

Young, J. S. (1959). J. Pathol. Bacteriol. **77**, 321

Zeidman, I., and Buss, J. M. (1952). Cancer Res. **12**, 731

Zeidman, I., Gamble, W. J., and Clovis, W. L. (1956). Cancer Res. **16**, 814

CHAPTER 9

Host organ/malignant cell interactions

9.1 Organ selectivity

Although metastases have been described in most if not all organs (Willis 1952), the most usual sites for blood-borne metastases are commonly described as the lungs and the bone marrow for systemic emboli, and the liver for portal emboli. This statement should be qualified to recognize the fact that in necropsies on human subjects, only parts of certain organs are selected for microscopic examination, and that the reported absence of secondary foci in at least some organs is essentially based on limited microscopic and/or naked-eye examinations. It is almost common knowledge that in experimental animals inoculated with tumours, rats bearing the Walker carcinosarcoma for example, parts of organs which appear tumour-free on careful histological and macroscopic examination, are capable of giving rise to new tumours on transplantation into fresh animals. From the strictly clinical viewpoint, occasional scattered tumour cells, or small emboli which are only apparent in serial sections of whole organs, are probably of less immediate importance to the patient than comparatively large more easily identifiable loci. Nonetheless, the absence of small numbers of tumour cells within an organ cannot be determined by simple histological examination (Greene 1965). Within these limitations, it is to be asked why recognizable metastases are more common in some organs than others.

Following the suggestions of von Recklinghausen (1891) and Ewing (1940), one school of thought has maintained that the main factor determining site of metastasis is the local blood supply to the organ in question. De Long and Coman (1950) showed that transplants from fibrosarcoma 241 into C57 mice, Walker 256 carcinosarcoma into Long–Evans hooded rats, and V2 carcinoma and the Brown–Pearce tumour into rabbits, took equally well in the spleens, adrenals, livers, kidneys and skeletal muscles of the respective animals. In fact, in the case of the rabbit spleen, tumour growth on a weight

339

basis was greater than in the other organs. The growth of implanted tumour tissues in the spleen of experimental animals was also described by Choi and Yun (1933). De Long and Coman interpreted their results to suggest that the scarcity of metastases in certain organs is not due to an inherent inability of these organs to support tumour growth, or to supply the metastasis with either stroma or an adequate vasculature. The explanation for absence of metastasis in particular organs should, according to De Long and Coman, be sought in the failure of tumour emboli to either reach organs or be arrested in them, or the inability of tumour cells to escape vessels. In the case of the spleen, naturally occurring metastases occur in about 2–4% of all fatal cases of human malignant disease (Herbut and Gabriel 1942; Willis 1952). However, it can be demonstrated by isotopic studies that of cells injected intravenously in mice and rats, many not only reach the spleen as would be expected, but also are arrested there (L. Weiss, unpublished data). It seems unlikely that the small vessels of the spleen in which arrest occurs can be structurally different from vessels of like size in the liver or lungs; however Pressman and Yagi (1964) have reviewed much work suggesting that immunological differences exist in the vascular beds of different organs. Although these differences must be reflected at a physico-chemical level, possibly in the subendothelial regions, they have not been correlated with either tumour invasion or ultrastructural appearance. Possibly, the main criticism of De Long and Coman's argument is that in transplants of the type made by them, tumour fragments were implanted in the various host organs, complete with their stromata. In natural metastatic phenomena, tumour cells probably do not take much stroma with them on leaving the primary lesion, and thus possibly have a less well protected microenvironment, which could be changed by the host organ to the detriment of the malignant cell. Willis (1948) has previously conjectured that the critical period for metastasizing tumour cells must be immediately following their lodgement, and before they have established stromal connections with the host organ. The demonstration of the free passage of tumour cells through capillary beds (Zeidman 1961) does not in itself provide a cogent argument against the mechanical filtration theories on which organ selectivity in metastasis is explained, since the emphasis should not be on the comparatively large percentage of cells passing through capillaries, but on the small percentage which do not, since on the mechanical theory these retained cells should be capable of producing secondary foci. Due to the existence of the vascular shunts described in the previous chapter, it is difficult to exclude the filtration theories, and indeed portocaval shunts for example have been suggested as an explanation for bizarre metastatic patterns (Lore et al. 1958). Nonetheless, the experimental evidence of Prinzmetal et al. (1948), shows that undeformable glass spheres up to about 370 μ in diameter can pass through both the spleen and the lungs, and indicates that the differences in metastases in these two organs cannot be explained simply in terms of mechanical trapping. It is be to noted that the liver would only permit the passage of beads corresponding to arteriovenous shunts of 50 to 180 μ diameter; however, the diameters of blood-borne tumour emboli are possibly below this. Although mechanical filtration may play a role in organ selectivity in metastasis, there is very little direct evidence in favour of it, and my own impression is that it is probably a minor one.

A second type of approach to organ selectivity is due to Paget (1889), who postulated that the growth of metastases in an organ is dependent on the local 'soil'. The local environment in this sense may be humoral or cellular, and will be discussed in some detail later. Willis' (1952) series of 179 primary tumours in areas with portal venous drainage were associated with metastases in the liver in 48%, and pulmonary metastases in 19% of the cases. Of 276 primary tumours in areas not draining into the portal veins, 40% had pulmonary, and 31% hepatic metastases. These data suggest that the liver is a more favourable site for metastases than the lungs. Lucké and his associates (1952) injected suspensions of V2 carcinoma cells both intravenously and intraportally into rabbits and noted that the takes in the liver were significantly greater in volume than those in the lungs; this was taken as evidence of the liver selectivity for V2 tumour cells. Haddow (1934) described the enhancing effect of a liver extract on tumour growth, but it is difficult now to comment on the nature of his material. The growth promoting effects on tumours of regenerating liver have been well demonstrated in rats given subcutaneous injections of malignant cells at the time of partial hepatectomy, which had developed larger hepatic metastases than controls after fourteen days (Paschkis et al. 1955). Fisher and Fisher (1959) observed that intraportal injections of seven different doses of the Walker carcinosarcoma, varying from 250 to 250,000 cells in 1 ml, gave increased incidence of hepatic metastases when the injection was immediately followed by partial hepatectomy. However, a similar operation 24 hours after injection had a lessened effect, and had no demonstrable effect at all 48 hours after injection. This could indicate either a hepatic growth-promoting factor or the impairment of some normal inhibition after partial hepatectomy. Sugarbaker (1952) injected tumour cell suspensions into the left ventricle of anaesthetized rats and showed that in addition to common sites, the Flexner–Jobling carcinoma produced metastases in the eye, the Walker carcinosarcoma involved muscle and subserosa, and sarcoma R39 involved the facial bones. These experiments were reasonably taken to indicate that different tumours have a propensity for metastasizing in specific organs. Elegant experiments pertaining to organ selectivity were made by Kinsey (1960) with the murine S-91 Cloudman melanoma, which metastasizes spontaneously exclusively to the lungs. Fragments of foetal lung were transplanted into the right thigh muscles of mice of the same inbred DBA strain. Successful intramuscular transplants of foetal kidney, heart, skin, thyroid or lung were made into the left thigh (liver transplants were unsuccessful). Ten days after transplantation the animals were given injections of S-91 cells into their tail arteries. Three to four weeks later, 37 out of 40 of the animals had developed melanotic tumours in the transplanted lungs, but in none of the other transplanted tissues. Willis (1952) notes that the average weights of the human liver, kidneys and spleen are about 1,500, 250 and 125 grammes respectively, giving weight ratios of $12:2:1$, and that in 500 necropsies blood-borne metastases were present in 36, 7.6 and 3% of cases respectively, suggesting that metastases at least in these three organs is proportional to weight rather than an inherent 'preference'. However, Warren and Davis (1934) reported that in a series of 1,140 necropsies, carcinoma of the breast metastasized to the spleen three times as frequently as to the kidneys, whereas carcinoma of the cervix uteri metastasized to the kidney three times as frequently as to the spleen. The overall impression is that the growth of different tumour cells is favoured by some organs and hindered by others. It is proposed to discuss some of the general reactions influencing tumour 'takes', but it should be made clear that at present, no explanation can be given for organ selectivity.

9.2 Host resistance to tumours

The literature on host resistance and tumour immunology is now so frighteningly vast that it would be difficult to summarize it in a monograph of this size, let alone one section of a single chapter. I shall review a few illustrative works on the topic, in an attempt to provide an immunological background to host–cell interactions which may be pertinent to metastasis. Whenever possible I will refer to work done on human tumours in preference to animal experiments, for reasons which will be discussed.

Before various host factors are discussed in detail, the evidence in favour of their existence in human malignant disease can be summarized partly according to Grace (1964), as follows:

(1) Cases of spontaneous regression of established tumours.

(2) Prolonged survival of patients after incomplete removal of their cancer, as exemplified by the case reports of Gordon-Taylor (1948), Kidd (1961) and many others. The incompleteness of the removal of malignant foci is suggested by the abrupt appearance of metastases after many years (Hutcheson 1952; Kidd 1961).

(3) Occasional regression of metastases after removal of the primary tumour (Everson and Cole 1956; Kidd 1961). It must be remembered that, in other cases, removal of the primary tumour has been associated with accelerated growth of metastases, leading to the concept of feed back control analogous to the maintenance of constant size in normal organs (Greene 1965).

(4) Enormous numbers of tumour cells may be present in the blood stream without the development of metastases. As discussed in chapter 8, this may or may not be due to circulating cytotoxic (? immune) factors.

(5) Histological evidence of infiltration of tumour domains by cells normally associated with the immune response (lymphocytes, plasma cells), and increased cellular activity in regional lymph nodes.

(6) The recognition and possible identification of tumour specific antigens.

(7) The appearance of antibodies detectable by *in vitro* tests, demonstrable hypersensitivity (skin tests) when tumour extracts are reimplanted into patients, and a low incidence of successful autografts of tumour tissues into cancer patients.

(8) Demonstrable changes in immunological response corresponding to clinically identifiable exacerbations and remissions in some malignancies.

Some of these points will now be considered under separate headings, although it will be obvious that such a division is arbitrary.

9.3 Spontaneous regression of tumours

Some support for an immune response in human tumours would be provided by well-substantiated evidence of tumour regression, since it might well indicate increased host resistance, although this in itself may be an unwarrantable assumption, since a number of so-called regressions in breast cancer for example, could be explained in terms of adrenal metastases which in effect perform an auto-adrenalectomy on the patient, and doubtless other non-immunological factors, such as infection, come into play. The most notable attempt to collect authentic cases of spontaneous regression in human malignancy is due to Everson and Cole (1956) who considered only cases reported since 1900 in the English language, where there was unequivocal histopathological diagnosis and no significant therapy. Even if all of the cases of true spontaneous regression described by Everson and Cole are acceptable on very rigid criteria, and Kidd (1961) makes it clear that he is not prepared to accept them all, then the incidence of spontaneous regression is still insignificant compared with the total number of patients dying from cancer. However, total regression of a diagnosable lesion may be an unrealistic parameter. When all the available various carcinogenic mechanisms are considered, it is perhaps notable that cancer is not a far commoner group of diseases than in fact recorded. It is arguable that immune and other homeostatic mechanisms are constantly destroying neoplastic foci when they are at the single cell stage, or even later than this, but before the foci are clinically detectable. When cancers are of such size as to be detectable clinically, this may imply that cell populations are not to be entirely destroyed by immunological mechanisms as is inherent in the concept of immunoselection (Hauschka et al. 1956), and that the reasonable outcome of such mechanisms would be retardation of tumour growth, not necessarily total regression.

The difficulties of assessing retardation or its absence, in the initial stages of the growth of human tumours, almost before they have been diagnosed, are obvious. Collins et al. (1956) and Schwartz (1961) took the approach that tumour growth is essentially exponential, and that measurements of comparatively small parts of the growth curve could be extrapolated backwards and forwards on the time axis, to indicate the entire growth history of the tumour. On the other hand, Laird (1965) of is the opinion that tumour growth may be generally characterized by a Gompertz function, interpreted to mean that an exponentially increasing retarding factor operates from the time of tumour initiation. It is possibly of significance here that Laird's experimental evidence comes from transplantable tumours in experimental animals; it is difficult to comment on the strict relevance to human solid cancers of growth in ascites tumours, with their almost unique nutritional support, and the well-defined immunological interactions of transplantable tumours as a whole (Snell 1953a, 1963; Hauschka 1957). The extension of Laird's viewpoint is that cancer is a self-limiting disease in which the patient dies before the tumour growth plateaus; although this may be true in very elderly patients, it is clearly not generally applicable. Hewitt (1966, personal communication) considers that retarding factors are terminal, and consist of host debility produced by excessive tumour mass. In the case of mouse tumours Hewitt notes that some growth curves which are described as non-exponential, only attain this form after reaching 20% of host body volume, by which time the animals are constitutionally exhausted and their haemo-globin levels may be as low as 25% of normal. In humans such retardation would not be expected until their tumours weighed more than 20 pounds. It would appear at present in humans, that tumour regression data do not in general unequivocally support the immunological concepts of cancer and that presently, insurmountable difficulties, concerned with controls and earlier diagnosis, render the more realistic problems of retardation of growth and homeostatic mechanisms operating on cell populations somewhat intractable.

9.4 Antigens associated with tumours

Immunity may be produced by antigens present in both normal and neo-plastic tissues which include the individual histocompatibility or transplantation antigens, and the tissue specific types which are the basis of auto-immune responses. In addition to these, neoplastic or premalignant cells may also contain specific antigens which are not found in normal tissues.

9.4.1. Histocompatibility antigens

The histocompatibility or H antigens, at least in the mouse, are determined by the H–2 gene locus (Snell 1948, 1953a, 1958a, b; Snell et al. 1953; Gorer 1956; and Hauschka and Amos 1957). As pointed out by Hauschka and Amos, the genetic determinants of graft failure do not necessarily all have to be immunological, but may be metabolic and simply mimic antigenic segregation; thus, transplantation data should always be backed up by sero-logical tests. In association with the changes of karyotype seen in malignant cells, some normal isoantigens may disappear (Hauschka and Levan 1953; Amos 1956). Hauschka and Amos (1957) have suggested that effectively diminished antigenicity may be brought about by increases in cell volume and changes in geometry associated with increases in ploidy, which may effect-ively reduce the density of antigenic sites, and 'upset' hypothetical critical antigen/antibody ratios necessary for inhibition of growth. On the other hand, crowding of peripheral antigenic sites on cells might result, as in the case of tetraploid lymphoma cells, in those having approximately double the volume of corresponding diploids, but only 1.5 times their computed surface area (Hauschka et al. 1956). Agglutination and immunofluorescence studies with H–2 specific antibodies have demonstrated the presence of H–2 antigen at the cell periphery (Gorer and Mikulska 1954; Möller 1961). Haughton (1965) has shown that lymph node cells, primary and transplanted lymphomas, and ascites tumour cells, all carry an approximate minimum of 80% of their total antigenic content at their peripheries. The H–2 antigens consist of insoluble lipoprotein particles, possibly associated with small amounts of carbohydrate (Kandutsch 1960; Herzenberg and Herzenberg 1961; Davies 1962; and Haughton 1964).

In man, information on the histocompatibility (H) systems is somewhat sparse, but much of the available information is reviewed by Batchelor (1965). It is known that extensive matching of all the presently known blood groups between graft donors and recipients provides no guarantee that grafts will take (Woodruff et al. 1963), and it might therefore be argued that erythrocyte peripheries do not contain immunologically significant amounts of H antigens. However, as Batchelor remarks, before this esssentially negative finding can be settled, it must be demonstrated that incompatible grafts do not induce the formation of haemagglutinins. Goldsmith (1965) has reviewed the evidence pertinent to the presence of H antigens in human leucocytes, and agrees with Walford (1960) that they are indeed carried by these cells. In support of this are the experiments of Friedman et al. (1961), who demonstrated accelerated rejection of skin grafts in recipients preimmunized with allogeneic peripheral leucocytes, and Walford et al. (1962), who demonstrated circulating leucocyte antibodies in patients who had received skin grafts. Much of the work on grafting which is relevant to the present discussion is covered in Publication No. 1229 of the National Academy of Sciences (U.S.), 'Histocompatibility testing' (1965).

The H–2 antigens are of great proven importance in tumour transplantation in allogeneic recipients, but their importance in spontaneous tumours is problematical and, at the moment cannot be regarded of proven importance in this situation, although they have been instrumental in furthering many advances in cytogenetics.

9.4.2. *Tumour specific antigens*

Tumour specific antigens have been demonstrated in a number of carcinogen-induced tumours of mice and rats as reviewed by Old and Boyse (1964) and Haddow (1965), and immunity to a number of these tumours can be induced in autochthonous hosts (Klein et al. 1960). In addition, tumour specific antigens which will induce immunity in isogeneic hosts, have been demonstrated in a number of virus-induced tumours (Old and Boyse 1965; Klein 1964). In contrast, studies on spontaneously arising tumours have been fewer and somewhat equivocal, although Day (1965), in his review of the literature, appears favourably disposed to the overall evidence suggesting that this class of tumours possess antigens which are either absent, or present in reduced amounts, in corresponding normal tissues.

These various antigens will be discussed under separate headings, namely: (1) antigens of chemically induced tumours, (2) antigens of virus-induced tumours, (3) antigens associated with spontaneous tumours.

(1) The antigens of chemically induced tumours have been reviewed by Prehn (1965), who emphasizes the fact that in general, tumours produced by different physical and chemical carcinogens do not cross-react. Furthermore, individual tumours produced by the same carcinogen, sometimes in the same animal, are immunologically distinct and one tumour cannot be used to immunize against another. Specific antigens in methylcholanthrene-induced tumours of mice have been demonstrated by Foley (1953), Prehn and Main (1957), Klein et al. (1960) and many others. Antigens have also been demonstrated in tumours induced by plastic films (Klein et al. 1963), ultra-violet light (Pasternak et al. 1964) and other physically or chemically induced malignancies. According to Prehn (1965) little is known about the physico-chemical nature of the antigens, apart from the fact that they neither contain the (chemical) carcinogens, nor are they chemically related to them. The antigens are characteristic of the tumour cells themselves, and Prehn presumes that they are present in the cell periphery.

(2) The antigens of virus-induced tumours are a well-recognized group, and in the case of animal tumours caused by oncogenic viruses, as briefly reviewed by Old and Boyse (1966), viral antigens are present at the peripheries of some infected cells, and may in fact function as transplantation-antigens. In an earlier review, Old and Boyse (1965) note that new antigens have been observed in all virus-induced tumours so far examined. These have been demonstrated by transplantation experiments in which animals previously infected with virus, rejected grafts of tumours induced in other animals by the same virus (Habel 1961); by the development of specific antibodies detectable by cytotoxicity or immunofluorescence following the injection of leukaemic cells or leukaemogenic virus (Fink and Malmgren 1963; Pope and Rowe 1964); and by the demonstration of complement fixation when antibody in the serum of animals bearing tumours produced by virus,

interacts with antigens of tumour cells produced *in vivo* and *in vitro* (Huebner et al. 1963).

Sabin and Koch (1964) describe how monkey sera which contain neutralizing and complement-fixing antibodies to SV40 virus, fail to react with complement-fixing antigens from the SV40 tumour. In addition, the sera of hamsters bearing tumours, which contain complement-fixing antibodies for tumour antigens, failed to react with virus antigen produced *in vitro*. However, when normal cells are producing SV40 virus at maximal rate soon after infection *in vitro*, complement-fixing antigen is produced which is indistinguishable from the specific complement-fixing antigen found in continuously transplanted SV40 tumours, and which is not demonstrable in the virus particles themselves. As the cytopathic effect of virus on cultures of normal cells near completion, 'tumour-like' infected normal cell antigens disappear, and the complement-fixing antigens of the infected viral particles reach maximum concentration. The complement-fixing antibodies in the sera of SV40 tumour-bearing hamsters interact with the transitory infected normal cell antigens. These data form the bases for Sabin and Koch's (1964) conclusion that the genetic information for the production of complement-fixing antigens of the SV40 tumours is derived entirely from either 'provirus or from another incomplete form of the SV40 viral genome continuously transmitted in the tumour cells'.

The cellular site of the antigen produced by oncogenic viruses can vary, and the homograft reactions against the tumours may well be most pronounced against those located at the cell periphery, such as the SV40-induced surface antigen demonstrated by Tevethia et al. (1965), in contrast to the internal 'T' antigen induced by the SV40 virus and described by Rapp et al. (1965). The surface changes associated with viral oncogenesis are discussed in detail in chapter 6.

It might well be noted that in contrast to the antigens of chemically or physically induced tumours, the antigens of virus-induced tumours are the same for the same virus, regardless of the host.

(3) There is much less available data on the antigens of spontaneous tumours, than on those induced chemically or by virus. In experimental animals, evidence of antigenicity was indicated by increased resistance of the host by Riggins and Pilch (1964), D. W. Weiss et al. (1964) and Attia et al. (1965). However, the possible viral origin of at least one of these antigens has more recently been demonstrated by Lavrin et al. (1965), and canine neoplasms examined by McKenna and Prier (1966). It seems likely, however, that the antigens from spontaneous tumours are weak, as least compared

with chemically induced tumours. Thus, Prehn (1960) showed that whereas host-resistance could be invoked in mice against sarcomata induced by polycyclic hydrocarbons, spontaneous fibrosarcomata produced little or no evidence of immunization (Prehn and Main 1957). Similary, although Klein et al. (1960) had shown that injection of irradiated cells from methylcholanthrene-induced murine sarcomata into isogeneic hosts produced immunity, Révész (1960) failed to demonstrate immunity using similar techniques with spontaneous adenocarcinomata or lymphomata. Baldwin (1966) failed to demonstrate immunity in rats following injection of heavily irradiated cells from either spontaneously developing reticulum cell sarcomata or squamous cell carcinomata into isogeneic hosts. In man, the presence of antigens is possibly suggested by *in vivo* anaphylactic reactions (Zilber 1958); and their presence in the sera of cancer patients has been described on the evidence of the Schultz–Dale test by Makari (1955, 1958), Burrows (1958) and Grace and Lehoczky (1959). In addition, DeCarvalho (1960) has demonstrated antigens in extracts of tumour cells by a gel diffusion technique.

McKenna and his associates (1964, 1966) have described the presence of a soluble specific 'G' antigen in a number of human tumours and cell lines derived from them, by immunodiffusion. The antigen was not demonstrable in a number of normal tissues or in benign tumours, and has not been identified in neoplastic mouse cells. The presence of the 'G' antigen shows some correlation with cell growth in the hamster cheek pouch. These authors have suggested that the antigen may be the manifestation of the genome of a common virus. Much of the work on the chemical nature of various postulated tumour antigens has been discussed by Day (1965), and quite obviously much of the early work was somewhat dubious. Of the more recent work on the chemical nature of specific tumour antigens, the studies of Rapport and his colleagues (see Rapport and Graf 1961) deserve special mention. Using a transplantable rat lymphosarcoma initially as a source of tumour material, Rapport and Graf (1955) discovered that mitochondria gave a better immunological response than other subcellular fractions, and that ethanol-ether extracts of this fraction or of whole tissues reacted with antibodies rather better than the intact tissues or organelles, as judged by complement fixation tests. The active antigenic material, cytolipin H, is a lipid hapten, which has since been identified in a number of human and other spontaneous tumours, but never in normal tissues. The structure of cytolipin H has been elucidated (Rapport et al. 1961a; Rapport et al. 1961b) and it is a ceramide lactoside, consisting of an almost entirely sphingosine 'base', with a fatty acid compo-

nent of variable chain lengths with C_{24} predominating, and glucose or galac-
tose in a lactose configuration. Rabbit antibodies prepared against lactose
coupled to non-rabbit protein by an azophenyl linkage, react with cytolipin
H (Graf et al. 1965); lactose was the only one of eleven sugars tested which
inhibited the reaction of cytolipin H and anti-choriocarcinoma serum.
Rapport and Graf (1961) therefore suggest that the carbohydrate moiety
is responsible for antigenic specificity. They also note that in contrast to
proteins which may possess many antigenic determinants in a single molecule, lipid haptens are essentially single antigenic determinants. Shapiro and
Rachaman (1964) synthesized N-lignoceroyl-1-D-sphingosyl-β-lactoside,
which Rapport and Graf (1964) showed was indistinguishable immunologically from cytolipin H. As the aggregation of these molecules into larger
units can occur by means of association of their fatty acid chains, cytolipin
H is possibly incorporated into the structure of various cell 'membranes'. If
in this position the hapten is associated with foreign protein, it will be converted into a complete antigen. Cytolipin H is considered on quantitative
data, to be quite distinct from cardiolipin and the Forssman hapten, which
are also present in human tissues. It will be of interest to determine whether
cytolipin H is present in quantity at the periphery of tumour cells in general,
since the work so far suggests that this may be the only currently identifiable
component which is exclusive to the malignant cell periphery.

It was mentioned above that the conversion of cytolipin H into a complete
antigen capable of involving an auto-immune response, required the presence
of foreign protein. In spite of numerous attempts, the amount of data available on tumour or patient specific proteins is extremely small. Korngold
(1960) discusses data showing that patients with myelomatosis possess
globulins carrying patient-specific antigens, as well as those normally associated with γ-globulins. The electrophoretic data of Whitcutt and Elson
(1962) on eight rat liver enzymes and other proteins, from normal organs,
during the process of azo dye-induced carcinogenesis, and from the
resultant hepatomata, show loss of some protein bands but fortification
of others.

The question of virus-induced antigens is obviously relevant to spontaneous tumours in man, particularly leukaemia.

9.4.3. *Antigenic loss*

In addition to the concept of antigenic gain by tumour cells the question of
antigenic loss must also be considered (Burnet 1957; Green 1959; Weiler

1959; Nairn et al. 1960), since both loss and gain could be reflected in altered recognition reactions by host cells to those of the tumour, as discussed by Witebsky (1961) and many others. Haddow (1965) has discussed the concept that the cancer cell has not essentially acquired inherent properties of unlimited growth, and there is a good deal of evidence from *in vitro* systems that normal cells possess equal growth potentialities. Growth in the cancer cell appears more due to loss of regulatory systems, and may well be connected with deletions. Thus, Weiler (1952, 1962), Baldwin (1963) and Kalnins and Stich (1963) demonstrated antigenic loss in rat liver cells following induction of malignancy by azodyes; loss of organ-specific antigenicity has been observed in the stilboestrol-induced renal carcinoma of the hamster (Weiler 1956a, b); antigenic simplification has been noted in leukaemic leucocytes (Seligmann et al. 1955; Milgrom et al. 1959 and Nelken 1963); loss of tissue-specific auto-antigen has been demonstrated in thyroid tumours (Goudie and McCallum 1963); and of tissue-specific antigens in gastro-intestinal tumours (Nairn et al. 1962).

Antigenic deletion may also occur in malignant cells, and Boyse et al. (1963) have described how when ERLD leukaemic cells, bearing the thymus leukaemia (TL) antigen are injected into C57BL/6 hosts, preimmunized with TL antigen, the cells grow, but without the TL antigen. When the leukaemic cells are transplanted back into a non-immune animal, the TL antigen reappears.

Antigenic loss, particularly at the cell periphery, may directly affect cell growth and division by altering the interaction of cells with environmental homeostatic factors, which may include other cells. On the other hand, antigenic loss in autochthonous tumours may bear no causal relationship to failure of response to homeostatic mechanisms at all, but may simply reflect intracellular change.

Green (1957, 1958) has proposed that carcinogens bind to intracellular specific proteins, giving rise to self-replicating complexes. Antibody combines with the complex and, in due course loss of the modified protein occurs by adaptive processes. Miller and Miller (1947) and Potter (1956, 1962) linked carcinogenesis with enzyme deletion, and much experimental work (e.g. Heidelberger 1959) has shown that chemical carcinogens interact with proteins and DNA. Certainly enzyme deletion could be reflected in total or partial loss of antigenic (or non-antigenic) constituents of the cell periphery. These constituents could be lipids, protein and/or carbohydrate. Whatever mechanisms are involved, the concept of antigenic deletion or dilution at the cell periphery seems well-supported by experimental evidence.

9.5 Host response

As data on the host response to autochthonous human tumours are sparse, much of our present understanding of this reaction is based on studies of grafts of normal and malignant tissues into experimental animals.

The reaction to implants containing foreign antigens may be manifest in (1) humoral, and (2) cellular responses. Although these responses will be discussed separately, they may overlap.

9.5.1. Humoral response

The early work of Clowes and Baeslack (1905), Beebe and Ewing (1906) Bashford and his associates (1908a, b), Jensen (1909), Coca (1912) and others, on the retardation or rejection of tumour development in experimental animals, by classical 'immunological techniques', led them to conclude that humoral antibodies are responsible for tumour regression. However, as Kidd (1961) has pointed out in an excellent critical review of this topic, it was soon demonstrated that induced resistance to tumours was short-lived and limited in application. In his detailed critical review of the literature up to 1929, Woglom (1929) concluded that no specific antibodies had been described to support the immunological concepts of cancer. It is also clear now that many of the immune responses noted earlier were invoked by antigens other than tumour-specific types.

The role of humoral antibody in the homograft reaction in general has been difficult to establish.

The recent evidence for participation of humoral antibody in the homograft reaction has been reviewed by Stetson (1963) and Russell and Monaco (1964). Russell and Monaco (1964) summarized the areas of experimentation that lead to the general scepticism of the significance of humoral antibody in homograft rejection.

(1) The early failure to detect humoral antibody in skin graft rejection in rabbits (Medawar 1946, 1948a).

(2) The experiments of Algire et al. (1957) in which allografts enclosed in millipore chambers, permitting passage of humoral but not cellular elements, survived for long periods of time even in a previously immunized host.

(3) Repeated failure to transfer allograft sensitivity by large doses of serum in a number of species (Billingham et al. 1954; Billingham et al. 1956).

These negative findings have been used as strong evidence against the role of humoral antibodies in homograft immunity (Medawar 1958a; Brent 1958;

Lawrence 1959) and focused the attention strictly on cellular immunity.

Some of these findings are no longer tenable and at the present time the homograft reaction is believed to be mediated through the production of both humoral and cell-bound antibodies (Hellström and Möller 1965).

It has been demonstrated conclusively that humoral antibody can be produced by both skin and tumour homografts using the cytotoxic reaction *in vitro* (Gorer and O'Gorman 1956; Möller and Möller 1962), the indirect fluorescent antibody technique (Möller 1964; Klein and Klein 1965) and complement fixation (Batchelor 1960; Winn 1962). The experiments of Algire (1954) and Algire et al. (1957) showing prolonged graft survival in cell-impermeable chambers were taken as evidence for lack of humoral response in homograft reaction; however, later studies (Amos and Wakefield 1958, 1959) have shown that humoral antibodies and complement penetrate the Millipore chambers with difficulty and that grafts can be inhibited or even destroyed in such chambers in the presence of appropriate levels of antibody alone. Similar findings have been observed by other investigators (Gorer and Boyse 1959; Gabourel 1961; Möller 1963a). Later Algire (1959) demonstrated that neoplastic cells of a plasma cell series were destroyed in these chambers, but some non-neoplastic donor cells survived. The observation that not all grafts are equally susceptible to destruction by serum factors was also noted by Gorer and Boyse (1959).

Although Billingham et al. (1954) were completely unable to achieve passive immunization against orthotopic skin grafts, by use of serum and whole blood, the capacity of humoral antibodies to inhibit tumour growth has been demonstrated in several tumour types. The inhibitory effect of humoral antibody has been studied mostly in leukaemias (Amos and Day 1957; Gorer and Kaliss 1959; Winn 1960), but has also been demonstrated in ascites carcinoma BP8 (Gorer and Kaliss 1959) and ascites tumour sarcoma 1 (Chouroulinkov et al. 1962; and Phillips and Stetson 1962).

The immunological enhancement of tumour growth by humoral antibody should also be noted here, and the reader is referred to the reviews by Kaliss (1958, 1965) and Möller (1963a). Enhancement is dependent on the antibody dose:tumour mass ratio; small ratios tend to produce enhancement of growth, and vice versa.

The literature on studies of specific antibody production in response to spontaneous tumours is confusing, in the sense that until quite recently,for every report describing positive findings, one could be found negating it. Osler (1961) has listed the various hypotheses to be considered, which include:

(1) Tumour cell growth in the absence of antibody formation implies that possibly the neoplastic change is not represented in antigenic changes in a positive way, or that tumour cells are actually deficient in antigens. Another possibility is that tumour cells can only proliferate when the host developes a state akin to acquired immune-tolerance or immunological paralysis.

(2) Tumour-specific antibodies are produced but are of the cell-dependent type and hence are not ideal for extensive *in vitro* investigation.

(3) Tumour-specific antibodies are cell-bound (Amos and Koprowski 1963).

(4) Circulating tumour-specific antibody is produced which reacts extensively with normal tissues.

It may be asked whether in man, humoral antibodies play a demonstrable role in controlling tumour progression in general, and the metastatic process in particular. Circulating antibodies in patients with various gynaecological cancers were demonstrated with complement-fixation tests in 12 out of 48 patients by Graham and Graham (1955), when the patients' sera were allowed to react with their own tumours. The majority of patients not having antibodies, had advanced neoplasia. The Grahams noted that the antibodies may have been specific for each patient, which would make future tests more difficult. By use of a haemagglutination technique, in which rabbit erythrocytes which had absorbed an extract of the patients' own tumour were agglutinated by the patient's serum, Parigot et al. (1958) obtained positive findings in 6 out of 21 cases. Grace and Kondo (1958) gave patients intradermal injections of aqueous extracts of their own tumours and, separately, normal tissues obtained by biopsy. In five patients with mammary carcinoma, two with Hodgkin's disease and one with lymphoma, all gave positive skin reactions consisting of wheals of more than 1 cm diameter. In contrast, none of the normal tissue extracts gave wheals larger than 0.5 cm diameter. In addition, patients and control sera were injected intradermally into other subjects, and 24 hours later, tumour extract injected into the same sites. Positive reactions were obtained only in those sites pretreated with serum from the patient providing the tumourous material. Experiments aimed at demonstrating the production of circulating antibodies in experimental animals by injection of human tumour extracts are questionable in the absence of rigid controls (e.g. Björklund 1961). The general impression is obtained that circulating antibodies are unlikely to be of major importance in the control of spontaneous human tumours, and that attention should be focussed on cell-bound antibodies. This view is also expressed and substantiated by Pilch and Riggins (1966).

9.5.2. Cellular response

An early systematic attempt to follow the cellular response to implants of tumours was made by Algire (1954) who inoculated the subcutaneous tissues of inbred strains of mice with fragments (0.2 mm^3) of tumour tissue within transparent chambers, where they could be observed by light microscopy. C3HBA mammary adenocarcinoma which originated in strain C3H mice, survived in this strain under the experimental conditions, for a mean of twelve days, but regressed after eight to ten days in C57BL mice. If C57BL mice were inoculated with the tumour twelve to seventeen days after the initial transplant, tumour regression occurred significantly earlier. Thus the graded responses to tumour inoculation could be visualized. In the C3H mice, capillaries developed within the graft some one to four days after implantation and, vascularization increased with tumour volume up to the eighth to tenth days. After this time, regression was evident by the increasing opacity of the graft, endothelial adherence of leucocytes, vascular narrowing and statis, and decrease in tumour volume. Concurrent with these changes, an inflammatory reaction occurred round the tumour with the usual vascular dilatation and leucocytic invasion. The vascular damage within the tumours did not precede tumour distruction but were concurrent with it. Thus, failure of vascularization does not play an obvious primary role in tumour destruction in the C3H mice under these conditions, just as it does not play a primary role in the rejection of first homografts of normal tissues (Medawar 1948a). Second interstrain grafts into C57BL mice failed to become vascularized, as might be expected from studies on homografts of normal (Medawar 1944; Merwin and Hill 1954) and malignant tissues (Mitchison 1954) in actively immunized animals. These non-vascularized tumour grafts did not grow initially, and became surrounded by leucocytes within two to three days, suggesting that in the immunized animal, initial vascularization is of some importance. In the case of an animal with a metastasizing tumour, a developing active immunity may well control the growth of the metastases through failure of vascularization.

Another dynamic technique for studying vascularization of tumour transplants in the cheek pouch of the hamster has been described by Goodall et al. (1965) and Warren and Shubik (1966), in which the transplant together with vascularized host tissue are also enclosed in transparent chambers where they can be observed by light microscopy, or removed for examination in the electron microscope. This resembles the technique developed earlier by Algire and Legallais (1949) in mice. If the assumption is made that such transplants form a useful model for developing metastatic deposits from spontaneous tumours, then the observations are instructive. The transplants induce endothelial proliferation in the host, and capillary sprouts invade the tumour. These sprouts become canalized at their tips and may fuse to form vessels which may or may not develop muscular coats. This stage of the vascularization process is similar to that described in the process of wound-healing by Cliff (1963) and Schoefl (1963) among others, and the lateral fusion of vessels has also been described in autografts in the rabbit ear chamber by Williams (1959). At the fine structural level, Warren and Shubik (1966) have described expansion of the plasma membranes of the endothelial cells in vessels near to the tumour grafts, together with the formation of numerous microvilli. The anastomosing capillary sprouts at first are most numerous near to the centre of the tumour but, as it grows, the vasculature becomes more peripheral. Host vessels become incorporated into the tumour mass as it expands. In the tumour proper, two types of vascular pathways are seen, thin-walled vessels composed of endothelium and supportive collagen, and sinuses lined by neoplastic cells.

The vascularization of tumour implants, the development of stroma and the survival or death of the focus is related to the type of cellular reaction around them. The primary cellular responses to tumour transplants in experimental animals have been classified by Gorer (1958) to include a type 1 response which is the classic type seen in most solid tumours in which the graft is supplied with a fibrovascular stroma by the host. Destruction of the graft is associated with lymphocytic and plasma cell infiltration. In actively immunized mice, no fibrovascular stroma is provided for the transplant, and the tumour degenerates into a thin-walled cyst (Russell 1908). Gorer's type 2, seen with some ascites sarcomata, is characterized by the opening up of capillaries as the tumour expands. The essential feature of this type is a local proliferation of histiocytes which invade the tumour and surround the neoplastic cells, which then die. Plasma cells are not seen in the region of the graft, and the graft is not invaded by lymphocytes. Type 3, seen with leukaemic transplants, is characterized by exudation of plasma, necrosis and histiocytic invasion with homograft rejection, and corresponds to the reactions observed by Potter and Findley (1935). Different types of tumours evoke various cellular responses, which may vary with the site of implantation.

Medawar (1944), in his classic description of the rejection of the full thickness allogenic skin grafts in rabbits, observed that the most common cells, on microscopic examination, resembled small lymphocytes. In the past two decades the role of the lymphoid cells in homotransplantation reactions has been intensively studied and the immunological activities of these cells in homograft transplantation have been reviewed by Gowans and McGregor (1965).

The most significant observation that demonstrated the essential role of cells of lymphoid series in solid homograft rejection was the transfer of homograft immunity to previously untreated recipients by means of sensitized lymphoid cells, by Billingham et al. (1954) in the case of skin, and Mitchison (1955, 1958) with tumours. Mitchison and Dube (1955) also showed that adoptive immunity against neoplastic cells can be readily transferred by immune lymphoid cells and not by serum. Numerous more recent studies have confirmed these findings with a variety of homografts (Elkins 1964; Ramseier and Billingham 1964).

The role of lymphoid cells in the destruction of homografts *in vivo* has also been substantiated by demonstrations that lymphoid cells obtained from specifically immunized animals have a cytocidal effect on appropriate homologous 'target' cells *in vitro* (Rosenau 1963; Brondz 1964). Wilson (1965) observed that lymphoid cells obtained from DA-strain rats sensitized by grafting of Lewis strain skin would produce lysis in Lewis tumour cells grown *in vitro*. He noted that the survival of target cells was inversely related to the number of sensitized lymphocytes. Lysis occurred in the absence of complement and was preceded by firm adhesion of lymphocytes to the target cells. Attempts to implicate a serum component or a soluble factor in the destruction of lymphocytes were unsuccessful.

Another method of demonstrating that small lymphocytes are involved in the homograft reaction is to deplete the animal of small lymphocytes. Although a variety of techniques have been used, they can provide only circumstantial evidence for the complicity of small lymphocytes in homograft reactions, because their application to the whole animal may cause widespread disturbances involving a number of cell types (Gowans and McGregor 1965).

By continuous drainage from thoracic duct fistulae in rats, McGregor and Gowans (1964) produced marked lymphopenia, reduction of weight of lymph nodes with depletion of cortical small lymphocytes. In such animals it was demonstrated that survival of first set allografts in a non-inbred albino colony was strikingly prolonged; however, the graft survival of first set homografts skin exchanged between albino and hooded rats was increased only by a few days. Woodruff and Anderson (1964) showed that survival of skin grafts between distantly related rats could be increased by combining the drainage of lymphocytes with injections of heteroimmune (rabbit–anti–rat) serum.

Animals thymectomized early in life show a depletion of lymphocytes during adult life (Waksman et al. 1962; Miller 1962; Cooper et al. 1966) and there is good evidence that the thymus is essential for the normal development of the lymphoid tissue (Miller et al. 1962; Metcalf 1964; Miller 1964). Miller (1962) showed that neonatal thymectomy, which prevents normal lymphocyte population of lymph nodes and spleen, and causes a lymphocytopenia, may be associated with an inability of the animal to reject homografts or even heterografts. Miller (1963) also showed that grafts of neonatal thymus, or injections of cells from lymph-nodes or spleens from adult syngeneic donors, restore the immunological response to previously thymectomized recipients.

The increased susceptibility of thymectomized mice and hamsters to tumour induction by carcinogens and polyoma virus has been described by Law (1966a, b) and Defendi and Roosa (1964). However, Fisher et al. (1965) failed to observe the promotion of growth of experimentally induced hepatic metastases, in rats which had been thymectomized at birth. These apparently contradictory results suggest that thymectomy may be more relevant to the case of strongly antigenic tumours or tumorogenic agents, than to control the progression of those tumours possessing weak antigens.

These homograft reactions which have been discussed so far in terms of lymphocyte function, are primarily concerned with the reactions of host against donor tissues. Another type of interaction must also be considered, in which the donor material (i.e. tumour) attacks the host. This graft versus host reaction, which requires the presence of immunologically competent cells in the graft, is probably not directly related to naturally occurring host response in the metastatic process. However, the question arises of whether the grafting of immunologically competent cells into patients with cancer can favourably influence the course of their disease.

Brent and Medawar (1963, 1964) showed that peripheral blood lymphocytes from guinea pig A, which had received grafts from guinea pig B, would produce a marked reaction when injected intradermally into guinea pig B. Similar experiments on humans have been made by Gray and Russell (1963), Moorehead and Patel (1964), Aisenberg (1965) and Amos et al. (1965). Although similar results indicating lymphocytic immunological activity have been obtained by all of these investigators, there appears to be a difference in interpretation of the data to indicate either a reaction of the donor lymphocytes against the recipient, or a reaction of the recipient against the donor lymphocytes. The usual reaction seen after injecting immune lymph-node cells into hamsters is abolished after irradiation of the recipient, indicating that the reaction is dependent on the presence of host lymphocytes to react with the graft (Ramseier and Streilein 1965). In humans, the reaction is depressed in uraemic patients (Bridges et al. 1964) and in the presence of ABO-group incompatibility (Moorehead and Patel 1964). Amos (1966) has reported interesting data on the injection of lymphocytes from normal subjects into cancer patients, when the overall response was much less marked than in normal recipients. From the host versus graft viewpoint, these experiments indicate that the host response was diminished, as also suggested by the transplantation experiments of Southam and Moore (1958) with cultured cells. The next experiments described by Amos (1966) consisted of ingeniously testing the functional state of lymphocytes from normal donors *in situ*, within cancer patients. When antigens to which the donor, but not the recipient, reacted, were injected into the recipient at sites previously inoculated with donor lymphocytes, markedly greater reactions were seen than with the donor lymphocytes alone. No positive reactions were observed in the recipient sites receiving either antigen alone or antigen after killed donor lymphocytes. The experiments indicate a primary 'reticulo-endothelial deficiency' in these cancer patients, and that the transplanted lymphocytes can function in a cancer host. This has obvious potentialities in the field of immunotherapy.

9.5.3. *Some possible mechanisms of lymphocyte function*

Gowans (1965) draws attention to the fact that small lymphocytes may be involved in both the initiation of graft/host interactions by contact with graft antigens, and in the graft destruction proper, when lymphocytes released from activated lymph nodes invade the grafts. Gowans considers that either antigens released by dead cells could travel in the lymph vessels, or, alternatively, as suggested by Medawar (1958a), lymphocytes might infiltrate the graft via the blood stream, 'react' with it, and then travel along the lymphatics to the regional lymph nodes where an immune response could be effected.

Experimental evidence suggests that cell death, produced by ligation of a tumour pedicle, can promote immune response, and certainly 'necrobiosis' is a familiar feature of tumour pathology. It is therefore conceivable that antigenic cell debris could leave the transplantation site and reach local nodes. As pointed out by Gowans, very little is known of how antigens from grafts reach the lymphoid cells of the hosts, and that it is generally assumed that the antigens leave the graft via lymphatic vessels draining into the local lymph nodes. Gowans quotes evidence in favour of this proposed route, from the survival of homografts in tissues where lymphatic vessels are absent, such as the brain (Medawar 1948a) and hamster cheek pouch (Billingham and Silvers 1962), and also the work of Billingham et al. (1954) and Mitchison (1954) showing that the regional lymph nodes play an important part in host response to homograft.

Neter (1963) has reviewed the evidence showing that antigens can become attached to erythrocytes and other cells, which raises the possibility that they may be transported on the surfaces of lymphocytes which have infiltrated the tumour, to antibody-forming sites. The transfer of antigenic material from the graft to the regional lymph node could be accomplished as a result of amoeboid movement of the lymphocytes over the cells of the graft, when as a result of the microruptures and exchange of 'surface' materials postulated by L. Weiss (1961) and detailed in chapter 4, antigenic material could be transported at the lymphocyte peripheries.

Although, the exact mechanism of antigen transport is not known, cellular changes occur in the regional lymph nodes, which are characterized by the appearance of large pyroninophilic cells (Scothorne and McGregor 1955; Burwell and Gowland 1960; André et al. 1962). Gowans and McGregor (1965) state that there is good evidence that the precursor of the large pyroninophilic cell is the small lymphocyte, which transports antigen to the lymph node. Gowans (1965) also considers that the 'activated' lymphocytes which are released from the nodes could conceivably be the progeny of the pyroninophils. This concept of a lymphocyte with changing function and morphology fits in well with current views that the potentially long-lived, recirculating small lymphocyte is not an 'end' cell but that it can enlarge and start dividing when appropriately stimulated.

The properties of lymphocytes which make them 'immunologically activated' have not been fully characterized. A demonstration of cell-bound immunity was made *in vitro* by Berrian and Brent (1958) based on the capacity of the cells to inactivate antigenic extracts. This neutralization could not be accomplished with humoral antigens in a similar test system. The lymphoid cells from immune animals were considered to have developed antibody-like reactive sites located peripherally and/or intracellularly which could reasonably be termed 'cell-bound antibodies'. This antibody should be distinguished from 'cytophilic' antibody (Boyden 1963) which is a globulin component of immune serum which *in vitro* absorbs to some cells in such a way that these cells become capable of specifically absorbing antigen.

At the present time, experiments aimed at the detection of cell-bound antibodies by adoptive transfer experiments are performed in the presence of antibody-producing cells and in this system the 'cell-bound' antibodies cannot be separated from the humoral 'cytophilic' antibody (Hellström and Möller 1965). However, there is evidence from *in vitro* experiments (Rosenau 1963 and Wilson 1965) that cytolysis of cells can occur without presence of humoral antibody and complement, and this may be taken as evidence for cell-bound antibody.

It seems possible that circulating immune lymphocytes enter the graft and destroy it by direct contact interactions with the target cells. However, experiments using immune lymphoid cells labelled with tritiated thymidine *in vivo* have failed to show the presence of significant numbers of labelled cells in the recipients' homografts (Najarian and Feldman 1962, 1963; Billingham et al. 1963). Using a somewhat different approach Prendergast (1964) demonstrated that cells originating from a regional node do reach skin homografts in significant numbers but they are not specifically attracted into the immunologically appropriate graft.

In contrast to the inconclusive *in vivo* evidence, it has been demonstrated that close contact of the immunized lymphocytes and target cells is necessary for cytolysis *in vitro* (Rosenau 1963; Wilson 1965). A millipore filter between target cells and immunized cells prevented target cell destruction. The contact between the immune lymphocyte and target cell and destruction of target cell can also be prevented by pretreating the target cell with humoral antibodies directed toward the same antigen as the immune lymphocyte (E. Möller 1965). The humoral antibody may thus act by competing for sites on target cell surfaces with lymphoid cells.

Pulvertaft (1959) has remarked that both normal and malignant lymphocytes apply themselves closely to other cells, and in some cases appear to be attracted by malignant cells, and that sometimes the lymphocytes appear to be 'licking' the surfaces of malignant cells. From the work done on the mechanics of cell movement and cell separation, it might be argued that when lymphocytes crawl around malignant cells, materials including bound antibodies at their peripheries might well be torn off the lymphocytes and deposited on the neoplastic cells, to their detriment.

In view of the intimacy of contact required between lymphocytes and their target cells, it is of interest that the lymphocyte may lead an intracellular existence. The presence of lymphocytes within other cells was noted in cultures of chick embryo spleen by Fischer and Dolschansky (1929), in mixed cultures of rat thymus and chick fibroblasts by Trowell (1949), in thyroid homografts in rabbits by Darcy (1952), and cinemicrographically by Koller and Waymouth (1953). Much of the older literature pertaining to the apparent intracellular location of lymphocytes in conventional histological preparations is reviewed by Trowell (1958), but in most cases this material did not permit a discrimination to be made between intracellular and pericellular location. The intimate association of lymphocytes with human tumour cells *in vitro* was observed in cinemicrographs by Humble et al. (1956), who noted that lymphocytes could apparently enter other cells, wander around inside them and, in some cases, leave them. This phenomenon was termed 'emperipolesis' (Gk 'inside, round-about wandering').

The intracellular existence of lymphocytes may function as a mechanism whereby they can escape destruction from host cells. Evidence in favour of this suggestion comes from experiments discussed earlier, on somatic hybridization of cells using viral-induced fusion. These experiments have lead Harris (1966) to conclude that there are no intracellular mechanisms in vertebrate cells for recognizing incompatibility. The logical extension of this argument is that recognition is governed by the cell periphery.

In humans, attempts have been made to correlate good prognosis with a marked lymphocytic infiltration, by MacCarty (1922), Black et al. (1955) and others. The correlation is not particularly convincing, and the difficulties in assessing prognosis are exemplified by Friedell et al. (1965) who report on 153 surgical specimens of carcinoma of the breast, where lymphocytic infiltration of blood vessel walls was associated with bad prognosis when vascular invasion and lymph-node metastasis were present, and with better prognosis in the absence of vascular invasion and presence of nodal metastases.

It is to be hoped that more attention will be given to the cellular response to spontaneous tumours and their metastases, as much of the work discussed in this section is dependent on the challenge provided to the host by histocompatibility antigens (Billingham and Brent 1959; Simonsen 1962) and the part played by tumour-specific antigens is not at all clear.

In addition to the cellular responses to tumours already described, the provocative work of Elias et al. (1964) on the morphology of metastatic carcinoma in the livers of human subjects suggests that normal liver cells in contact with the tumour may undergo malignant conversion and be incorporated into the tumour. Pulvertaft (1959) had previously speculated on the possibility that in primary tumours, lymphocytes may be involved in such conversion processes.

9.5.4. *Some comments on the macrophage*

Histological studies of first-set homografts have emphasized the difficulties in identifying the types of host cell involved, and generally a mixture of lymphocytes, plasma cells and macrophages is implicated (Waksman 1963; Wiener et al. 1964).

A study of the rejection of sarcoma 1 ascites tumours in A/JAX and C57BL /6K mice, by Baker et al. (1962), illustrates another aspect of cellular interactions which may be relevant to the establishment or rejection of metastases. Following intraperitoneal injection, 100% of the A/JAX subline die, whereas the tumour is rejected in 100% of C57BL/6K mice. Observations on short-term cultures of cells taken at various times after inoculation suggest that the tumour cells are destroyed as a result of the 'contact activities' of peritoneal macrophages, because:

(1) among the host cells of the ascites population the macrophage was the only cell type showing a marked increase in concentration before the onset of tumour destruction;

(2) the peritoneal macrophage was the only host cell that showed a marked affinity for tumour cells;

(3) passive transfer of tumour immunity from the C57BL/6K to the A/JAX subline was accomplished with macrophage-rich ascitic fluid from actively immunized animals, but not with serum, cell-free ascitic fluid, extracts of spleen or peritoneal cells from these animals and

(4) when tumour cells were enclosed in millipore chambers, which were impermeable to cells, and implanted in the peritoneal cavities of actively immunized animals, they remained viable for at least three weeks, compared with the complete rejection that occurs in free cells by the eighth day. Similar observations have also been made by Granger (1964), who summarizes the previous work in this area.

9.5.5. *Defective immune response in cancer*

In addition to the rather doubtful increases in immunological response, well-characterized immunological defects have been observed in patients with malignancies involving the reticuloendothelial system such as leukaemia, lymphosarcoma, multiple myeloma and particularly Hodgkin's disease. Much of the literature has been reviewed by Grace (1964), who draws attention to work done by Reed (1901–1902) over 60 years ago, in which tuberculin tests were negative in 5 out of 8 patients with Hodgkin's disease. Sokal and Primikirios (1961) studied skin test responses in patients with Hodgkin's disease and lymphosarcoma, to tuberculin, trichophyton and *Candida antigens*, and reported a depression in skin reactivity which they correlated with increased activity of the disease, judged clinically. Patients who were tuberculin-positive during remission often became tuberculin-negative during clinical exacerbations. Diminished antibody production in patients with Hodgkin's disease and brucellosis was also noted by Dubin (1947). In contrast, Hoffmann and Rottino (1950) reported good production of antibodies in patients with Hodgkin's disease after immunization with *Salmonella antigens*, and Schier et al. (1965) noted that such patients gave a normal response to mumps virus vaccine. Grace (1964) remarks that while variable impairment of humoral antibody response may occur in this group of diseases, the diminished response is most consistently shown in those processes involving cellular responses, such as homograft rejection. Evidence in favour of this is provided by the prolonged skin graft survival in 19 out of 43 patients with lymphomatoses reported by Miller et al. (1961). Interestingly enough, these workers found no consistent correlation between graft rejection, which is a phenomenon involving cellular response, isohaemagglutinin titre, antibody titre following injections of *Salmonella antigens* or to skin tests with tuberculin or *Candida antigens*.

9.6 Other host factors influencing metastases

In addition to the questions of organ selectivity and host resistance in terms of immune response or its lack, other factors are thought to affect the development of metastases in various organs. Probably the best explored system is the development of hepatic metastases in Sprague–Dawley rats, given intraportal injections of Walker tumour cells, as described in a series of papers by the Fishers, and recently summarized by them (Fisher and Fisher 1965). Partial hepatectomy performed just before or after injections of tumour cells resulted in a significant increase in number and size of metastases compared to animals either not operated on at all, or in which a dorsal skin incision was made. On the other hand, coeliotomy, particularly with liver manipulation, injection of air, hepatoxic toxic doses of chloroform, and to a lesser extent, ether anaesthesia, all produced more and larger hepatic metastases. It was concluded that parenchymal damage was condusive to the development of metastases. Agostino and Cliffton (1965) have essentially confirmed and extended the earlier observations of the Fishers on the importance of trauma, in a series of experiments in which systemic injections of Walker 256 tumour cells produced recognizable metastases in the lungs of over 90% of rats, but none in their other organs. However, if liver damage was produced by the administration of carbon tetrachloride, hepatic metastases were also produced in 73% of the animals. When homogenates of their liver, kidney, heart, testis or brain were made four hours after the intravenous injection of tumour cells into rats, and then injected subcutaneously into fresh animals, tumours grew at the injection sites, indicating the presence of viable cells in these organs, even though metastases did not develop in them subsequently. If glass fragments were implanted in the liver, kidney and mesentery of rats before systemic injection of tumour cells, metastases subsequently developed in these organs, but not in spleens carrying glass fragments. Although trauma in these experiments clearly was associated with metastasis development, its physiological relevance is somewhat doubtful.

The mechanism of trauma on the production of metastases in Agostino and Clifton's experiments is possibly explicable in terms of haemodynamic alternations in the organs receiving glass implants, but the Fishers' experimental data cannot readily be accounted for in this way. The Fishers (Fisher and Fisher 1963) studied the incidence of hepatic metastases in parabiotic pairs of rats, and observed that tumour cells injected intraportally into one parabiont only produced hepatic metastases in that animal. If the other animal then had its liver traumatized there was no significant increase in metastases in the liver of the animal receiving the tumour cells. These experiments were taken to indicate that a humoral metastasis-promoting factor is not demonstrably released from damaged liver; they did not however exclude the possibility that a locally acting factor was released, and when tumour cells were mixed with homogenized normal liver prior to injection, a subsequent enhancement of tumour growth was observed both within the liver and soft tissues of the groin (Fisher and Fisher 1962). Contrary to common belief among pathologists, the induction of cirrhosis (with CCl_4) did not decrease the incidence of hepatic tumours, but caused an increase, and reference to their own human necropsy data by the Fishers revealed that there was a difference in the incidence of hepatic metastases from extrahepatic primary tumours in cirrhotic and non-cirrhotic patients.

The data from a series of elegant surgical procedures which altered the oxygenation of the liver via the hepatic artery suggested that decreased oxygen supply also promoted the development of metastases, as previously proposed by Willis (1948) and others. The Fishers also studied the effect of host nutrition on growth of tumours in the liver, and their findings indicate that while a low protein diet, which reduces the amount of liver protein, does not influence the arrest of tumour cells, their subsequent growth is retarded. On the other hand, a high fat choline-free diet was associated with a higher incidence of hepatic foci than in controls on an isocaloric diet. While the Fishers argue that the hepatic parenchymal cells in animals on a high fat diet swell, occlude sinuses and trap tumour cells, a more likely explanation is that the high fat diet acts by interference with the blood-clotting mechanisms of the host, as discussed in the previous chapter.

Endocrine organs may also play a role in the development of tumours by virtue of their effects on nutrition.

The presence of a tumour produces many changes in host tissues which do not contain malignant cells, and which cannot readily be ascribed to haemorrhage, infection or malnutrition. Begg (1958) has reviewed much of the evidence related to this type of tumour–host relationship as it affects the alteration of host metabolism and nutrition, enzymatic activity, hormone balance, etc., which will not be considered further here. Whether or not these various changes in the host are in any way specific to cancer is undecided. Boyd et al. (1960) compared the effects of chlorpromazine-induced cachexia in rats, with the cachexia induced by the growth of the Walker 256 carcinosarcoma. In both types they noticed similar histopathological changes in many organs, associated with similar shifts in weight, water, neutral fat, cholesterol and phospholipid content. Most similar work has also failed to uncover changes specific to malignancy.

9.7 Conclusions

(1) The experimental evidence on spontaneous human tumours suggests that tumour-specific antigens are present. The reasons for the apparent final ineffectiveness of the patient's immune response against his own tumour are very possibly due to his depressed immunological reactivity, which is in some way manifest in functional deficiencies of lymphocytes.
(2) Humoral antibodies by themselves appear to be ineffective against malignant foci, and it may be predicted that anti-cancer sera will not be of clinical use, by themselves.
(3) Although the immune response is diminished in patients with advanced cancer, potentiation of the antigenic stimulus in patients at earlier stages of the disease appears worthy of testing, particularly with a view to control-

ling metastases. Potentiation may possibly be brought about by killing all or part of the primary tumour and leaving it in the patient (Lewis and Aptekman 1952), by chemical methods discussed, or by injections of autogenous vaccines prepared from the patient's own tumour, with or without adjuvant. It may be mentioned that extensive tests of the latter by Graham and Graham (1962) were disappointing; however, in clinical practice it is generally, and correctly from an ethical standpoint, not the rule to use new therapeutic techniques on patients with early cancer.

(4) Injection of lymphoid cells from normal subjects or possibly from cultures, appears to offer the best feasible hope at the moment for immunotherapy. This field is currently being intensively investigated but not enough clinical data is available to comment further.

References

Agostino, D., and Clifton, E. E. (1965). Cancer Res. **25**, 1728
Aisenberg, A. C. (1965). J. Clin. Invest. **44**, 555
Algire, G. H. (1954). J. Natl. Cancer Inst. **15**, 483
Algire, G. H. (1959). J. Natl. Cancer Inst. **23**, 435
Algire, G. H. and Legallais, F. Y. (1949). J. Natl. Cancer Inst. **10**, 225
Algire, G. H., Weaver, J. M., and Prehn, R. T. (1957). Ann. N. Y. Acad. Soc. **64**, 1009
Amos, D. B. (1956). Ann. N. Y. Acad. Sci. **63**, 706
Amos, D. B. (1966). In, The mechanism of invasion of cancer. U.I.C.C. Symposium
Amos, B., and Koprowski, H. (1963). Cell-bound antibodies. Wistar Institute Press, Philadelphia
Amos, D. B., and Day, E. D. Eds. (1957). Ann. N. Y. Acad. Sci. **64**, 851
Amos, D. B., Nicks, P. J., Peacocke, M., and Sicker, H. O. (1965). J. Clin. Invest. **44**, 219
Amos, D. B., and Wakefield, J. D. (1958). J. Natl. Cancer Inst. **21**, 657
Amos, D. B., and Wakefield, J. D. (1959). J. Natl. Cancer Inst. **22**, 1077
André, J. A., Schwartz, R. S., Mitus, W. K., and Damashek, W. (1962). Blood **19**, 313
Attia, M. A., DeOme, K. B., and Weiss, D. W. (1965). Cancer Res. **25**, 451
Baker, P., Weiser, R. S., Jutila, J., Evans, C. A., and Blandau, R. J. (1962). Ann. N. Y. Acad. Sci. **101**, 46
Baldwin, R. W. (1963). Acta, Unio Intern. Contra Cancrum. **19**, 545
Baldwin, R. W. (1966). Intern. J. Cancer **1**, 257
Bashford, E. F., Murray, J. A., and Cramer, W. (1908a). 3rd Sci. Rept. Imperial Cancer Res. Fund. 315
Bashford, E. F., Murray, J. A., and Haaland, M. (1908b). 3rd Sci. Rept. Imperial Cancer Res. Fund. 359
Batchelor, J. R. (1960). Immunology **3**, 174
Batchelor, J. R. (1965). Brit. Med. Bull. **21**, 100
Beebe, S. P., and Ewing, J. A. (1906). Brit. Med. J. **2**, 1559

Begg, R. W. (1958). Advan. Cancer Res. **5**, 1

Berenbaum, M. C. (1958). J. Clin. Pathol. **11**, 543

Berrian, J. H., and Brent, L. (1958). Ann. N. Y. Acad. Sci. **73**, 654

Billingham, R. E., and Brent, L. (1959). Phil. Trans. Roy. Soc. B **242**, 439

Billingham, R. E., Brent, L., and Medawar, P. B. (1954). Proc. Roy. Soc. B **143**, 58

Billingham, R. E., Brent, L., and Medawar, P. B. (1956). Brit. J. Exptl. Pathol. **37**, 566

Billingham, R. E., and Silvers, W. K. (1962). In, Ciba foundation symposium on transplantation, Churchill, London, p. 90

Billingham, R. E., Silvers, W. K., and Wilson, D. B. (1963). J. Exptl. Med. **118**, 397

Björklund, B. (1961). Cancer Res. **21**, 1238

Black, M. M., Opler, S. R., and Speer, F. D. (1955). Surg. Gynecol. Obstet. **98**, 725

Boyd, E. M., Jarzylo, S., and Shannas, M. N. (1960). Cancer **13**, 850

Boyden, S. V. (1963). In, B. Amos and H. Koprowski, eds., Cell-bound antibodies. Wistar Inst. Press, Philadelphia, p. 7

Boyse, E. A., Old, L. J., and Luell, S. (1963). J. Natl. Cancer Inst. **31**, 987

Brent, L. (1958). Ann. N. Y. Acad. Sci. **69**, 804

Brent, L., and Medawar, P. B. (1963). Brit. Med. J. **ii**, 269

Brent, L., and Medawar, P. B. (1964). Nature **204**, 90

Bridges, J. M., Nelson, S. D., and McGeown, M. (1964). Lancet **1**, 581

Brondz, B. D. (1964). Folia Biol. **10**, 164

Burnet, F. M. (1957). Brit. Med. J. **1**, 779

Burrows, D. (1958). Brit. Med. J. **1**, 368

Burwell, R. G., and Gowland, G. (1960). Nature, Lond. **188**, 159

Choi, C. Y., and Yun, I. S. (1933). Trans. Soc. Pathol. Japan **23**, 707

Chouroulinkov, I., Boyse, E. A., and Old, L. J. (1962). Proc. Soc. Exptl. Biol. Med. **111**, 263

Cliff, W. J. (1963). Trans. Roy. Soc. B **246**, 305

Clowes, G. H. A. and Baeslack, F. W. (1905). Med. News **87**, 968

Coca, A. F. (1912). Z. Immunitätsforsch. **13**, 524

Collins, V. P., Loeffler, R. K., and Tivey, H. (1956). Am. J. Roentgenol. **76**, 988

Cooper, M. D., Peterson, R. D. A., South, M. A., Good, R. A. (1966). J. Exptl. Med. **123**, 75

Darcy, D. A. (1952). Phil. Trans. Roy. Soc. B **236**, 463

Davies, D. A. L. (1962). Biochem. J. **84**, 307

Day, E. D. (1965). The immunochemistry of cancer. Thomas, Springfield, Illinois

De Carvalho, S. (1960). J. Lab. Clin. Med. **56**, 333

Defendi, V. and Roosa, R. A. (1964). In, Defendi, V. and D. Metcalf, eds., The thymus, Wistar Institute Press, Philadelphia, p. 121

De Long, R. P. and Coman, D. R. (1950). Cancer Res. **10**, 513

Dubin, I. N. (1947). Ann. Internal Med. **27**, 898

Elias, H., Bierring, F., Grunnet, I. (1964). Oncologia **18**, 210

Elkins, W. L. (1964). J. Exptl. Med. **120**, 329

Everson, T. C. and Cole, W. H. (1956). Ann. Surg. **144**, 366

Ewing, J. (1940). Neoplastic diseases. 4th edition. Saunders, Philadelphia

Fink, M. A. and Malmgren, R. A. (1963). J. Natl. Cancer Inst. **31**, 1111

Fischer, A., and Dolschansky, E. (1929). Arch. Entwicklungsmech. Organ. **116**, 123

Fisher, B., and Fisher, E. R. (1959). Cancer **12**, 929

Fisher, B., and Fisher, E. R. (1962). Cancer Res. **23**, 1651

Fisher, B., Fisher, E. R., and Sakai, A. (1965). Cancer Res. **25**, 993

Fisher, E. R., and Fisher, B. (1963). Cancer Res. **23**, 1532

Fisher, E. R., and Fisher, B. (1965). Acta Cytol. **9**, 146

Foley, E. J. (1953). Cancer Res. **13**, 835

Friedell, G. H., Betts, A. and Sommers, S. C. (1965). Cancer **18**, 164

Friedman, E. A., Retan, J. W., Marshall, D. C., Henry, L. and Merrill, J. P. (1961). J. Clin. Invest. **40**, 2162

Gabourel, J. D. (1961). Cancer Res. **21**, 506

Goldsmith, K. L. G. (1965). Brit. Med. Bull. **21**, 162

Goodall, C. M., Sanders, A. G. and Shubik, P. (1965). J. Natl. Cancer Inst. **35**

Gordon-Taylor, G. (1948). Ann. Roy. Coll. Surg. **2**, 60

Gorer, P. A. (1956). Advan. Cancer Res. **4**, 149

Gorer, P. A. (1958). Ann. N. Y. Acad. Sci. **73**, 707

Gorer, P. A. and Boyse, E. A. (1959). In, F. Albert and P. B. Medawar, eds. Biological problems of grafting. Oxford, Blackwell, p. 192

Gorer, P. A., and Kaliss, N. (1959). Cancer Res. **19**, 824

Gorer, P. A. and Mikulska, Z. B. (1954). Cancer Res. **14**, 651

Gorer, P. A. and O'Gorman, P. (1956). Transpl. Bull. **3**, 142

Goudie, R. B. and McCallum, H. M. (1963). Lancet **ii**, 1035

Gowans, J. L. (1965). Brit. Med. Bull. **21**, 106

Gowans, J. L. and McGregor, D. D. (1965). Progr. Allergy **9**, 1

Grace, J. T. (1964). Ann. N. Y. Acad. Sci. **114**, 736

Grace, J. T. and Kondo, T. (1958). Ann. Surg. **148**, 633

Grace, J. T., and Lehoczky, A. (1959). Surgery **46**, 238

Graf, L., Yariv, J., and Rapport, M. M. (1965). J. Immunochem. **2**, 145

Graham, J. B., and Graham, R. M. (1955). Cancer **8**, 409

Graham, J. B., and Graham, R. M. (1962). Surg. Gynecol. Obstet. **114**, 1

Granger, G. A. (1964). Science **145**, 1427

Gray, J. G., and Russell, P. S. (1963). Lancet **ii**, 863

Green, H. N. (1957). Ann. N. Y. Acad. Sci. **68**, 268

Green, H. N. (1958). Brit. Med. Bull. **14**, 101

Green, N. H. (1959). In, Ciba Foundation Symposium, Carcinogenesis mechanisms of action, Churchill, London, p. 131

Greene, H. S. N. (1965). Acta Cytol. **9**, 160

Habel, K. (1961). Proc. Soc. Exptl. Med. Biol. **106**, 722

Haddow, A. (1934). Am. J. Cancer **22**, 308

Haddow, A. (1965). Brit. Med. Bull. **21**, 133

Harris, H. (1966). Discovery **27**, 10

Haughton, G. (1964). Transplantation **2**, 251

Haughton, G. (1965). Science **147**, 506

Hauschka, T. S. (1952). Cancer Res. **12**, 615

Hauschka, T. S. (1957). In, Proceeding of Canadian Cancer Res. Conf. Academic Press, New York, **2**, 305

Hauschka, T. S., and Amos, D. B. (1957). Ann. N. Y. Acad. Sci. **69**, 561

Hauschka, T. S., Kvedar, B. J., Grinnell, S. T., and Amos, D. B. (1956). Ann. N. Y. Acad. Sci. **63**, 683

Hauschka, T. S., and Levan, A. (1953). Exptl. Cell Res. **4**, 457

Heidelberger, C. (1959). In, Ciba Foundation Symposium on Carcinogenesis, mechanisms of action. Churchill, London
Hellström, K. E. (1959). Transpl. Bull. **6**, 411
Hellström, K. E., and Möller, G. (1965). Progr. Allergy **9**, 158
Herbut, P. A., and Gabriel, F. R. (1942). Arch. Pathol. **33**, 917
Herzenberg, L. A., and Herzenberg, L. A. (1961). Proc. Natl. Acad. Sci. **47**, 762
Hoffmann, G. T., and Rottino, A. (1950). Arch. Internal. Med. **86**, 872
Huebner, R. J., Rowe, W. P., Turner, H. C., and Lane, W. T. (1963). Proc. Natl. Acad. Sci. (U.S.) **50**, 379
Humble, J. G., Jayne, W. H. W., and Pulvertaft, R. J. V. (1956). Brit. J. Haematol. **2**, 283
Hutcheson, J. B. (1952). Arch. Pathol. **54**, 314
Jensen, C. O. (1909). Z. Krebsforsch. **7**, 279
Kaliss, N. (1958). Cancer Res. **18**, 992
Kaliss, N. (1965). Federation Proc. **24**, 1024
Kalnins, V. I., and Stich, H. F. (1963). Nature **200**, 189
Kandutsch, A. A. (1960). Cancer Res. **20**, 264
Kidd, J. G. (1961). Cancer Res. **21**, 1170
Kinsey, D. L. (1960). Cancer **13**, 674
Klein, E., and Klein, G. (1965). Cancer Res. **25**, 851
Klein, G. (1964). In, P. Emmelot and O. Mühlbcck, eds., Cellular control mechanisms and cancer. Elsevier, Amsterdam, p. 236
Klein, G., Sjögren, O., and Klein, E. (1963). Cancer Res. **23**, 84
Klein, G., Sjögren, H. O., Klein, E., and Hellström, K. E. (1960). Cancer Res. **20**, 1561
Koller, P. C., and Waymouth, C. (1953). J. Roy. Microscop. Soc. **72**, 173
Korngold, L. (1960). Natl. Cancer Inst. Monograph **2**, 57
Laird, A. K. (1965). Brit. J. Cancer **18**, 490
Lavrin, D., Dezfulian, M., and Weiss, D. W. (1965). Proc. Am. Assoc. Cancer Res. **6**, 38
Law, L. W. (1966a). Cancer Res. **26**, 1121
Law, L. W. (1966b). Cancer Res. **26**, 551
Lawrence, H. S. (1959). Physiol. Rev. **39**, 811
Lewis, M. R., and Aptekman, P. M. (1952). Cancer **5**, 411
Lore, J. M., Madden, J. L., and Gerold, F. P. (1958). Cancer **11**, 24
Lucké, B., Breedis, C., Woo, Z. P., Berwick, L., and Nowell, P. (1952). Cancer Res. **12**, 734
MacCarty, W. C. (1922). Ann. Surg. **76**, 9
Makari, J. G. (1955). Brit. Med. J. **ii**, 1291
Makari, J. G. (1958). Brit. Med. J. **i**, 358
McGregor, D. D., and Gowans, J. L. (1964). Lancet **1**, 629
McKenna, J. M., and Prier, J. E. (1966). Cancer Res. **26**, 137
McKenna, J. M., Sanderson, R. P., and Blakemore, W. S. (1964). Cancer Res. **24**, 754
McKenna, J. M., Sanderson, R. P., Davis, F. E., and Blakemore, W. S. (1966). Cancer Res. **26**, 984
Medawar, P. B. (1944). J. Anat. (Lond) **78**, 176
Medawar, P. B. (1946). Brit. J. Exptl. Pathol. **27**, 15
Medawar, P. B. (1948a). Brit. J. Exptl. Pathol. **29**, 58
Medawar, P. B. (1948b). Quart. J. Microscopic Soc. **89**, 239
Medawar, P. B. (1958a). Harvey Lect. **52**, 144

Medawar, P. B. (1958b). Proc. Roy. Soc. B **148**, 145

Medawar, P. B. (1958c). Proc. Roy. Soc. B **149**, 145

Merwin, R. M., and Hill, E. L. (1954). J. Natl. Cancer Inst. **14**, 819

Metcalf, D. (1964). In, V. Defendi and D. Metcalf, eds., The thymus. Wistar Institute Press, Philadelphia, p. 52

Milgrom, F., Seligmann, M., Bernard, J., and Grabar, P. (1959). Rev. Hématol. **14**, 309

Miller, D. G., Lizardo, J. G., and Snyderman, R. K. (1961). J. Natl. Cancer Inst. **26**, 569

Miller, E. C., and Miller, J. A. (1947). Cancer Res. **7**, 468

Miller, J. F. A. P. (1962). Proc. Roy. Soc. B **156**, 415

Miller, J. F. A. P. (1963). Lancet **i**, 43

Miller, J. F. A. P. (1964). In, R. A. Good and A. E. Gabrielson, eds., The thymus in immunobiology. Harper and Row, New York, p. 436

Miller, J. F. A. P., Marshall, A. H. E., and White, R. G. (1962). Ado. Immunol. **2**, 111

Mitchison, N. A. (1954). Proc. Roy. Soc. B **142**, 72

Mitchison, N. A. (1955). J. Exptl. Med. **102**, 157

Mitchison, N. A. (1958). Symp. Soc. Exptl. Biol. **12**, 225

Mitchison, N. A., and Dube, O.L. (1955). J. Exptl. Med. **102**, 179

Möller, E. (1965) J. Exptl. Med. **122**, 11

Möller, E., and Möller, G. (1962) J. Exptl. Med. **115**, 527

Möller, G. (1961). J. Exptl. Med. **114**, 415

Möller, G. (1963a). J. Natl. Cancer Inst. **30**, 1205

Möller, G. (1963b). On the rôle of isoimmune reactions in tissue transplantation, T. Balder AB, Stockholm

Möller, G. (1964). Methods in Biol. Res. **10**, 58

Moloney, J. B. (1960). J. Natl. Cancer Inst. **24**, 933

Moorehead, J. F. and Patel, A. R. (1964). Brit. Med. J. **ii**, 1111

Nairn, R. C., Fothergill, J. E., McEntegart, M. G., and Richmond, H. G. (1962). Brit. Med. J. **i**, 1791

Nairn, R. C., Richmond, H. G., McEntegart, M. G., and Fothergill, J. E. (1960). Brit. Med. J. **i**, 1335

Najarian, J. S. and Feldman, J. D. (1962). J. Exptl. Med. **115**, 1083

Najarian, J. S. and Feldman, J. D. (1963). J. Exptl. Med. **117**, 449

Nelken, D. (1963). Vox Sanguinis **8**, 638

Neter, E. (1963). In, B. Amos and H. Koprowski, eds., Cell-bound antibodies. Wistar Inst. Press, Philadelphia, p. 35

Old, L. G. and Boyse, E. A. (1964). Ann. Rev. Med. **15**, 167

Old, L. J. and Boyse, E. A. (1965). Fed. Proc. **24**, 1009

Old, L. J. and Boyse, E. A. (1966). Med. Clin. N. Am. **50**, 901

Osler, A. G. (1961). Cancer Res. **21**, 1187

Paget, S. (1889). Lancet **1**, 571

Parigot, J., Lacour, F., and Lacour, J. (1958). Bull. Assoc. Franc. Etude Cancer **45**, 454

Paschkis, K. E., Cantarow, A., Stasney, J., and Hobbs, J. H. (1955). Cancer Res. **15**, 579

Pasternak, G., Graffi, A., and Horn, K. H. (1964). Acta Biol. Med. Ger. **13**, 276

Phillips, M., and Stetson, C. A. (1962). Proc. Soc. Exptl. Biol. Med. **111**, 256

Pilch, Y. H., and Riggins, R. S. (1966). Cancer Res. **26**, 871

Pope, J. H., and Rowe, W. P. (1964). J. Exptl. Med. **120**, 121

Potter, J. S. and Findley, M. D. (1935). Proc. Soc. Exptl. Biol. Med. **32**, 1338

Potter, V. R. (1956). Cancer Res. **16**, 658
Potter, V. R. (1962). In , The molecular basis of neoplasia. Univ. Texas Press, Austin, p. 367
Prehn, R. T. (1960). Cancer Res. **20**, 1614
Prehn, R. T. (1965). Fed. Proc. **24**, 1018
Prehn, R. T. and Main, J. M. (1957). J. Natl. Cancer Inst. **18**, 769
Prendergast, R. A. (1964). J. Exptl. Med. **119**, 377
Pressman, D. and Yagi, Y. (1964). In Small blood vessel involvement in diabetes mellitus. A.I.B.S., p. 177
Prinzmetal, M., Ornitz, E. M., Simkin, B., and Bergman, H. C. (1948). Am. J. Physiol. **152**, 48
Pulvertaft, R. J. V. (1959). Proc. Roy. Soc. Med. **52**, 315
Pulvertaft, R. J. V., and Humble, J. G. (1956). Rev. Hématol. **11**, 349
Ramseier, H., and Streilein, J. W. (1965). Lancet **i**, 622
Ramseier, H., and Billingham, R. E. (1964). Ann. N. Y. Acad. Sci. **120**, 379
Rapp, F., Butel, J. S., Feldman, L. A., Kitahara, T., and Melnick, J. L. (1965). J. Exptl. Med. **121**, 935
Rapport, M. M., and Graf, L. (1955). Cancer **8**, 538
Rapport, M. M., and Graf, L. (1961). Cancer Res. **21**, 1225
Rapport, M. M., and Graf, L. (1964). Nature **201**, 879
Rapport, M. M., Graf, L., and Yariv, J. (1961a). Arch. Biochem. Biophys. **92**, 438
Rapport, M. M., Skipski, V. P., and Sweeley, C. C. (1961b). Lipid Res. **2**, 148
Recklinghausen, I. von (1891). Festschr. zum Rudolf Virchow's 71. Geburtstage
Reed, D. M. (1901–1902). Johns Hopkins Hosp. Rept. **10**, 133
Révész, L. (1960). Cancer Res. **20**, 443
Riggins, R. S., and Pilch, Y. H. (1964). Cancer Res. **24**, 1994
Rosenau, W. (1963) In, B. Amos and H. Koprowski, eds., Cell-bound antibodies. Wistar Inst. Press, Philadelphia, p. 75
Russell, B. R. G. (1908). 3rd Sci. Rept. Imperial Cancer Res. Fund. p. 341
Russell, P. S., and Monaco, A. P. (1964). The biology of tissue transplantation. Little, Brown and Company, Boston
Sabin, A. B., and Koch, M. A. (1964). Proc. Natl. Acad. Sci (Wash) **52**, 1131
Schier, W. A., Roth, A., Ostroff, G., and Schrift, M. H. (1956). Am. J. Med. **20**, 94
Schoefl, G. I. (1963). Virchows Arch. Pathol. Anat. Physiol. **337**, 97
Schwartz, M. (1961). Cancer **14**, 1272
Scothorne, R. J., and McGregor, I. A. (1955). J. Anat. Lond. **89**, 283
Seligmann, M., Grabar, P., and Bernard, J. (1955). Sang. **26**, 52
Shapiro, D., and Rachaman, E. (1964). Nature **201**, 878
Simonsen, M. (1962). Progr. Allergy **6**, 349
Snell, G. D. (1948). Genetics **49**, 87
Snell, G. D. (1953a). J. Natl. Cancer Inst. **14**, 691
Snell, G. D. (1953b). In, F. Homburger and W. H. Fishman, eds., The physiopathology of cancer, P. B. Hoeber, Inc., New York, p. 338
Snell, G. D. (1958a). J. Natl. Cancer Inst. **20**, 787
Snell, G. D. (1958b). J. Natl. Cancer Inst. **21**, 843
Snell G. D. (1963). Conceptual advances in immunology and oncology. M. D. Anderson Hosp. Symp., University of Texas
Snell, G. D., Smith, P., and Gabrielson, F. (1953). J. Natl. Cancer Inst. **14**, 457

Sokal, J. E., and Primikirios, N. (1961). Cancer **14**, 597

Southam, C. M., and Moore, A. E. (1958). Ann. N. Y. Acad. Sci. **73**, 635

Stetson, C. A. (1963). Advan. Immunol. **3**, 97

Sugarbaker, E. D. (1952). Cancer **5**, 606

Tevethia, S. S., Katz, M., and Rapp, F. (1965). Proc. Soc. Exptl. Biol. Med. **119**, 896

Trowell, O. A. (1949). J. Physiol. **110**, 5P

Trowell, O. A. (1958). Intern. Rev. Cytol. **7**, 235

Waksman, B. H. (1963). Lab. Invest. **12**, 46

Waksman, B. H., Arnason, S., and Jankovic, B. D. (1962). J. Exptl. Med. **116**, 187

Walford, R. L. (1960). In, Leukocyte antigens and antibodies, Grune and Stratton, London, p. 119

Walford, R. L., Carter, P. K., and Anderson, R. E. (1962). Transplant. Bull. **29**, 16

Warren, S., and Davis, A. H. (1934). Am. J. Cancer **21**, 517

Warren, B. A., and Shubik, P. (1966). Lab. Invest. **15**, 464

Weiler, E. (1952). Z. Naturforsch. **76**, 237

Weiler, E. (1956a). Brit. J. Cancer **10**, 553

Weiler, E. (1956b). Brit. J. Cancer **10**, 560

Weiler, E. (1959). In, Ciba Foundation Symposium, Carcinogenesis. mechanisms of action. Churchill, London, p. 165

Weiler, E. (1962). In, M. J. Brennan and W. L. Simpson, eds., Biological interactions in normal and neoplastic growth, Churchill, London, p. 141

Weiss, D. W., Faulkin, L. J., and DeOme, K. B. (1964). Cancer Res. **24**, 732

Weiss, L. (1961). Exptl. Cell Res. Suppl. **8**, 141

Whitcutt, J. M., and Elson, L. A. (1962). Biochem. J. **83**, 11P.

Wiener, J., Spiro, D., and Russell, P. S. (1964). Am. J. Pathol. **44**, 319

Williams, R. G. (1959). Anat. Record. **133**, 465

Willis, R. A. (1948). Pathology of tumours. C. V. Mosby Company, St. Louis, Missouri, p. 179

Willis, R. A. (1952). The spread of tumours in the human body. Butterworth, London

Wilson, D. B. (1965). J. Exptl. Med. **122**, 143

Winn, H. J. (1960). J. Immunology **4**, 530

Winn, H. J. (1962). Ann. N. Y. Acad. Science **101**, 23

Witebsky, E. (1961). Cancer Res. **21**, 1216

Woglom, W. H. (1929). Cancer Review, **4**, 129

Woodruff, M. F. A., and Anderson, N. F. (1964). Ann. N. Y. Acad. Sci. **120**, 119

Woodruff, M. F. A., Robson, J. S., Nolan, B., Lambie, A. T., Wilson, T. I., and Clark, J. G. (1963). Lancet **ii**, 675

Zeidman, I. (1961). Cancer Res. **21**, 38

Zilber, L. A. (1958). Advan. Cancer Res. **5**, 291

Epilogue

It will be obvious to the reader that it is just not possible at the moment to give a clear-cut picture of the metastatic process at cellular or physico-chemical levels. The necessary experimental data for such a synthesis may already be present in the papers to which I have referred, on the other hand, most of the quoted papers may be irrelevant.

My own feelings are best summed up in the following paragraph taken from Pulvertaft (1959) ... 'We must ask ourselves in what way these observations may be related to the development and propagation of the malignant process. Here we enter the realm of hypothesis, and I do so without apology, for observations and experiments are useless unless they point the way to new conceptions. Research is like 'blind man's buff': we touch our target for a moment in the darkness but can neither hold nor name it; only at long last do we grasp it firmly and claim with confidence to recognize it without a doubt. For most of the time we must be content with half-knowledge and uncertain guesses. At any one time 'the truth' is merely the closest approximation to reality which we can attain in the light of our present knowledge'.

Pulvertaft, R. J. V. (1959). Proc. Roy. Soc. Med. **52**, 315

Index

Acetal phosphatide, 27
acetylcholine esterase, 77, 78
β-N-acetylglucosaminidase, 93
acids (peripheral)
    linoleic acid, 22
    α-phosphatidic acid, 25, 264
    fatty acids, 21, 25
        species variations in, 29
        variations with diet and disease, 29
        monolayers of, 39
    N-acetyl neuraminic acid, 31, 32, 109, 166, 209
    amino acids, 62
    hyaluronic acid, 209, 284
    sialic acids, 31–33, 61, 87, 106, 107, 109, 205, 207
        assay of, 33, 247
        in relation to tumours, 265, 266
        in relation to electrophoretic mobility, 267–269, 302
        in relation to virus-induced cell conversion, 283
Acrasiales, 123, 124
acrasin, 124
actomyosin, 122
adenosine deaminase, 77
    loss of during isolation of nuclei, 19
adenosinetriphosphatases, 58, 78, 79
adenylpyrophosphatase, 78
Aerobacter aerogenes, 166, 167
Amblystoma tigrinum, 140
aminopeptidases, 318
amoebae
    preparation of, for electron microscopy, 52
    trilaminar structure in, 60, 119

modulation of cell periphery of, 85, 86
movement of, 117–123
contact among, 183, 184
locomotive force of, 187, 188
electrophoretic mobility of, 187
zeta potential of, 187
Amoeba dubia, 249
Amoeba proteus, 118, 119, 120
amoebocytes, 131, 135
amylase, 307
antigens
    of the cell periphery, 30, 31, 197, 280–283
    M and N antigenic activity of erythrocytes, 32
    H-antigens, 34, 35, 345, 346, 362
        H-2 antigenic activity of ascitic fluid, 35
        test of H-2 antigenic activity, 35
    P_1 blood group, 34
    Rh antigenic sites, 34
    immobilising antigen of *Paramecium aurelia*, 76
    synthesis during cell development, 81
    changes in surface antigenicity, 84, 85
    of bacteria and viruses, 85
    D and M in *Paramecium aurelia*, 85
    in *Salmonellae*, 89
    of myxamoebae surface, 134, 135
    of cell surface of sponges, 136, 137
    role in cell aggregation, 140
    in the nucleus, 281
    associated with tumours, 345, 351
    tumour specific, 346–350, 362
    of chemically and virus-induced tumours, 347, 348

375

SV40 induced antigens, 348
of spontaneous tumours, 348
G antigen in human tumours, 349
cytolipin H, 349, 350
transport on surfaces of lymphocytes,
360
antisera
effect on lysosomal activation, 97, 210,
211
effect on mouse bones, 98
effect on the cell periphery, 97, 98
effect on cell aggregation, 137, 140
effect on cell separation from glass, 211
cytotoxic effects of, 210, 211
Arbacia punctulata, 250
arginase, 305, 307
ascites tumour cells
isolation of membranes from, 18
alteration of the periphery of, 61
temperature-dependent sodium fluxes in,
106
asparaginase, 77
autolysis
sublethal, 92, 93, 98, 303, 307
generalized, 94
autoradiographic studies
of spiral cord, 82

Bacillus cereus, 102
Bacillus subtilis, 101, 102
bacteria
modifying erythrocyte agglutination, 31
enzyme induction in, 77
modulation in, 84, 85
lysogenic, 88, 89, 279
electrophoretic mobility of, 102
adsorption of phage to, 180
phagocytosis of, 220
bacteriophages, 88–90
adsorption to bacteria, 180
bilayers
bimolecular lipid leaves, 41, 42
as biological model, 42
bimolecular lipid layers, 43, 44, 50, 51, 53
capacitance of, 48
blastoderm, 151–153
blood groups

genetic control of, 30, 76
substances, 30, 31, 34
receptors type P, 33
Rhesus (Rh), 34
P_1 antigen, 34
H substance, 34
Bordetella pertussis, 84, 85
Brownian movement, 165, 169, 185, 214,
275
Busycon canaliculatum, 249

Calcium
content in tumours, 271
content of cells in relation to age, 272
influence on cell separation and adhesion, 296, 297
roles in cell adhesion, 297
effect on electrical double-layer, 297
binding to carboxyl groups, 297
interaction with polyelectrolytes, 298
function in the cell periphery, 299, 300
Candida, 364
cardiolipin, 27, 59, 350
casein, 62
cathepsins, 38, 93, 94, 97, 305, 307, 318
cells
surface of, 17
permeability of, 64
differentiation of, 75
fusion between, 90, 91
biological activities of, 94
extracellular matrix, 129
isolation from tissues, 141
locomotory energy of, 186, 187, 214
dissociation of, 189
electrokinetic surface of, 207, 231
deformability of, 215, 216
calcium content in relation to age of, 272
changes associated with viruses, 277–284
pH influences on, 291
cell adhesion
and antigens, 134, 136, 137
in sponges, 137, 138
to glass, 145, 146, 205
to account for movements, 149
time courses of, 176
forces of, 188–193